O

N

Physical Education and Health in the Elementary School

Physical Education
and Health in the
Elementary School

by CHARLES A. BUCHER
*Professor of Education and Director of Graduate
Studies in Physical Education, New York University*

and EVELYN M. READE
*Professor of Physical Education and Chairman,
Department of Health and Physical Education,
New Jersey State College, Glassboro*

The Macmillan Company, New York
Collier-Macmillan Limited, London

Dedicated to

Classroom and Physical Education Teachers Responsible for
Educating Children in Early and Middle Childhood Grades

PREFACE

The tender years of childhood are most important from the standpoint of social, physical, and mental-emotional development. Personality is being molded, attitudes are being formed, symbols are being learned, and social values are being acquired. The direction of the child's development will depend to a great extent upon his educational experiences and the leadership provided to guide these experiences.

Play, which is often referred to as the child's work, is an educational medium with tremendous potentialities for the optimum development of children. Play offers children opportunities for discovering and expressing themselves, acquiring useful skills, developing strong, healthy bodies, learning how to get along with others, making decisions, and gaining other qualities essential to good citizenship.

Play can be adapted to so many different phases of education in the elementary school that the physical education program is integral to general education. (In the physical education program, under the leadership of the classroom teacher and the physical education specialist, educational goals can be brought nearer to accomplishment.) Such goals are not achieved, however, merely by having physical education periods in the schools. The results depend on the teacher's ability to teach.

The school health program also has deep implications for the child's education. Good health is basic to effective learning. Within the elementary school program, there should be health instruction, health services, and a healthful environment. Although health and physical education are separate fields, they are closely related. Particularly in the elementary school with the self-contained classroom, the classroom teacher and the physical education specialist have important responsiblities to know and understand what constitutes both the health program and the physical education program.

In recent years, the classroom teacher has played an important part in directing physical education and health programs in the elementary grades. Although there is a recognized need for the physical education and the health specialist to conduct certain aspects of the program, the classroom teacher's day-to-day role is often the key to success. This development has given the classroom teacher the responsibility of adequate preparation in two phases of education that have become major parts of the curriculum because of their indispensable contribution to the proper growth and development of children. This book has been designed to provide the classroom teacher with the background of principle and the specifics of practice needed to provide a rich physical education and health offering to all of the children with whom he or she works from day to day.

This book will also prove very helpful to the physical education specialist, who must understand the total aspects of the elementary school physical education and health program if he or she is to provide proper leadership in both areas. The text offers an entirely new approach, with a new format, new ideas, and activities never before published.

The book is divided into two major parts, the first concerned with physical education in the elementary school and the second with the elementary school health program. In addition, there are appendixes containing suggestions for such essentials as books, visual aids, records, ways to make equipment, sources of free and inexpensive materials, game and dance diagrams, and materials from the *AAHPER Youth Fitness Test Manual*.

Part One, "Physical Education in the Elementary School," covers such topics as philosophy, child growth and development characteristics, and the program of activities. Special attention has been given to the role of physical education in schools and the important factors necessary for fulfilling its objectives. In addition, provisions have been made for such current topics as physical fitness, movement education, and creativity.

The book traces the role of physical education in education and the way in which play can be used as a medium through which educational objectives are achieved. It shows that physical education is not an appendage to the school curriculum but instead an integral part of general education. It stresses new developments in elementary education that offer challenges and opportunities for teachers. It discusses the child as a growing and developing personality and the teacher as the guide who utilizes play as an educational medium to help the child. The classroom teacher and physical education specialist will find principles and information on planning the organization and administration of desirable physical education programs, adapting general instructions to individual classes, providing the program progression needed from grade to grade, correlating physical education with other phases of the curriculum, organizing noon-hour and free-play programs, and teaching almost 500 activities arranged according to the grade levels, the indoor or outdoor play areas, and the occasions to which they are appropriate. In addition, the book discusses problems—

such as evaluation, safety, legal liability, and camping and outdoor education—with which every classroom and physical education teacher should be familiar.

The second part of the book is concerned with the elementary school health program. A detailed treatment is given to the health education, health services, and healthful school living phases of this important part of the elementary school program. The aim of the authors has been to cover in a factual and condensed manner the practical aspects of what the classroom and physical education teacher must know about school health. The nature and scope of the school health program are first discussed in terms of such basic topics as objectives, the factors that influence the child's health, health problems of elementary school youngsters, the school health team responsible for protecting the pupil's health, and the relation of health to physical education. Next, there is a discussion of a well-planned health education program—a discussion that includes the bases for selecting curriculum experiences, health needs and interests of students, psychological principles that promote learning, samples of teaching units, proposals for curriculum development, methods of teaching, sources of free and inexpensive health materials, and principles for evaluation. Finally, there is a chapter covering the component parts of a healthful school environment, both mental and physical, and the services necessary to maintain and improve the child's health.

The authors are confident that the inclusion of physical education and health within the covers of one textbook will contribute to a better understanding and appreciation of both of these specialized fields, especially in those professional-preparing institutions where physical education and health are combined into one course.

CHARLES A. BUCHER
EVELYN M. READE

ACKNOWLEDGMENTS

The authors wish to express their appreciation to the many individuals whose contributions have made this book possible. Particular thanks are due to the children and teachers who helped develop and test the new activities and to the many colleagues who gave invaluable suggestions for the revision of the text.

Assistance with photographs has been provided by Dr. Thomas Robinson, Dr. Eva Aronfreed, Mr. Michael Briglia, and Mr. Roy Butz of Glassboro State College and its Campus School; Irving Eiseman and the Fairview Day Camp of Philadelphia; The SAFE Fencing Co.; Seaboard Pools; Panetrol, Inc.; Miracle Equipment Company; Atlantic-Pacific Manufacturing Corp.; Carl Purcell, National Education Association; and San Diego Public Schools. Appendix E, containing materials from the *AAHPER Youth Fitness Test Manual,* has been included through the courtesy of the American Association for Health, Physical Education and Recreation. The permission from the President's Council on Physical Fitness, Washington, D.C., to reprint the many developmental activities is very gratefully acknowledged.

CONTENTS

PART ONE *Physical Education*

in the Elementary School

THE PHILOSOPHY

CHAPTER 1

Physical Education in the Elementary School

Physical education is a much publicized subject in today's world. Large posters in public places ask if children are getting organized physical activity in the schools. Commercials on television stress the need for regular exercise. Spot announcements on radio advise, "It Pays to Play." All sorts of games, exercising equipment, records, books, and gadgets are advertised in the nation's press. Parents are cautioned to provide for their child's rest, nutrition, dental care, and bone growth. Children in the schools are exposed to calisthenics, push-ups, obstacle courses, physical fitness tests, and isometrics.

Educators are as much concerned about physical education as are parents. They are confronted, however, with many different philosophies on what constitutes a good educational program. Some school people advocate great amounts of formal exercise, such as calisthenics and push-ups, as the way to get children into good physical shape. Other persons say that athletic programs are the answer and that leagues and tournaments should be organized in many different sports. A third group says that physical

education should be concerned with more than the physical aspects of development. This group advocates that consideration be given also to social and mental development.

The classroom teacher and the specialist in physical education are in the midst of all this wrangling and discussion. The classroom teacher, not being a specialist, wonders at times what is the best approach to follow and what type of a program to initiate in his or her classes. Many times he or she finds the easiest solution is to succumb to the pressures of townspeople and provide the program they advocate without thought of the part physical education plays in total education.

This book is written for the guidance of those classroom teachers and specialists who are responsible for physical education classes in the elementary school. Herein are provided the ingredients for a sound program of physical education. Here is a guide that will enable the teacher to proceed with confidence, knowing that she or he has the answers to what is in the best interests of the child and sound education.

MOVEMENT—THE FOUNDATION OF PHYSICAL EDUCATION

Children play dodgeball, dance the polka, climb the jungle gym, tumble on the mat, swim in the pool, stand on their heads, throw balls, and engage in many different physical activities. Running through each of these activities is a common denominator

5

with which the physical educator is very much concerned—MOVEMENT.

Movement is essential to life. How terrible it would be if human beings could not jump, skip, throw, stretch, run, or leap. Their bodies would not develop properly. Their lives would be uninteresting. They would be sickly and weak persons. They would never experience the joy that comes from catching a fish, hitting a ball, going down a ski trail, flying through space on ice skates, or possessing enough strength to hurl a stone at a tin can.

The job of the physical education teacher is the development of skillful, meaningful, satisfying movement in the untold and limitless plethora of activities in which children engage. This is an important contribution to the child, who is the recipient of such instruction, and to society, which profits from such a service. To develop effective and skillful movement requires a sound foundation of knowledge with biological, psychological, and sociological roots. In addition, principles of physics come into play, for the body relates to such factors as space, time, and force. The teacher must have some of this background information if he or she is to help each child effectively find his own movement patterns and responsibilities.

Although this book cannot provide all the depth of information needed, it has delineated that material which is thought to be most essential for the teaching of physical education in the elementary school. It informs the teacher at each grade level how he can be most useful in helping the child to use various balls, ropes, apparatus, and other equipment for movement possibilities as well as to use his body in rhythms, the dance, and the formal and more highly organized games and activities. It shows how the teacher and the child can both be creative, one in the teaching approach, and the other in the area of movement expression. It helps the teacher to give the child an awareness of his body and its place and role in day to day living. It shows the relationship of physical education to health education, and the relationship of both to the welfare of the whole child.

THE FUNCTION OF THE ELEMENTARY SCHOOL

Approximately 360,000 elementary schools throughout the nation have important roles to play in modern education. Through their doors each year walk millions of youngsters. This is the first school experience for most of these children. The attitude they develop toward learning, the degree to which their basic mental equipment is activated, how they look at themselves and the world in which they live, and the degree to which they are interested in their physical wellbeing will be sharply affected by these first few years of formal education. Children can be molded in many different ways. Education should be designed to mold them in the right directions.

Most children who come to school are enthusiastic about the educational process. They have heard mothers, fathers, brothers, and sisters talk about reading, games, spelling, writing, and arithmetic. Their appetites have been whetted and they have a strong desire to partake of the educational fare. Their motivation for learning is probably as great at this point as it ever will be in their lifetimes. The teacher and the school can exploit this enthusiasm, this desire for learning, and make it a very satisfying experience, or they can dampen enthusiasm by poor and uninspired teaching.

Some of the experiences in which the child should have a successful, challenging, and satisfying role and the outcomes that should accrue in the elementary school are as follows:

1. *The child should develop mentally.*

There should be training and experience in the basic mental skills. There should be opportunities for study in such areas as language, arithmetic, and spelling. There is need for training in logical thinking and clear self-expression. It is essential for children to learn to read material and comprehend what has been read. It is important for them to be exposed to such fields as literature, music, natural history, and simple physical and natural science, and the manner in which these areas of learning affect the world in which they live. An acquisition of knowledge, and the fundamental abilities and skills basic to formal learning, together with the development of a wholesome attitude toward learning, are the primary functions of elementary education.

2. *The child should develop socially.*

The child must learn to live effectively with other people. The elementary school years can provide an excellent laboratory for the development of many desirable social qualities. For example, elementary school experiences can help the child develop a respect for the rights of others and an understanding of the values inherent in society and the family. There should be a change from the "I" concept with the stress on the individual to the "we" concept with the stress on being a cooperating member of society. There should be emphasis on self-fulfillment, with equal emphasis on expanding home, community, national, and international obligations.

3. *The child should develop physically.*

There needs to be stress on health habits and physical wellbeing in the elementary school. This function is especially necessary during the growing years. It is important that the child be emotionally well-balanced. It is necessary that the child have a self-controlled, physically fit body. An interest in physical development and a consciousness of proper body care should be impressed upon each pupil. Finally, there is need for large amounts of big muscle activity during this period because various parts of the body are developing. This activity is essential to healthy growth. The

Figure 1–1. Learning skill in dribbling.

elementary years are an important time for educating the pupil for his proper health development because organic foundations are being laid, skills are being learned, and attitudes developed which will influence his health all through his years.

4. *The child should develop the foundations for the wise use of leisure time.*

The world is faced with increasing amounts of leisure as new kinds of automated aids develop. The hours of work will be important, but the non-working hours will be equally important. Whether or not children achieve their full potential in the world in which they live today and in the future will depend upon their attitudes, skills, and understanding of the part that leisure plays in their full development.

WHAT IS PHYSICAL EDUCATION?

The word *physical* refers to the body and to things physical, such as muscle, bones, skin, hair, and blood. The word *education* refers to principles and practices which have to do with learning or the instruction and study which helps to develop the mind and character. Physical education, therefore, refers to the instruction or learning that takes place through the body. One important point to understand clearly is that the term *physical education* implies that learning takes place.

What kind of learning takes place in physical education? It is obvious that much can be learned about the body itself. Children can learn about some of the important parts of the body and how such organs as the heart, lungs, stomach, and liver function. Furthermore, they can understand why it is important to take care of bodily equipment and its relationship to optimum physical functioning and being well and happy. Of course, there is other subject-matter information that children can be taught and through which they will have a better understanding of the world about them and their own future role in society.

The elementary school teacher needs to recognize that physical education does not merely mean getting young bones and muscles into action. The activity does not take place in a vacuum. There are other reasons for engaging in physical activities and for activating one's body than the exercise that takes place. The more clearly that children realize this, the more they will be motivated throughout life to be physically active and provide for the needs of their bodies.

Another type of learning that takes place in physical education is that of physical skill. An expression that has received considerable use in the advertising world is "that it's easier to start a habit than to stop one." In other words, if a skill is taught correctly it will heighten the learning process. Poor habits and wrong ways of performing skills will not have to be undone. Once a skill has been learned the wrong way it takes considerable time and effort to correct the error. The object, therefore, is to help youngsters during their early years learn to throw, jump, run, skip, tumble, stand, sit, and dance the right and skillful way. The more complex skills used in the highly organized sports and physical activities in which the child will engage at a later age are combinations of such fundamental movements as running, jumping, and leaping. Therefore, during the elementary school years a broad foundation of skillful physical performance should be instilled so that new and more difficult skills will be easily learned and enjoyed later on in life.

A third type of learning that takes place is what happens to the individual child in his or her relationships with the other youngsters. The physical education class period offers a wonderful opportunity to teach such qualities as courage, initiative, leadership, followership, honesty, and dependability. It helps a child to appreciate better the individual abilities of others and the value of one's own playing according to the rules. When games are being played, many situations arise where the youngster must determine what is the right course of action to follow. Under expert and qualified leadership, the right decision will be made.

Physical education, therefore, is not just education of the physical body. It is not merely exercising, sweating, puffing, and building strength and stamina. It goes beyond these and, in addition to developing physical wellbeing, it uses the body as a vehicle through which knowledge is gained, attitudes are developed, and desirable social qualities are acquired. It is education through and by means of physical activity.

The *physical* part of physical education is the way or means and not the end in itself. If all we hope to achieve is neuromuscular skills, strength, agility, and comparable physical growth, we cannot logically call it physical *education*. It would be more correctly called *physical training,* the term used years ago. However, through the physical and by means of many different kinds of physical experiences, we have opportunities to assist in reaching other educational objectives.

The worthy objectives of physical education are as follows:

1. To provide for big-muscle activity in order to aid in the growth and development of the body.

2. To develop neuromuscular skills so that the child may participate in various activities such as running, jumping, throwing, catching, dancing, and so on.

3. To maintain an interest in and a love of physical activity by teaching activities based on the needs, interests, and abilities of all children.

4. To teach activities which may be used during the child's leisure time.

5. To teach fair play, sportsmanship, respect for fellow players and officials, and an understanding of abiding by the rules of games and sports.

6. To teach safety as it relates to each activity used in the program, and to instill a regard for safety at all times in activities in which the child engages.

7. To teach health as it correlates with physical education. (Why is exercise and physical development beneficial to all? Why is it not wise to drink ice cold water when participating in strenuous activities? And so on.)

To get a child to run, jump, or skip is not the only function of physical education. It is designed to get him to think about his bodily makeup, his physical needs, the relation of his body to his total self, and the contribution that physical education makes to his whole development.

SOME MISCONCEPTIONS

After a discussion of the meaning of physical education in education it is readily apparent there are misconceptions about this field today. A few of the more common of these misconceptions may be briefly summarized as follows:

1. *Physical fitness is the same as physical education.*

The great amount of stress on physical fitness today has had many excellent results for physical education. It has, however, tended to distort the role of physical fitness in physical education. Physical fitness is one objective of physical education. It is very important to develop strong boys and girls but to be content with the accomplishment of this one objective is not sufficient. To plan a program so that it is focused mainly on this objective (calisthenics, obstacle courses, and apparatus) is not in accordance with sound educational practice. There must be as much, or more, concern for the development of skills, the imparting of knowledge, and the acquisition of desirable social traits.

2. *Interschool athletics are a vital part of the elementary school physical education program.*

America is a very sports-minded country. This sports-mindedness has rubbed off on education. School athletics started out in the colleges and were then imitated in the senior high schools. The junior high schools looked at the senior high schools and liked what they saw and today approximately 85 per cent of the junior high schools in this country have some form of interschool athletics of a varsity pattern. In recent years some elementary schools have looked at the junior high schools and decided this is something that is good for grade school students, with the result that some elementary schools in this country have athletic programs.

There is a question as to whether interschool athletics should ever become part of the elementary school physical education program. Many outstanding educators and child-growth and development specialists say "no." Ample evidence is available that the objectives of elementary school physical education, including physical fitness, can be accomplished without offering any form of interschool athletics. Furthermore, the establishment of interschool athletics of a varsity type for junior high schools is severely questioned in many educational quarters. Therefore, if they are questionable for grades seven, eight, and nine, it would seem wise not to have them in grades one through six in the elementary school. The leadership, facilities, time, and money needed for interschool athletics can be used to greater advantage in other parts of the physical education program.

3. *Physical education is the same as health education.*

There is confusion in the thinking of some parents, as well as some educators, in regard to the meaning of physical education and health education. Physical education, as has been pointed out, is concerned with all types of physical activities which are used as a medium for building desirable physical qualities and also for mental, skill, and social reasons. Health education in the schools is concerned with instructing children in regard to such health matters as what constitutes nutritious food in their diet, providing them with a healthful environment in which to live, both physical and psychological, and seeing that the essential health services, such as medical examinations, first aid, and communicable disease control, are provided. Health instruction should be performed by a person who has had special training in the field of health education. A physical educator may or may not have had such training.

Figure 1–2. Dance is an important part of the program.

COMPONENT PARTS OF THE ELEMENTARY SCHOOL
PHYSICAL EDUCATION PROGRAM

There are three main components of a well-rounded elementary school physical education program—(1) the required class program, (2) the adapted program, and (3) the intramural program.

The *required class program* is the component part for all students in the elementary school. It is instructional in nature and should be provided on a daily basis throughout the elementary school years. It should consist of a variety of activities including story plays, rhythms and dances, games of low organization, mimetics, self-testing activities and stunts, classroom games, individual activities, team games, and aquatics. These activities should be presented in a progressive manner, ranging from the simple and informal to the complex and the more highly organized. The activities should be presented to meet the physical, mental, social, and emotional needs of the students.

The *adapted program* refers to that phase of the physical education program which meets the needs of the individual, who, because of some physical inadequacy, functional defect capable of being improved through exercise, or other deficiency, is temporarily or permanently unable to take part in the regular physical education program. The adapted program has implications for pupils with such characteristics as faulty body mechanics, nutritional disturbances (overweight and underweight), heart and lung disturbances, postoperative and convalescent problems, hernias or weak and flat feet, nervous instability, low physical fitness, and crippling conditions. Provisions for restricted and/or remedial physical activity are made for such pupils, both during regular class and special classes, utilizing special conditioning exercises, aquatics, and recreational sports. The adapted program is predicated upon harmonious working relationships with school and home medical and nursing personnel.

The *intramural program* is designed to provide competition within the same school in games, sports, and other physical activities for elementary school students. Such a program is most frequently offered in the intermediate grades (fourth, fifth, and sixth). Whereas the required class program is instructional in nature, the intramural program is designed to provide an opportunity for students to utilize learned skills in actual competitive situations. Such competition should be friendly and informal, with an absence of pressures usually generated by publicity, gate receipts, and spectators. The competition should be voluntary in nature, conducted during out-of-class hours, and should provide for a variety of activities based on the needs and interests of pupils.

SOME FACTORS AFFECTING THE ELEMENTARY SCHOOL PHYSICAL EDUCATION PROGRAM

Whether or not the physical education program in the elementary school is a successful experience for the child and a dynamic part of the educational offering depends upon several factors. Some of the more important of these follow.

Administrative Philosophy

The philosophy of education as expressed by the community, the board of education, the superintendent of schools, and the principal, plays an important part in determining the place and role of physical education in the total educational program. Upon these people depend the type of facilities that will be provided, the amount of money allocated in the budget, the respect given to the physical education specialist, the time provided in the school day, and the personnel who are hired. The administration that endorses a philosophy of education that gives lip service to the physical needs of pupils but fails to follow through and provide adequate tangible support for meeting these needs can be questioned as to its sincerity for this phase of the educational program. School administrators and communities are needed who clearly see the important contribution that a meaningful physical education experience can provide boys and girls and who are willing to back up this philosophy with action in terms of scheduling, facilities, time, personnel, and other essentials.

Time

The amount of time in the school program allocated for physical education will influence the type of experience provided elementary school pupils. On the primary level, the classroom teacher and physical education specialist should try to provide a minimum of thirty minutes each day for purposes of class instruction. In addition, there should be at least thirty minutes of supervised play in which the youngsters engage in activities in the gymnasium, on the playground, or in the swimming pool. In the intermediate grades the time allocation should be increased to forty or forty-five minutes daily for the instructional phase of the program and twenty to thirty minutes daily for supervised play.

Facilities, Equipment, and Supplies

Not all elementary schools have fine gymnasia, swimming facilities, and an ample supply of balls, bats, and other equipment. In fact, there are many schools that do not have any facilities or materials with which to work. However, this does not mean teachers should throw up their hands and do nothing about physical education. For the creative teacher, much can be done through improvisation. It may mean using the playground for more months during the year, utilizing the corridors in the school as a play area, adapting activities to the classroom, and collecting broom handles, ropes, and supplies from outside sources. The ingenious teacher, however, will provide for the physical education of her pupils.

Boards of education and community-minded people are increasingly recognizing the importance of physical education facilities. Teachers of elementary school physical education showed be familiar with the following standards and make recommendations accordingly.

1. The playground area should be located near the building and be easily accessible to classrooms.

2. Kindergarten children should have a section of the playground for their exclusive use consisting of a surfaced area, a grass area, and a place for sand and digging. The sand area should be enclosed to prevent the sand from being scattered. It is also wise to have a shaded area where storytelling and similar activities may be conducted. Essential equipment would include swings, slides, seesaws, climbing structures, tables, and seats.

3. Children above kindergarten (grades one through six) should have play space which includes turf, apparatus, shaded, multiple-use paved, and recreation areas. The turf area provides space for many games and other activities and the apparatus area for such climbing equipment as a jungle gym, horizontal bars, and giant strides. There should be ample space to provide for the safety of the participants. The shaded area may provide space for such activities as marbles, hopscotch, or ring toss, and also storytelling. The multiple-use paved area may be used for a variety of purposes and activities on a year-round basis by both school and community. It can house basketball, tennis, and handball courts, games of low organization, and other activities. This area should be paved with material that takes into consideration resiliency, safety, and durability. Rapid and efficient drainage is essential. Lines may be painted on the area for the various types of games. The schools should allow additional space adjacent to this area for possible future expansion.

4. Gymnasia for elementary schools should have a minimum floor area of at least 50 by 80 feet and include such general construction features as smooth walls, hardwood floors (maple preferred), recessed lights, recessed radiators, adequate and well-screened windows, and storage space for the apparatus and other equipment. It is also generally agreed that it is best to have the gymnasium located in a separate wing of the building to isolate the noise and a convenient location for community groups anxious to use such facilities.

5. Suggested equipment and apparatus may be found in Chapter 6.

Personnel

A controversial issue in elementary

school physical education is whether the classroom teacher or the specialist should teach physical education. A discussion of this subject appears later in this book. At this point it will suffice to say that both the physical education specialist and the classroom teacher must work closely together in carrying out this important function. The classroom teacher in many school systems is assigned the responsibility but there is a physical education specialist upon whom she or he may call for advice, materials, and help.

Some of the important qualifications of the classroom teacher are as follows:

1. *A philosophy of education that appreciates physical education as an important part of education.* The classroom teacher must see physical education as an important part of the educational program. Frequently, the classroom teacher appreciates reading, arithmetic, and language as important phases of elementary education but does not have the same feeling for physical education. In such cases, this philosophy and feeling is reflected in what the teacher does during the physical education period. There are some classroom teachers who use this period as a time to sun themselves while the children play on their own, to chat with other teachers who have their classes on the playground at the same time, or to stay in the classroom and grade papers while the youngsters run and jump outside. A disservice is being done when such conditions exist. It is just as though the teacher failed to carry out the teaching assignments in history or in science.

2. *An interest in children and their play activities.* The classroom teacher who recognizes that boys and girls have a love of play and a desire for action and appreciates and wants to direct these desires into educational channels will do an excellent job in physical education. She or he will recognize

that this medium is a natural part of the growth and development of children and will nurture and use it for educational purposes.

3. *A desire and determination to know what physical education is all about.* Unfortunately, most classroom teachers have insufficient training and preparation in physical education. Many have no formal course work whatsoever. Some have had a three-hour credit course which covered the activities, the philosophy, and other aspects of physical education. A few have had more extensive training. This means, therefore, that much of the training and information must be self-taught and gained on the job. The classroom teacher can get much of this information and do much toward his or her own self-education by (a) contacting the physical education specialist for help and advice and (b) developing a professional library on physical education. There may be a specialist assigned to the elementary school. If not, there are some in the community who will be most anxious to offer help and assistance. It might be wise to ask to be notified when physical education staff meetings are held and then attend them. There are also many excellent books on physical education and many fine periodicals that contain helpful articles which will keep the teacher in touch with new trends, provide new methods for teaching classes, and help solve the problems that continually arise.

4. *A diligent effort to provide a good physical education program.* The classroom teacher should make an honest attempt to provide a physical education program for his or her pupils which is in accordance with professional standards. This program should be based upon the needs and interests of pupils and should mesh with the program of the preceding grade and the grade following.

QUALIFICATIONS OF THE ELEMENTARY SCHOOL PHYSICAL EDUCATION SPECIALIST

The qualifications of the elementary school physical education specialist should exceed those of the classroom teacher:

1. *Professional preparation*—graduation from an approved teacher training institution with a major in physical education, and accredited by the American Association of Colleges of Teacher Education.

2. *General education*—preparation in such general education areas as English, science, psychology, foreign languages, and the arts.

3. *Elementary education*—preparation in and an understanding of the elementary school child and the program of studies and activities with which he should be provided, together with an appreciation of how physical education fits into the total pattern.

4. *Health*—freedom from any physical or mental defects which would prevent successful teaching in physical education. Because of the important part that a teacher plays in shaping a child's life, it is necessary that specialists have good mental and physical health. Furthermore, in building healthy bodies they should be good testimony for their preachments.

5. *Personality suitable for teaching*—possession of such personality traits as enthusiasm, friendliness, cheerfulness, industry, cooperation, self-control, integrity, social adaptability, and likeableness. Whether or not the right social traits are developed in children will depend largely on the personality of the leader.

6. *Sincere interest in the teaching of physical education*—possession of a deep conviction that he or she is rendering a service to mankind. Physical educators should have an interest in serving children through the teaching of physical activities and in helping them to develop into better adults.

7. *Acceptable standard of motor ability*—possession of skills in the activities he or she teaches. Physical skills are basic to the physical education profession and proficiency in some of them is important to success in this type of work.

8. *Sense of humor*—possession of a lighter side to his or her personality, a requisite for the teacher who works with children. It will make physical education more interesting for students.

QUESTIONS AND PRACTICAL PROBLEMS

1. What role does movement play in the physical education program?

2. Do you think John Dewey was in favor of physical education? Why?

3. To what extent did the physical education program in which you participated in elementary school contribute to your physical, social, mental, and emotional welfare?

4. Why is there a great need for understanding the true meaning of physical education? What are your responsibilities to interpret the work correctly? Explain your answer in as much detail as you can.

5. Define the term *education*. What do you consider an acceptable definition of an educated person to be? What are the advan-

tages of being an educated person in light of your definition?

6. What is meant by each of the following terms: hygiene, physical culture, gymnastics, physical training, athletics? What is the relation of each to physical education?

7. What is the classroom teacher's role in physical education in the elementary school? What qualifications should he or she have?

8. How can the elementary classroom teacher prepare herself to do an effective job of teaching physical education? Outline what you consider to be a practical in-service program.

SELECTED REFERENCES

BUCHER, CHARLES A., *Administration of School Health and Physical Education Programs,* St. Louis, The C. V. Mosby Company, 1963.

———, *Foundations of Physical Education* (Fourth edition), St. Louis, The C. V. Mosby Company, 1964.

DUNCAN, RAY O., and HELEN B. WATSON, *Introduction to Physical Education,* New York, The Ronald Press Company, 1960.

JENNY, JOHN H., *Physical Education, Health Education, and Recreation,* New York, The Macmillan Company, 1961.

NIXON, EUGENE W., *et al., An Introduction to Physical Education,* Philadelphia, W. B. Saunders Company, 1959.

PAPE, LAURENCE A., and LOUIS E. MEANS, *A Professional Career in Physical Education,* Englewood Cliffs, N.J., Prentice-Hall, Inc., 1962.

SMITH, HOPE, and MARGUERITE CLIFTON, *Physical Education—Exploring Your Future,* Englewood Cliffs, N.J., Prentice-Hall, Inc., 1962.

VAN DALEN, DEOBOLD B., and MARCELLA M. VAN DALEN, *The Health, Physical Education and Recreation Teacher,* Englewood Cliffs, N.J., Prentice-Hall, Inc., 1956.

CHAPTER 2

The Contribution of Physical Education to General Education

A set of plans used to build a house 150 years ago could not successfully be utilized today. Times have changed. The availability of land was not a problem a century and one half ago. Today over 180,-000,000 Americans live in the United States and thousands are trying to find a place to live—many of them in or near already crowded cities. The cost of lumber has increased, carpenters' wages have jumped to more than $4 an hour, taxes are high, and zoning laws have been established to meet the problems connected with modern-day living. These are only a few of the changes that have occurred which make plans developed 150 years ago almost worthless for today's builder.

The same thing that is true of building houses is true of many other things—business, medicine, transportation, communication, and certainly education. Schools of great-grandfather's day would not satisfy the needs of today's children. During the American colonial period, such subjects at Latin, Greek, and rhetoric, conducted in a severe and serious atmosphere, were believed to provide the best type of education for those few who came to school and were primarily interested in becoming lawyers, ministers, and doctors. Educators felt these subjects, plus drills and rigid discipline, met the needs of children and youth. Even within the lifetimes of people living today, many elementary schools were restricted to teaching the three R's and to drilling in the facts of history, geography, and literature. Secondary schools were primarily concerned with mathematics, languages, and science. Such subjects as music, dramatics, home economics, manual arts, and physical education were not considered important. Extracurricular activities did not even exist.

THE CHANGING ELEMENTARY SCHOOL CURRICULUM

Brown has outlined the changes in the subject matter of the elementary school from 1800 to 1945. The reader can see in Table 2–1 the tremendous changes that have been made during this period of time.

Today, there are even more new ex-periences offered children in the schools of the nation. In addition to such regular offerings as arithmetic, writing, geography, and spelling, new experiences which include camping, outdoor education, safety, and health are taking their place in curricular

TABLE 2–1. *Changes in the Subject Matter of the Elementary School, 1800–1945*[1]

1800	1850	1900	1945
Reading	Reading	Reading	Reading
Spelling	Declamation	Literature	Literature
Writing	Spelling	Spelling	Spelling
Catechism and Bible	Writing	Penmanship system	Printing and script writing
Arithmetic	Manners and conduct	Conduct	Citizenship
	Mental arithmetic	Arithmetic	Arithmetic
	and ciphering	Oral language	Oral presentation
	Grammar	Grammar	Correct usage
	Geography	Geography	Geography
	U.S. history	U.S. history	History
	Object lessons	Constitution	Local
		Object lessons	National
		Elementary science	Backgrounds
		Drawing	Constitutions
		Music	General science
		Physical exercises	Art
		Manual training	Music
			Hygiene
			Physical education
			Vocational education
			Homemaking
			Foreign language
			Trips and excursions
			Extracurricular activities

[1] Francis J. Brown, *Educational Sociology* (Second edition), Englewood Cliffs, N.J., Prentice-Hall, Inc., 1954, p. 376. Reprinted by permission of the publisher.

patterns. The school is rapidly becoming a setting where the child receives training and preparation for meeting successfully the problems involved in modern-day living. Many of the responsibilities formerly viewed as the sole prerogative of the home are being shifted to the school. This places an increased load and responsibility on the classroom teacher. If she is to do a good job, she must be versatile and adept in many areas and disciplines. Since physical education is an important part of the elementary school program, she needs to have a good grounding in this specialized field.

EDUCATION AS PREPARATION FOR LIFE

Education has changed over the years to meet a changing society. It has adjusted its curricula to meet the needs and interests of people who are required to live in a changing world. It is designed to help individuals meet their responsibilities in day-to-day living. Education is preparing individuals for fruitful and useful lives. Life is not concerned merely with facts. It is also concerned with such things as ethics, human relations, mental health, citizenship, and emotions. Subject matter and discipline are not enough. The total culture to which man is exposed and which influences his actions must be considered. He has not been born in a vacuum. He has been born into a way of life which he should help to preserve and improve for future generations.

George Counts, writing on principles of education, pointed to the value of having an education that was geared to the needs and interests of the individual. Through an illustration involving a dialogue between teacher and pupil, he accented the need for meeting the day-to-day problems with which children and adults are faced:

Greeting his pupils, the master asked:
    What would you learn of me?
And the reply came:
    How shall we care for our bodies?
    How shall we rear our children?
    How shall we work together?
    How shall we live with our fellowmen?
    How shall we play?
    For what ends shall we live?
And the teacher pondered these words, and
    sorrow was in his heart, for his own
    learning touched not these things.[2]

THE MEANING AND OBJECTIVES OF GENERAL EDUCATION

The term *education* has different meanings for various individuals. Some define it as a training process which involves study and instruction; others say it is the sum total of human experiences; and still others say it means growth and adjustment. John Dewey, an educator who did as much as anyone to influence modern educational thinking, defined education as the reconstruction of events which compose the lives of individuals so that new happenings and new events become more purposeful and more meaningful. Furthermore, through education, individuals will be better able to regulate the direction of ensuing experience. Education as defined by Dewey is a "doing" phenomenon. One learns through doing. Education takes place in the classroom, in the library, on the playground, in the gymnasium, and in the swimming pool.

The job of education is to provide experiences for the student which will be most meaningful in life. Since education is the preparing of individuals for worthwhile lives, the schools should enable one to live a more purposeful, interesting, and vigorous life. They should help him to live the "good life." The Educational Policies Commission, in discussing policies for education in American democracy, states the following as the purpose of education:

. . . The primary business of education in effecting the promises of American democracy is to guard, cherish, advance, and make available in the life of coming generations the funded and growing wisdom, knowledge, and aspirations of the race. This involves the dissemination of knowledge, the liberation of minds, the development of skills, the promotion of free inquiries, the encouragement of the creative or inventive spirit, and the establishment of wholesome attitudes toward order and change—all useful in the good life for each person, in the practical arts, and in the maintenance and improvement of American society, as our society, in the world of accomplishment. It does in fact,

[2] J. Crosby Chapman and George S. Counts, *Principles of Education,* Boston, Houghton Mifflin Company, 1924, Foreword.

if perfection be expected; but such is the primary business of public education in the United States; theory supports it; practice inadequately illustrates and confirms it.[3]

Education Is More Than Absorbing Knowledge

Education cannot restrict itself to the dispensing of knowledge, according to the Educational Policies Commission. In addition, other factors are essential. As this commission says, "The nature of the knowledge to be disseminated is qualified by the condition, 'useful in the good life and in the maintenance and improvement of American society.' Both ethics and the nature of American civilization are drawn into immediate and inescapable consideration."

The Educational Policies Commission further points out that education is as much concerned with the training of the body and spirit as with the transmission of knowledge. It states:

It is not merely with the transmission of knowledge that education is deeply concerned. The functions of the schools are not fully described by a summary of programs, curriculum, and methods. No written or spoken words do, or can, completely convey the meaning of education as the day-to-day living force that it is in fact and may be—in the transactions of pupil and pupil, and in the experiences of the library and athletic field. Here are exchanges, bearings, and influences too subtle for logical expression and exact measurement. Yet we cannot doubt their existence, at least those of us who recall our own educational experiences and see teachers at work. Here, in the classroom, the auditorium, laboratory, and gymnasium, are in constant operation moral and cultural forces

just as indispensable to civilization as knowledge or any material elements—indeed primordial in nature and the preconditions for the civilized users of material things.[4]

The above statements well define and express the role of education as it relates to our educational systems. It is within this pattern that all experiences should be formulated.

Objectives of General Education

The goals toward which American education is striving have been enumerated many times in the nation's history. The compilation of objectives which, it seems, has received the most publicity is the list set forth by the National Education Association in 1918. This list received the label "Cardinal Principles of Education" and included such well-known aims as health, command of fundamental processes, worthy home membership, vocation, citizenship, worthy use of leisure, and ethical character. Although these principles were stated 40 years ago, to a great degree they are still reflected in educational thinking today. Over the years, Americans have consistently held a constant point of view as to what they felt their schools should accomplish.

Another group of aims reflects the social-economic goals for education as presented in ten characteristics which are desired for the individual American. These characteristics were stated in 1937 by a committee that included a philosopher, a lawyer, a sociologist, a superintendent of schools, and two secretaries of state education associations. They include hereditary strength; physical security; skills, technics, knowledge, values, and standards for effective participation in an evolving culture; an active, flexible

---

[3] Educational Policies Commission, *Policies for Education in American Democracy*, Washington, D.C., National Education Association and the American Association of School Administrators, 1946, p. 60.

[4] *Ibid.*, p. 64.

personality; suitable occupation; economic security; mental security; equality of opportunity; freedom; and fair play. Also included in the report of this committee, of which John Dewey and Willard E. Givens were members, were statements that "education must be universal in its extent and application, universal in its materials and methods, and universal in its aim and spirit."

In 1946, the Educational Policies Commission, one of the most influential groups affecting the direction of American education, set forth four groups of objectives in discussing the purpose of education. These objectives have become guides for teachers in our schools. On careful analysis, it will be discerned that they reflect the thoughts of previous committees and commissions. The four groups are objectives of self-realization, objectives of human relationship, objectives of economic efficiency, and objectives of civic responsibility.

The objectives of self-realization deal with such important items as the desire for learning; the ability to speak, read, and write effectively; an acquisition of knowledge and habits concerned with healthful living; and the ability to use leisure time in a wholesome and satisfying manner.

The objectives of human relationship are concerned with such things as an appreciation of the home, friendships, courtesy, the value of human welfare, and the ability to work harmoniously with one's fellow men.

The objectives of economic efficiency pertain to producer and consumer education. On the one hand, they stress such things as the importance of good workmanship, careful selection of one's vocation, and occupational adjustment, appreciation, and efficiency; on the other hand, they stress such factors as consumer judgment, buying, and protection.

The objectives of civic responsibility involve the citizen's responsibility to his

fellow men, to his country, and to the world; his responsibility for developing a tolerant, scientific, critical, sympathetic, and cooperative attitude within himself; and his responsibility for developing an unswerving loyalty to the democratic way of life.

A few years ago, a White House Conference on Education was called by the President of the United States. This meeting re-emphasized the many objectives of education that have been listed in this section. The conference clearly pointed out the desire of the American people that the schools prepare their children mentally, physically, emotionally, and socially for the tasks that lie before them. The White House Committee in its report to the President of the United States stressed that it saw a "genuine public demand" for what historians may look upon as a new concept of education. This concept was stated in the following words:

Schools are now asked to help each child to become as good and as capable in every way as native endowment permits. The schools are asked to help children to acquire any skill or characteristic which a majority of the community deems worth while. The order given by the American people to the schools is grand in its simplicity; in addition to intellectual achievement, the schools must foster morality, happiness, and any useful ability. The talent of each child is to be sought out and developed to the fullest. Each weakness is to be studied and, so far as possible, corrected. This is a very majestic ideal, and an astonishingly new one. Schools of that kind have never been provided for more than a small fraction of mankind.

This concept of the White House Conference places additional importance on the development of the "whole" child, and the "physical" is an important aspect of this "whole" development.

The goals of education as presented by various groups and individuals indicate that a heavy responsibility rests upon the shoulders of teachers who spend a large share of their time with the children and youth of today. If experiences are provided which are satisfying, successful, and directed toward enriching an individual's life, these purposes of education will be accomplished. However, if this responsibility is shunned, if an indifferent attitude is assumed, if attention is not focused on the child, if children are allowed to grow up without having experiences which build for the good life—then education, as provided through organized institutions, is not realizing its potentialities. Each teacher has within his or her power the ability to aid in the fulfillment of the objectives of education. The education that takes place in the total program of the school can accomplish the "majestic ideal"—in the words of the White House Conference—of America.

THE MEANING AND OBJECTIVES OF PHYSICAL EDUCATION[5]

The term *physical education* takes on a new meaning after a consideration of the word *education*. The word *physical* refers to the body. It is often used in reference to various characteristics such as physical strength, physical development, physical prowess, physical health, and physical appearance. It refers to the body as distinct from the mind. Therefore, when you add the word *education* to the word *physical* and use the words *physical education,* you are referring to an educational process concerned with activities which develop and maintain the human body. When an individual is playing Run Sheep Run, swimming in the pool, dancing in the gymnasium, skating on the pond, or performing any of the activities which aid in the development and maintenance of his body, education is taking place. This education may be conducive to the enrichment of the individual's life, or it may be detrimental. It may be a satisfying experience, or it may be an unhappy one. It may help to achieve educational objectives, or it may result in antisocial behavior. Whether or not physical education helps or inhibits the attainment of educational objectives depends to a great extent upon the

[5] Charles A. Bucher, *Foundations of Physical Education* (Fourth edition), St. Louis, The C. V. Mosby Company, 1964.

leadership that is responsible for its direction.

Physical education is a very important part of the general educational process. It is not a frill or an appendage to the school program. It is, instead, a vital part of education. It can be defined as follows: *Physical education, an integral part of the total education process, is a field of endeavor which has as its aim the development of physically, mentally, emotionally, and socially fit citizens through the medium of physical activities that have been selected with a view to realizing these outcomes.*

The aim of all education is to enable one to live an enriched and abundant life. This is the ultimate goal on which all who are concerned with education have trained their sights. The objectives of physical education are more definite and specific than this aim, and through these objectives, the ultimate goal is brought nearer to realization.

A study of the child reveals four general directions or phases in which growth and development take place: physical development, skill development, mental development, and social development. Each of these phases contributes to the making of a well-rounded individual who will become a worthy member of society. Physical education can play a very important part in contributing to each of these phases of child growth and development. Physical education will prove its vital importance as a part of the educational process if it can accomplish these objectives.

Physical Development Through Directed Play

Play excels as a contributor to the health and physical development of the child. It is essential to optimum physical development—to a healthy heart, lungs, and other organs of the body—and to the development of such characteristics as strength, endurance, agility, speed, and accuracy. All are essential to a healthful, vigorous, and satisfying life.

The physical development objective is concerned with the program of activities which builds physical power in an individual. It results in the ability to sustain adaptive effort, recover, and resist fatigue. The value of this objective rests on the premise that a person will be more active, have better performance, and be healthier if the organic systems of the body are adequately developed and functioning properly.

Exercise plays an important part in the development of the organic systems of the body. The term *organic* refers to the digestive, circulatory, excretory, heat regulatory, respiratory, and other systems of the human body. These systems are stimulated through activities which involve such basic movements as hanging, climbing, running, throwing, leaping, carrying, and jumping. The activity should be of a vigorous nature so that the various organic systems are sufficiently stimulated.

Through regular, vigorous exercise several beneficial results are achieved. The heart beats slower and provides better nourishment to the entire body. It pumps more blood per stroke, hence more food is delivered to the cells and there is better removal of waste products. There is a longer rest period between beats. After exercise it returns to normal much more rapidly. As a result, a person who exercises regularly over an extended period is able to perform work for a greater length of time, with less expenditure of energy, and much more efficiency. This trained condition is necessary to a vigorous and abundant life because from the time a person rises in the morning until he goes to bed at night he is continually in need of vitality, strength, endurance, and stamina to perform routine tasks, to be prepared for emergencies, and to lead an active life.

This objective is especially important for the elementary school child. This is his formative period. Play is his work—it helps him to grow and develop, to build the sound organic base which is so essential to a healthy and vigorous existence. According to some recent studies, American children are soft compared to European youngsters. Although the evidence is not conclusive, there is a danger of young people getting soft because all of the laborsaving devices and other gadgets that modern technology is giving this country tend to result in a lack of the sufficient physical activity necessary to develop strong, flexible bodies. The possibility of a weak youth has attracted the attention of many doctors, educators, and even the President of the United States. There is a growing urgency to do everything possible to build a strong, physically fit youth. Elementary school teachers, in particular, should realize the importance of this objective and strive to organize and administer physical education programs which fulfill this important need.

Skill Development Through Directed Play

The skill development objective is concerned with performing various physical movements with as little expenditure of energy as possible in a proficient, graceful, and aesthetic manner. This has implications for one's work, play, and anything else that requires physical movement.

Effective skill is dependent upon a harmonious working of the muscular and nervous systems. It allows for peak performance over fairly long periods of time. It is needed in activities involving running, hanging, jumping, dodging, leaping, kicking, bending, twisting, carrying, and throwing. It enables one to perform his daily work much more efficiently and without tiring too quickly.

In physical education activities, the function of efficient body movement or neuromuscular skill, as it is often called, is to provide the individual with the ability to perform with a degree of proficiency. Among other benefits, it will result in greater enjoyment of participation. Most persons enjoy doing those things in which they have acquired a degree of mastery or skill. For example, if a child has mastered the ability to throw a ball consistently to a designated spot and has developed batting and fielding power, he will like to play baseball or softball. If he can swim 25 or 50 yards without tiring and can perform several advanced dives, he will enjoy being in the water. If he can dance the tango, waltz, or cha cha cha, he will like to get out on the dance floor. A person enjoys doing those things in which he or she excels. On the other hand, people do not enjoy participating in activities in which they have little or no skill. Therefore, it is an objective of physical education to develop in each child as many physical skills as possible so that his interests will be wide and varied. This will not only result in more enjoyment for the participant, but at the same time will allow for better individual adjustment to groups.

Physical skills are not developed in one easy lesson. It takes years to acquire co-ordinations, and the most important period of their development is during the formative years of a child's growth. The building of coordinations starts in childhood when an individual attempts to synchronize his muscular and nervous systems for such things as creeping, walking, running, and jumping. A study of kinesiology shows that many muscles of the body are used in even the most simple coordinated movements. Therefore, in order to obtain efficient motor movement or skill in many activities, it is necessary to start training early in life and to continue it into adulthood. Further, a child does not object to the continual trial and error process of achieving success in the performance of physical acts. He does not object to being observed as an awkward, uncoordinated beginner during the learning period. Most adults, however, are very self-conscious when going through the period of learning a physical skill. They do not like to perform if they cannot perform in a creditable manner. As a result, the skills they do not acquire in their youth are many times never acquired. Therefore, the classroom teacher and the physical education teacher should do everything possible to ensure that much skill learning takes place when a person is young, willing, and laying the foundation for adult years.

Mental Development Through Directed Play

Children develop mentally when they play. This is sometimes hard for educators and parents to understand. Through play youngsters gain knowledge, learn to reason and make judgments, and develop other intellectual powers. Gesell points out how much children learn and develop through their play. Many observing parents and teachers have noticed it while they watched boys and girls in action. Babies learn that a *ball* will *bounce* but a block won't. If you *push* some toys a *bell* will *ring*. When you chew on a spoon it is *hard* and *cold,* but a teddy bear's foot is *soft* and *fuzzy*. Through trial and error in play children learn many basic facts. Parents often take these things for granted because this knowledge is so fundamental, but these symbols have to be mastered—a child isn't born with an understanding of them. Many other mental concepts are developed through play. Young children learn simple arithmetic in rope jumping: "Mary, after the rope turns *four* times, you run in and take *ten* jumps." When the boys plan a softball diamond they must *compute angles* and handle *measurements*. The baseball team uses *percentages* in figuring batting *averages*. Children dance and march in *circles, squares, rectangles,* and *parallel lines*. Every activity has a learning situation, if the proper leadership is present to bring it out.

The individual also acquires knowledge about games. Such things as rules, techniques, and strategies are learned. Basketball can be used as an example. In this sport the participant should know the rules, the strategy in offense and defense, the various types of passes, the difference between screening and blocking, and, finally, the values that are derived from playing the sport. Techniques which are learned through experience result in knowledge. For example, a ball travels faster and more accurately if one steps with a pass, and time is saved when the pass is made from the same position in which it is received. Furthermore, a knowledge of followership, leadership, courage, self-reliance, assistance to others, safety, and adaptation to group patterns is very important.

Knowledge concerning health should play an important part in the program. All individuals should know about their bodies, the importance of disease prevention, exercise, sanitation, and a well-balanced diet, and the values of good health habits and attitudes. This knowledge will contribute greatly to physical prowess as well as to general health. Through the accumulation of a knowledge of these facts, activities will take on a new meaning and health practices will be associated with definite purposes. This will help each individual to live a healthier and more purposeful life.

A store of knowledge will give each individual the proper background for interpreting the new situations which inevitably confront him from day to day. Unless there is knowledge to draw from, he will become helpless when called upon to make important decisions.

Social Development Through Directed Play

The child's social development is greatly advanced through play. Many times he forms his values, ideals, and standards from those utilized and practiced by his teachers and playmates. Directed play should provide suitable social relationships between the child and his playmates and teacher. Constructive behavior patterns of helpfulness, kindness, truthfulness, justice, and sociability should result. Individual qualities such as aggresiveness, ambition, perseverance, and courage should be directed so they will not become objectionable. They can be disciplined through play. Good manners, courtesy, truthfulness, consideration for others, and a belief in the Golden Rule are worthy objectives which can be accomplished. Properly guided play does not give the child an opportunity to develop antisocial qualities. As Adler in his book *Understanding Human Nature* says, "The manner in which a child approaches a game, his choice and the importance he places upon it, indicates his attitude and relationship to his environment and how he is related to his fellowmen."

The teacher who plays with her children can be a very influential person in shaping their character development. In play she observes them in their most natural state. The personality of the child is displayed in his play reactions. When he misses a ball is he always looking for an excuse? "Tom threw it too hard." "It wasn't anywhere near me." When he is about to be tagged in a running and fleeing game does he "accidentally on purpose" fall down? If he is poor at some particular activity or skill, does he project his defense on others. "Sam can't play as well as I can even if I can't hit the ball."

Many individual traits or characteristics may be identified through play. Many can also be corrected by the wise and understanding teacher. The teacher, however, must avoid planning activities for play which are too complex. If the play requires skills beyond the capacity of the child, the challenge may appear too great and he will retreat. The same might be true if attainable results are too elementary and have no challenge—he may retreat from the group and choose something for himself which offers more of a challenge.

All human beings should experience success. This factor can be realized through play. Through successful experience in play activities, a child develops self-confidence and finds happiness in his achievements. Physical education can provide for this successful experience by offering a variety of activities and developing the necessary skills for success in these activities.

If children are happy, they will make the necessary adjustments. An individual who is happy is much more likely to make the right adjustment than the individual who is morbid, sullen, and in an unhappy state of mind. Happiness reflects friendliness, cheerfulness, and a spirit of cooperation, all of which help a person to be content and to conform to the necessary standards which have been established. Therefore, physical education should instill happiness by guiding children into those activities where this quality will be realized.

In a democratic society all individuals should develop a sense of group conscious-

Figure 2–1. Dance teaches social development.

ness and cooperative living. This should be one of the most important objectives of the physical education program. Whether or not a child will grow up to be a good citizen and contribute to the welfare of society will depend to a great extent upon the training he receives during his childhood and youth. In various play activities the following factors should be stressed: aid for the less-skilled players, respect for the rights of others, subordination of one's desires to the will of the group, and realization that co-operative living is essential to the success of society. In other words, the Golden Rule should be practiced. The individual should be made to feel that he belongs to the group and has the responsibility of directing his actions in its behalf. The rules of sportsmanship should be developed and practiced in all activities that are offered in the program. Such things as courtesy, sympathy, truthfulness, fairness, honesty, respect for authority, and abiding by the rules will help a great deal in the promotion of social efficiency. The necessity for good leadership and followership should also be stressed as important to the interests and the ideals of our society.

People's actions can be controlled through proper education. This education can result in effective citizenship, which is the basis of sound, democratic living. Effective citizenship is not something that can be developed by artificial stimuli. It is something that is achieved only through activities in which indivduals engage in their normal day-to-day routines. Since play activities have such a great attraction for children and youth, and since it is possible to develop desirable social traits under proper guidance, physical education should realize its responsibility. It should do its part in contributing to good citizenship—the basis of a democratic society.

PHYSICAL EDUCATION AS A PART OF GENERAL EDUCATION

It can be seen that through the fulfillment of its objectives of physical, skill, mental, and social development, physical education can contribute a great deal to the whole development and growth process. It is important, however, to be able to see more clearly how this phase contributes to each of the objectives set forth for education in general. For purposes of organization, such a discussion may be grouped under the four headings which represent the objectives of general education as set forth by the Educational Policies Commission. By realizing how physical education, as an integral part of education, contributes to the fulfillment of each of these objectives, the teacher will have a clearer conception of how physical education fits into a total integrated educational pattern.

The Objectives of Self-realization

The objectives of self-realization are aimed at developing the individual so that he realizes his potentialities and becomes a well-adjusted member of society. Physical education can contribute to the objectives of self-realization in many ways.

1. *Contributing to an inquiring mind.* New and interesting phases of living are opened up to the child through activity. His motor mechanism enables him to explore,

to cruise, and to see and discover the nature of many phases of his environment. It stimulates his curiosity.

2. *Contributing to knowledge of health and disease*. Physical education contributes to knowledge by giving the child information as to the importance of such things as nutrition, rest, sleep, and exercise; by instructing him in measures that should be taken to guard against disease; by developing an understanding of why the body needs vigorous outdoor activity; by instilling an appreciation of wholesome health attitudes and habits; by giving him knowledge about the correction of physical defects; by stressing safety factors for the prevention of accidents; and by showing the importance of adequate health services.

3. *Contributing to family and community health*. Physical education can create, within the student, a realization of his responsibilities for his own health and for the health of others. He comes to realize that health is a product that increases as it is shared with other individuals. He has a responsibility for the health of others in school, at home, and in the community of which he is a part.

4. *Contributing to skill as a participant and spectator in sports*. Physical education develops skill in many activities. The child, as a result, can enjoy and derive the many advantages that come from actually engaging in a game or other similar experiences. At the same time, an interest and knowledge of other activities is presented so that the value of spectator enjoyment is also enhanced.

5. *Contributing to resources for utilizing leisure hours in mental pursuits*. Education is concerned with developing mental resources for the utilization of leisure hours. Physical education contributes by providing the material for interesting sports stories and biographies of great athletes, such as Bob Cousy, Willie Mays, and Arnold Palmer.

In addition to motivating reading, sports can contribute to many interesting hobbies such as designing, building, and caring for equipment, research on the many statistics involved in sports, and a study of various aspects of nature which would be aroused by an interest in sports.

6. *Contributing to an appreciation of beauty*. The educated person develops an appreciation of the beautiful which can be fostered in early childhood. In addition to beauty of architecture, painting, and music, the child should also appreciate the beauty of trees, animals, the sky, and other aspects of the environment which he meets in his play. He should develop an appreciation for the beauty of his body, and of physical movement, which in sports situations can produce the ultimate in grace, rhythm, and coordination.

7. *Contributing to the direction of one's life toward worthwhile goals*. The educated person conscientiously attempts to guide his life in the proper direction. Physical education can contribute to the child's direction during the early formative years by giving guidance as to what is right and proper, which goals are worth competing for, the difference between intrinsic and extrinsic values, autocratic and democratic procedures, and antisocial and acceptable conduct. The child is a great imitator, and the beliefs, actions, and conduct of the teacher are often reflected in the beliefs, actions, and conduct of the student.

The Objectives of Human Relationships

Human relationships may be defined as the manner in which individuals get along with each other. Good human relations imply that people live together, work together, and play together harmoniously. Physical education can make a worthwhile contribution in this area in a variety of ways, of which the following are significant:

1. *Placing human relations first.* Activities are planned with the needs and interests of children in mind; rules and regulations exist for the benefit of the player's welfare; the less skilled are given due attention; and the program is child-centered. If human relations come first, a spirit of good will, fellowship, and cooperation exists.

2. *Enabling each child to enjoy a rich social experience through play.* Such an experience can help develop a child's personality by teaching him to adapt to the group situation, by developing proper standards of conduct, by creating a feeling of belonging, and by developing a sound code of ethics. There are limitless possibilities for social experiences in "tag" and "it" games. Here the child learns behavior traits which are characteristic of a democratic society. Because of his drive for play, he will be more willing to abide by the rules, accept responsibility, contribute to the welfare of the group, and respect the rights of others.

3. *Helping children to play cooperatively.* The physical education program should stress cooperation as the basis for achieving the goals an individual or group desires. It should also stress leadership and followership traits. The success of any venture depends on good leadership and good workers or followers. Everyone cannot be captain of the relay team. Everyone does not have leadership ability. Those who are good leaders should also be good followers. A leader in one activity might possibly make a better follower in another activity. The important thing is that both leaders and followers are needed for the accomplishment of any enterprise. All contribute to the undertaking. All deserve commendation for work well done. Cooperation by every member of the group in whatever way each one is best equipped to contribute will insure success for the group endeavor.

4. *Teaching courtesy, fair play, and good sportsmanship.* The amenities of social behavior are a part of the repertoire of every educated person. Such characteristics as courtesy, fair play, and good sportsmanship can be developed in the child as he plays with his classmates and others in game situations.

5. *Contributing to family and home living.* The teacher of physical education is often the individual in whom a child puts his trust and confidence and whom he desires to emulate. The nature of physical education work and its appeal to youth are probably the major reasons for this tendency. Consequently, the teacher in charge of the physical education class should utilize his advantageous position to become better acquainted with the youth and his home and family life. Many times a child's home and parent problems can be helped through such knowledge. Proper counseling and guidance, helping children to experience success in play activities, talks with parents, and home visits are often useful.

The Objectives of Economic Efficiency

A third objective of education deals with the production and consumption of goods and services. Education has the opportunity of informing children in respect to both the vocational aspects of living and the consumer aspects. Both are important and are necessary for a happy and successful life. Physical education can aid in more efficient production of goods and services and also can aid in the establishment of certain standards which will guide the public in the wise consumption of certain goods.

1. *Recognition of the need for good workmanship.* Work is an essential for all individuals. Through work one contributes goods and services to the community of which he is a part. Children should have the

opportunity to work. As part of their educational training children should be assigned tasks in the home and also in school. In physical education, children could help develop playfields, care for equipment, and instruct those with less skill. Through regular duties, they can discover that they are contributing to the welfare of the group and are providing services which will help others to enjoy their activity experiences more fully.

2. *Recognition of the need for successful work.* The success of any job depends to a great degree upon the health and physical fitness of the worker. Experience in physical education activities contributes to physical health, mental health, human relations, and other social assets which help to contribute to better work. As each child develops a strong organic base for future years, he becomes prepared to do a better job.

3. *Recognition of the need for professional growth.* The teacher of physical education should be continually interested in developing new skills, understandings, and an appreciation of the contribution that his area of education can make to child growth and development. Physical education is a growing profession. New awareness and knowledge in the fields of biology, psychology, and sociology are continually evolving which have implications for helping the physical education teacher do the best job possible. Only if the teacher is constantly studying such new developments can he make the greatest contribution to children.

4. *Recognition of the need for wise consumption of goods and services.* The educated person buys his goods and services with wisdom. He is well informed as to the worth and utility of various goods and services. Physical education helps to develop in children the relative values of goods and services that influence their health and physical fitness. Such things as the need to seek qualified advice in health matters, the dangers of self-medication, and the importance of critical evaluation of advertisements and other material on health cures can be discussed.

The Objectives of Civic Responsibility

Civic responsibility falls upon each member of society. Only as each individual assumes his civic responsibility and contributes to group welfare will democratic ties be strengthened.

1. *Recognition of the need for humanitarianism.* Children should be well informed as to the needs of mankind everywhere. A humanitarian view of the conditions of mankind should become a part of every student. Physical education can, within limits, provide democratic play experiences in which children see the importance and value of cooperative living and contributing to the welfare of all. Here is an ideal setting for developing humanitarian values. Children of all creeds, colors, and races and from all walks of life, are brought together for a social experience. Interest and a natural drive for activity provide a laboratory for actual practice in developing these values.

2. *Recognition of the need for tolerance.* It is the prerogative of every person to think out solutions to various problems, form his own opinions, and attempt to bring others around to his point of view. The physical education class can be a place where tolerance is developed in regard to other people's opinions in the various activities they conduct. Children may be educated to participate intelligently in the discussion of common problems that develop in a game situation. All can be encouraged to contribute their thinking. Thoughts and ideas are respected by all and final settlement of the problem can be made by the group.

3. *Recognition of the need for the conservation of natural resources.* Physical education should be especially interested in

preserving such natural resources of the nation as forests, soil, scenic beauty, water, and wild life. They have implications for active forms of recreation. Children should understand the value of such resources to the health and physical fitness of the country. Through an educational program which points out that natural resources are directly related to the welfare of each resident of this country, much good can be done in conserving this form of the nation's wealth.

4. *Recognition of the need for conformance with the law.* In a democracy laws are made by the people and for their benefit. Obedience is essential to a well-ordered society. Physical education can contribute to the development of a law-abiding attitude in youth. The rules of the game and the rules of safety that have been established for the playground, gymnasium, and other places where activities are held should be made clear to each student. Furthermore, the purpose behind such rules and the individual's responsibility in each case should be understood.

5. *Recognition of the need for civic responsibility.* It is the responsibility of every citizen to have a clear understanding of his civic duties and to see that they are carried out in an intelligent manner. Physical education can show how games and various aspects of the school program are analogous in many ways to what the child's responsibilities will be in an adult community. The importance of selecting good leaders, living according to high standards of conduct, abiding by the rules, and contributing to the welfare of the group are a few examples.

6. *Recognition of the need for democratic living.* The educated citizen believes in the democratic way of life and his every action is symbolic of his loyalty to its ideals. Physical education can contribute, together with other areas of the school program, by making experiences on the playground or in the gymnasium ones where democratic principles prevail and where such important concepts as respect for the individual, the rights of others, and freedom of action are honored.

QUESTIONS AND PRACTICAL PROBLEMS

1. Survey an elementary school in your community and list by year the main subject-matter areas that have been covered over the last decade.

2. Evaluate America's way of life today and describe the factors that are essential for living sucessfully in the twentieth-century.

3. Do a research paper, finding as many lists of objectives as possible for education as proposed since 1800 by associations, committees, and commissions. Determine the similarities and differences.

4. Make a drawing of the circulatory system of the body, showing the changes that take place during exercise.

5. Discuss the nervous system of the body in relation to the development of skills.

6. What is the "needs theory" of education? How can these needs be met through physical education?

7. Comment on the statement, "All education takes place within the walls of the public schools."

8. List the objectives of self-realization, human relationship, economic efficiency, and civic responsibility in four columns on a piece of paper. Place a check mark after each objective to which physical education contributes. Opposite each list itemize as many contributions physical education makes to each objective as you can.

9. Examine a history book and determine how the objectives of present-day physical education compare with the objectives of physical education in Ancient Greece. How might the Greek development of physical education be related to the development of democracy?

10. Make a list of points which show the unique features of physical education that contribute to general education objectives.

SELECTED REFERENCES

BRAMELD, THEODORE, *Philosophies of Education in Cultural Perspective,* New York, The Dryden Press, 1955.

BROUDY, HARRY S., *Building a Philosophy of Education,* Englewood Cliffs, N.J., Prentice-Hall, Inc., 1954.

BUCHER, CHARLES A., *Administration of School Health and Physical Education Programs,* St. Louis, The C. V. Mosby Company, 1963.

———, *Foundations of Physical Education* (Fourth edition), St. Louis, The C. V. Mosby Company, 1964.

———, *Methods and Materials in Physical Education and Recreation,* St. Louis, The C. V. Mosby Company, 1954.

EDUCATIONAL POLICIES COMMISSION, *Education for All American Children,* Washington, D.C., National Education Association of the United States and the American Association of School Administrators, 1948.

———,*Education and the Defense of American Democracy,* Washington, D.C., National Education Association of the United States and the American Association of School Administrators, 1940.

———, *Education of Free Men in American Democracy,* Washington, D.C., National Education Association of the United States and the American Association of School Administrators, 1941.

———, *Policies for Education in American Democracy,* Washington, D.C., National Education Association of the United States and the American Association of School Administrators, 1946.

HETHERINGTON, CLARK W., *School Program in Physical Education,* New York, World Book Company, 1922.

MCCLOY, CHARLES H., *Philosophical Bases for Physical Education,* New York, Appleton-Century-Crofts, Inc., 1940.

NASH, JAY B., *Physical Education: Interpretations and Objectives,* New York, A. S. Barnes and Company, 1948, Chapters 6–12.

NIXON, EUGENE W., and FREDERICK W. COZENS, *An Introduction to Physical Education,* Philadelphia, W. B. Saunders Company, 1959.

PARK, JOE, *Selected Readings in the Philosophy of Education* (Second edition), New York, The Macmillan Company, 1963.

WHITEHEAD, ALFRED N., *The Aims of Education,* London, Williams and Northgate, Ltd., 1929.

WILLIAMS, JESSE FEIRING, *The Principles of Physical Education,* Philadelphia, W. B. Saunders Company, 1963.

CHAPTER 3

Play—The Child's Work

The fifth-grade children of the Salamanca Elementary School were restless and impatient. Fidgeting in their seats they watched the hands of the clock slowly work toward eleven o'clock. Then, as the bell rang marking the end of the period, their faces lit up with smiles, and there were uncontrollable whoops of joy. Little arms and legs moved at double time to the school exit and on toward the playground. As they left the confinement of school corridors behind, the fast walk turned into a gallop. There were cheers and yells. Jack Worth, the ten-year-old pride and joy of the town banker, shouted, "Come on Rich, let's get the balls." Doris Brown and six other girls legged it as fast as they could to try and beat them out.

These children were anxious and in a hurry to get where they were going. The eager looks on their faces, tenseness of their muscles, and explosive, limitless energy demonstrated that play is a child's work. It carries its own drive. It is something children want to do. As Arnold Gesell, the well-known child psychologist says, "[Play] rises spontaneously out of instinctive promptings which represent developmental needs. It prepares for maturity. It is a natural enjoyable exercise of growing powers." He continues, "Play never ceases to be a major business throughout childhood. Nature plants strong play propensities in every normal child to make sure that certain basic needs of development will be satisfied."

Nature has not left children's play to chance. It has literally kicked them into activity. It has pushed them into action so that their heart, lungs, muscles, and the rest of their body will develop properly.

Observe elementary school children over a period of hours. They are a mass of activity. It is hard for them to sit still. They must have action. It is not deviltry created in the mind of the child in order to annoy the teacher. It is a drive that cannot be suppressed—it must be expressed. This desire for activity is being satisfied when they burst out of the schoolroom doors onto the playground. It is being met as they climb through the maze of the jungle gym. It expresses itself in creative dance movements. Growth and development are proceeding in harmony as the girls jump rope.

Some years ago an Eastern university conducted an experiment. The investigators asked Mel Ott, a professional baseball player, to come to the playground at nine o'clock one morning. They also requested six-year-old Johnny Beckett to be there. Mel was asked to do everything Johnny did for as long a time as he could. It was a "follow the leader" game and in this case Johnny was the leader. Mel started out enthusiastic and eager to go. Every time Johnny took a somersault, Mel followed suit. When Johnny ran,

Figure 3–1. Play requires intense concentration.

Mel ran. After Johnny, Mel came swishing down the slide. As Johnny wiggled through the bars on one side of the jungle gym, Mel twisted and turned up and down on the other side.

Those who are familiar with children know the result of such an experiment. Although Mel was in excellent physical condition, he became very tired by eleven o'clock, exhausted at twelve, and had to give up a short time later. Johnny's thirst for activity, his boundless energy, and his continual craving for something more to do proved too much for an adult.

W. R. Smith, a psychologist, says, "Play is the most direct motivation possible and is the vocation of youth and avocation of the mature." *Webster's* defines it as an exercise or series of actions intended for amusement or diversion. Joseph Lee, many years ago in his book *Play in Education*, termed it an instinctive activity, looking toward an ideal. John Dewey, well-known educator, believed play consists of activities not consciously performed for the sake of any results beyond themselves. *The Dictionary of Education* defines it as any pleasurable activity carried on for its own sake, without reference to ulterior purpose or future satisfactions. *The Encyclopedia of Modern Education* states: "Play is defined not by the type of activity engaged in but by the distinctive attitude which the players take toward activity. In play, it is the activity itself, rather than the results, that counts."

These are a few definitions of play. To a great degree they all say the same thing: play is a natural activity which carries its own drive and is characterized by joy, pleasure, and happiness.

EDUCATION THROUGH PLAY

Play is one of the most significant ways in which the needs and interests of children are met. At the same time it is something that boys and girls enjoy and are anxious to do. Why not take this natural phenomenon, therefore, and direct it into constructive channels? Let's have *education through play*.

To obtain the most value from play experiences, proper attitudes, knowledge, and skills must be provided. By focusing attention on play and utilizing this innate compulsion for educational purposes, a tremendous new avenue for learning is opened. Children can learn and have fun doing it. Thorndike proved that the best education takes place when experiences are satisfying. What is more satisfying than a child's play? As Professor Thomas Briggs used to say to his students at Columbia University, "Let's help people to do better those things they are going to do anyway." Children are going to play whether adults and teachers want them to or not. Nature, a much greater force than man, has dictated this. Therefore, if play can be utilized to help develop young boys and girls into the types of adults the world needs, it might be said that "two birds are being killed with one stone." Children are satisfying an innate drive and at the same time real education is taking place.

Play is universal. Proof can be found throughout history that people in all ages and in all countries played. Scientists have found toys and trinkets in their excavations of ancient Egypt and Babylonia. Dancing, contests, singing, arts and crafts are some of the types of expression used by people in most parts of the world.

As an ingredient which is common to people everywhere, play offers an excellent medium for education—for preparation for living. It can serve as an excellent tool for learning.

ACCEPTANCE OF PLAY AS AN EDUCATIONAL TOOL

Play is not universally accepted as an educational tool. There are those who maintain that they do not send their children to school to play. They want them to spend all their time learning the three R's and to forget such foolishness as running and jumping. Some cannot visualize play as an effective medium for education. Some still feel that play should occupy only hours after school, at night, and on Saturdays.

History gives us a partial answer to the reason why some individuals today feel play has no educational value. Asceticism, Scholasticism, and Puritanism offer some of the answers to the dilemma. These three doctrines have affected play adversely.

Asceticism

Asceticism, a doctrine that permeated the minds of individuals in the Middle Ages, exalted the spirit and degraded the body. The soul could be saved only through the deprivation and torment of the body. The wants and actual needs of the body were ignored. Therefore, it was felt the body should be disciplined and persecuted in the belief that the spirit would be strengthened. In fact, the body was termed by early leaders as a "lion chained to the spirit mind."

As a result of Asceticism, things associated with the body came to be thought of as evil and those with the mind and spirit as good. Therefore, play, since it was associated with the body, could not be considered education. The so-called cultural subjects—languages, science, arithmetic, and geography —which were more closely associated with the mind, received the emphasis.

Scholasticism

Scholasticism was another dominant Christian philosophy of the Middle Ages. This doctrine is reflected in some educational thinking even today. It exalted the intellect. The physical body and the emotions were ignored. It stressed logic, metaphysics, and theology. It emphasized facts—if one knew the facts, he was educated.

Play, on the other hand, emphasized the body as well as the mind. It stressed the "whole" individual. It was not concerned solely with facts but with living, as well.

Puritanism

Puritanism was a doctrine that developed during the seventeenth century in England and Europe which had both religious and political implications. It came to America largely as a religious doctrine and contained many of the concepts of Asceticism. The Puritans felt that schools should be characterized by sternness, strict discipline, work, and emphasis on things spiritual. The school was not a place to play. Puritanism stressed a fear of showing emotions and playing. Play in any form was looked upon as sin. Work was all the physical activity needed for the good of the individual.

A stanza from an early church hymnal characterizes this philosophy

> Work for the night is coming,
> Work through the morning hours;
> Work while the dew is sparkling,
> Work 'mid springing flowers;
> Work when the day grows brighter,
> Work in the glowing sun;
> Work, for the night is coming,
> When man's work is done.

Everything centered around work. The child was taught that living was a serious business. Things should not be too easy; he should not enjoy himself too much.

Modern Educational Thinking

Although such doctrines as Asceticism, Scholasticism, and Puritanism dominated the thinking of the past and even reach into the present, the importance of play is rapidly expanding. Since the late eighteenth century it has been increasingly recognized as an educational tool.

Outstanding educators began to support play as an educational medium. Pestalozzi, the great Swiss educator of the late eighteenth and early nineteenth centuries, stressed play. He believed it to have great value from a recreational point of view and also as a means of achieving the harmonious development of mind, body, and soul.

Froebel, the renowned German educator, during this same period in history, developed the kindergarten. He strongly believed that one of the best ways to educate children was through play. He felt that youngsters express themselves more readily in their play than in any other way.

John Locke, the English philosopher of the seventeenth century, stressed activity. His words have lived through history. "A sound mind in a sound body is a short but full description of a happy state in this world. He that has these two has little more to wish for." Locke believed that play could aid in the achievement of this worthwhile goal.

Rousseau in *Émile* stressed the important part that play can render in the rearing of children. Dewey and others who followed also recognized the importance of play as a means of educating the young. Although there has been a lag in the acceptance of play as an educational medium, more and more educators are coming to realize the tremendous potential it has for guiding children in the right direction. Play, a medium which has its own drive, cannot be overlooked as an educational device.

DIRECTED PLAY

Play is a medium for the education of children but *it must be properly directed* if it is to achieve desirable outcomes. There must be qualified leadership lest it become misdirected and diverted into destructive channels. This fact was well illustrated recently at a school where there were no planned activities or leadership during a long noon hour. A factory, two short blocks down the railroad tracks from the school, had recently closed and moved its business out of town. At the end of the noon hour the first day after the industry had been vacated, 300 panes of glass were broken by the boys from this school. Was this "play"? The answer is "Yes." Was it directed? The answer, of course, is "No." The fellow who won this noon-hour game was the one who broke the most panes of glass. Pleasure was gained by the boys and they gratified their desire to play. This play was destructive in nature. It was misdirected because of lack of planning and qualified leadership. No planned activities of a constructive type were offered by the school. The school had failed to provide equipment, facilities, and leadership for wholesome play.

The question can be asked, is it necessary to teach a child to play? In a sense the answer is "No." It is not necessary to teach him, but it is necessary to direct his play to worthwhile activities. Again referring to what Professor Briggs stated, education should help an individual to do better those things he is going to do anyway. The child is going to play. But the school has not fulfilled its responsibility unless this play is properly and meaningfully directed and guided.

The play of children is spontaneous. Educators should work *with* this motivation and not *against* it. Through play they can help to develop the most sound standards for living.

Achievement of Children's Goals Through Directed Play

Every child has certain goals which represent basic human needs. Each of these may be satisfied in many ways. Play is one important way. A few of these goals are discussed.

1. *Child's desire for new experiences and adventure*. The child desires new experiences and adventure. He constantly wants new challenges to meet, new mysteries to

unravel, and new adventures to stir his blood. In play he is constantly meeting these new experiences. Each game affords a different adventure depending on its nature, where it is played, and with whom it is played. New learnings are outcomes of these new experiences. Those which are satisfying he will seek again. Those which are annoying will be avoided. As he grows older and his backlog of experiences becomes greater, his store of knowledge, attitudes, skills, and understandings will be richer. An individual is the sum of his experiences. Therefore, it is important that as many rich and satisfying experiences as possible be provided. Play is one avenue for achieving this goal.

2. *Child's desire for security.* The child needs security. It is one of the most important essentials for a happy life. It may or may not come from his father and mother. It can come to the child from his own group in school. How secure is he with them? Do his buddies include him in their play when they go on a hike or to a birthday party? Is he standing on the sideline at the playfield hoping Jim will want him on his team? Through play and proper leadership each child can be provided with the opportunity for the success and security that he needs.

3. *Child's desire for recognition.* The development of self requires recognition. Each individual wants others to know he exists and has something to contribute to the group. It is human nature to want to receive some form of recognition. Through play the teacher can provide varying situations where each child has the opportunity to be acknowledged.

4. *Child's desire for participation.* All children want to participate, either with a group or with another individual. Each wants to be able to contribute something to this individual or group. Basically, no child wishes to stand on the sideline and be a wallflower. No child wishes to be left out of the plans for the Christmas party or ball game. Play offers innumerable situations where all can participate regardless of skill and ability.

5. *Child's desire for pleasant emotions.* Every child wants to feel happy. His physical and mental well-being are dependent on it. Each desires the satisfaction of those things which bring pleasant emotions. The natural urge to play and the joy that it brings help to satisfy this basic need.

It can be seen that play offers many avenues for satisfying the desires and wishes of children. As such, it can be utilized in an educationally constructive way. It offers an excellent medium for guiding the child toward adulthood. As Slavson in his *Recreation and the Total Personality* says, "Play is a means whereby a child in fantasy comes to know reality." The child scales down the world about him to simpler patterns he can understand, gaining greater security and acquiring power as he does so. The adult world to the child is threatening and forbidding and in play he reduces its complexity to the levels of his powers and understandings. As he grows . . . his play activities generally fuse with reality."

ADAPTING PLAY TO THE CHILD

In order to achieve the greatest possible benefits, play *must be adapted to the needs of the individual child.* Individuals differ. They vary in respect to intelligence, emotions, physique, social background, race, economic standards, educability, and in many other ways. In respect to play, individual differences are significant.

Physical Differences

The body comes in many sizes, shapes, and models. Sheldon, in his *Varieties of Human Physique*, found there are 76 different body types. There are the fat, the lean, the short, the tall, and the many combinations of these. In respect to physical aspects, there are also those who are strong, weak, sickly, healthy, well skilled, poorly skilled, and many other variables. Each physical characteristic has its influence on the total response of the child. One must consider these factors in play. The child who is overweight will not have the same endurance, skill, or perhaps even the same interest in a fast running game as one who is an alert live wire of normal size and weight. A wise teacher notes all these factors and works accordingly with each individual child—not insisting that what is good for one is good for all.

Intellectual Differences

The fact that intellect varies with each individual has implications for the benefits each individual will derive from play situations. All of the children participating in activities will not learn the same things or at the same rate. This will mean more individual guidance and help for some, clearer explanations, more time to grasp the rules and understand the strategies involved, and helpful demonstrations. The learning curve of each boy and girl will differ. The progress of each must be analyzed and noted separately. A wise teacher knows this is true when the child is attempting to solve a mathematical problem. It is also true in a play situation.

Neuromuscular Differences

The ability to perform such fundamental activities as hopping, skipping, jumping, throwing, running, leaping, and combinations of these movements varies with each individual. One has only to watch a group of children to observe the differences. Mary can skip on her right foot but not on her left. John can throw a ball pretty well but cannot catch one at all. Each child differs as to the skills he possesses and the rate at which he is capable of learning new ones. Each individual should be guided to develop to the best of his or her ability. Neuromuscular differences, as well as physical differences, intelligence, and other factors, determine what each child will achieve.

Emotional and Social Differences

Temperament plays a part in play. What is the emotional range of the child? Is he optimistic or pessimistic? Is he a good competitor? Does he have self-assurance or is he timid? Such factors may determine the success of a child in his relations with fellow students and group participation in play. The very factor of timidity, for example, may slow him considerably in developing skills. Through careful guidance the teacher may give the timid child needed assurance in developing a skill and may help cheer the pessimist through his accomplishments. This is also true of other emotional traits. Some children lack the desire to excel. Others have too much for their own good. Some are too easily satisfied with just the bare necessities of life and never accept a challenge to go further or do more than merely meet these. Others go too far in the opposite direction. The child with the drive to be always on top, the child with the revenge drive, and the child who refuses to accept reality and habitually rationalizes—each of these may possess too strong a desire to excel. These drives may be good or bad, depending on the direction in which they are guided. The play situation is an opportune place for these traits to appear and to be properly directed.

WHY HUMAN BEINGS PLAY[1]

Sociologists have advanced many theories as to why people play. Some of the more prominent are (1) The Surplus-Energy or Spencer-Schiller Theory; (2) The Recreation Theory; (3) The Inheritance or Recapitulation Theory; (4) The Relaxation Theory; (5) The Instinct or Gross Theory; and (6) The Social-Contact Theory.

a revitalizer. After sitting at a desk for many hours, being confined to a classroom, or spending many hours in work, the body needs to be refreshed. Play acts as a refreshing change in one's routine. Play aids in the recovery of exhausted energies. It is an antidote for tense nerves, mental fatigue, and emotional unrest.

The Surplus-Energy or Spencer-Schiller Theory

The Surplus-Energy Theory is reflected in the statement, "Let them go out to the playground and get rid of that excess steam and energy." Those who advocate this theory believe that children have developed many powers which cannot all act at once. As a result of this phenomenon there is an overabundance of vigor not utilized in providing for immediate needs. Many powers are inactive for considerable periods of time. Active, healthy nerve centers, during these inactive periods, accumulate more and more energy, and hence are eventually brought to a point where there must be a release of the pressure. Play is an excellent medium for letting off the steam that has developed as a result of the continual bombardment of stimuli on the organism.

The Recreation Theory

The Recreation Theory rests on the premise that the human body needs play as

The Inheritance or Recapitulation Theory

The Inheritance Theory maintains that the past is the key to play. Play has been passed down from generation to generation from earliest times. Play and games are a part of each individual's inheritance. Society repeats the fundamental activities of play that were utilized by earliest man. Such activities as running, throwing, striking, climbing, leaping, carrying, and jumping have been part of daily life for generations. Sports and games played today are just variations of these old activities.

The Relaxation Theory

The Relaxation Theory is similar to the Recreation Theory. It asserts that such activities as reading, which utilizes the small muscles of the eyes, and writing, which utilizes the small muscles of the hand, are hard,

[1] Charles A. Bucher, *Foundations of Physical Education* (Fourth edition), St. Louis, The C. V. Mosby Company, 1964.

tedious, and very fatiguing. The organism, in order to function in an optimum manner, must have some means whereby it can relax after such ordeals. Play offers this medium. Such activities as dancing, tumbling, circle games, ball games, and swimming relax and rest the child and leave him refreshed and ready to pursue another session of work.

The Instinct or Gross Theory

The Instinct Theory of play was expounded by Professor Gross of Gorlitz, Germany. The Gross Theory believes that play is an instrument that came into the world to serve the purpose of education. This theory declares that human beings have an instinctive tendency to be active at various stages of their lives. A child breathes, laughs, cries, creeps, pulls himself up, stands, walks, runs,

and throws at various periods of his development. These are instinctive with him and appear naturally during the course of development. Therefore, play is something that just naturally happens as part of growth and development. It is not planned or purposely injected as a means of utilizing time. Instead, it is something that is natural and part of a child's make-up.

The Social-Contact Theory

Children are born of parents. The parents are members of a certain group, culture, and society. Consequently, to a great extent, the human being adopts activities from his surroundings. A child will play the games of the group of which he is a part. In the United States this may be One-O'-Cat, Dodge Ball, or Hopscotch.

TYPES OF PLAY

Play may take several forms, all of which may be beneficial and contribute to the educational program. There should be proper balance among the various types. Three types are discussed: (1) active, (2) passive, and (3) intellectual.

Active Play

Active play includes physical movement and participation in various forms of activity such as tumbling, swimming, and tag. The children are active participants and the exercise and activity are beneficial to each child. This is the most desirable form of play for growing children. Only by being a participant can the child realize many

physical, mental, social, and emotional dividends.

Passive Play

In the passive type of play, the spectator approach is used. One does not take part as an active member of the group or team but gains enjoyment by watching others participate in play or athletic contests. It takes place at a big-league baseball game, a tennis match, or a play, sports, or field day in the local school. Fun, relaxation, and other values can be gained from such activity. However, it should be recognized that the majority of values from play can only be gained by active participation.

Figure 3–2. Active play.

Intellectual Play

The last type of play is the intellectual kind. This does not mean that the intellect is not used in the other forms of play. However, as in chess or checkers, this type requires deep thinking and concentration. Again, it should be reiterated that children need active physical play for optimum results. Young bodies need vigorous movement and exercise in order to grow and develop and gain a sound, strong physical organism for the many years to follow. But a physical education program should include intellectual play.

PLAY—THE FOUNDATION FOR BALANCED ADULT LIVING

Dr. William Menninger, the famous psychiatrist and physician, has stated that too few adults know how to play. He also stresses that play is essential to balanced living. In one study he compared a group of psychiatric patients with a group of well-adjusted individuals. One characteristic of the well-adjusted group that was lacking in the psychiatric patients was that they had many hobbies, knew how to play, and took their play seriously. Dr. Menninger concluded from years of studying maladjusted individuals that play is very important to enriched living.

The proper attitudes toward play, the skills for play, and many other foundations are developed during the elementary school years. However, teachers who do not understand its importance are sometimes responsible for destroying this drive and making play unpalatable. Consequently, some individuals as they grow older, shy away from play and seek other pursuits. Some of these persons are in mental hospitals today. They had no healthy form of release from the tensions of modern-day living. They had no wholesome outlet for their aggressive drives. They could not find relaxation from their competitive living. They did not know the formula for good mental health. It is estimated that one out of every twelve children in our schools today will someday find his way into a mental hospital. Every teacher should recognize the importance of giving each child the foundational equipment to use play for balanced living. This is true education. This is living. This is teaching children how to live rich and happy lives. This is meeting a basic need of society. This is the responsibility of every teacher who comes into contact with a child in any type of play situation.

QUESTIONS AND PRACTICAL PROBLEMS

1. From your own experience give several examples of children whom you have observed demonstrating the fact that play is a child's work.

2. Study an elementary school child and prepare a report on how play is affecting his growth and development.

3. Describe several desirable goals possible of accomplishment through the use of play as an educational tool.

4. Cite examples in modern-day education where the doctrines of Asceticism, Scholasticism, and Puritanism continue to leave their imprint.

5. Read Rousseau's *Émile* and present a report to the class, pointing out the role of play in Rousseau's view of education.

6. Critically evaluate the following statement: "Play contributes only to the physical development of the child."

7. Write a paper on the topic "Play Contributes to Meeting the Basic Needs of Children."

8. Discuss the various theories that have been set forth as to why human beings play. Illustrate each.

9. Interview 10 adults to determine the role that play had in their lives as children and how those play experiences are affecting them as adults.

10. Describe how the attitude of educators toward play has changed in the last 100 years. Cite examples, if possible, from the actual writings of educators, then and now.

SELECTED REFERENCES

BRECKENRIDGE, MARIAN E., and E. LEE VINCENT, *Child Development* (Fourth edition), Philadelphia, W. B. Saunders Company, 1960.

BUCHER, CHARLES A., *Foundations of Physical Education* (Fourth edition), St. Louis, The C. V. Mosby Company, 1964.

———, *Methods and Materials in Physical Education and Recreation*, St. Louis, The C. V. Mosby Company, 1954.

COWELL, CHARLES C., *Scientific Foundations of Physical Education*, New York, Harper and Brothers, 1953.

HARTLEY, RUTH, *et al., Understanding Children's Play*, New York, Columbia University Press, 1952.

ILG, F. L., and L. B. AMES, *Child Behavior*, New York, Harper and Brothers, 1955.

JERSILD, A., *Child Psychology* (Fifth edition), Englewood Cliffs, N.J., Prentice-Hall, Inc., 1960.

JONES, HAROLD E., *Motor Performance and Growth*, Los Angeles, University of California Press, 1949.

JOYSON, D. C., *Physical Education for Children*, New York, Philosophical Library, 1955.

O'KEEFE, PATRICIA R., and HELEN FAHEY, *Ed-

ucation Through Physical Activities (Second edition), St. Louis, The C. V. Mosby Company, 1955.

OLSON, W. C., *Child Development* (Second edition), Boston, D. C. Heath and Company, 1959.

VAN DALEN, DEOBOLD B., *et al., World History of Physical Education,* Englewood Cliffs, N.J., Prentice-Hall, Inc., 1953.

WOODY, THOMAS, *Life and Education in Early Societies,* New York, The Macmillan Company, 1949.

CHAPTER 4

Physical Fitness and the Elementary School

The subject of fitness is a topic of much interest to people in America. Ever since test results indicated there was a tendency toward softness among American children as compared with European children, the question in professional circles as well as among many civic and business groups has been "How can we improve the fitness of our children?" The active enthusiasm of the Presidents of the United States toward this problem has acted as a catalyst, pushing it to the front lines of American thought. The national government has been especially concerned since a pilot program conducted by schools in several states for the President's Council on Physical Fitness showed that almost half the 200,000 school children in grades four through twelve who were tested failed minimum physical achievement tests. In addition, the Council has pointed out that only about 28 per cent of the nation's schools have adequate physical education and health education and that more than 50 per cent of our children have no daily physical education period. Statistics such as these have justly aroused alarm.

WHAT DOES FITNESS MEAN?

Although the word "fitness" means different things to different people, the professions of health, physical education, and recreation subscribe to the concept of total fitness—physical, mental, emotional, social, and spiritual well-being. The Director of Selective Service for the Federal Government gives this definition: "Fitness is that quality, inherent and acquired, which renders a person qualified to serve to the limit of his or her physical strength; to render the maximum of his or her mental capabilities and capacities, and on a high moral plane, and which recognizes, fully, his or her obligations to the family, the neighbor, the community, the state, and the nation."

Fitness is the ability of the individual to live a full and balanced life. The totally fit person has a healthy and happy outlook on life. He satisfies basic needs, such as physical wellbeing, love, affection, security, and selfrespect. He likes people and lives happily with them. As he grows older, he develops a maturity that is characterized by submersion of self and an interest in serving humanity. He makes peace with his God and believes in and exemplifies high ethical standards.

The American Association for Health, Physical Education and Recreation stresses that fitness is the ability of the individual to function, which means that he possesses organic health, coordination, strength, vitality, emotional stability, social consciousness, knowledge, desirable attitudes, and spiritual and moral qualities.

WHAT DOES PHYSICAL FITNESS MEAN?

Although it is recognized that the various aspects of fitness are closely interrelated, physical fitness is discussed separately because of its close relationship to our professional fields of endeavor.

Physical fitness is one aspect of total fitness. The term has been defined in different ways. Gallagher and Brouha [1] provide an excellent description when they point out that physical fitness is composed of (1) static or medical fitness which refers to soundness of the organs of the body such as the heart and lungs; (2) dynamic or functional fitness, or the degree to which the body functions efficiently under strenuous work; and (3) motor skills fitness which refers to coordination and strength in the performance of activities.

Physical fitness is related to the tasks the person must perform, his potential for physical effort, and the relationship of his physical fitness to his total self. The same degree of physical fitness is not necessary for everyone. It should be sufficient to meet the requirements of the job plus a little extra as a reserve for emergencies. The student who plays football needs a different type of physical fitness than the student who plays in the school orchestra. The question "Fitness for what?" must always be asked. Furthermore, the physical fitness of a person must be determined in relationship to that person's own human resources and not those of others. It depends on his potentialities in light of his own physical make-up.

[1] J. R. Gallagher and L. Brouha, "Physical Fitness," *Journal of the American Medical Association,* **125**:834–838, July 23, 1944.

Finally, physical fitness cannot be considered by itself, but, instead, as it is affected by mental, emotional, and social factors as well. Human beings function as a whole and not as segmented parts.

Achieving Physical Fitness

Physical fitness is not achieved solely through exercise. It is a complex quality which depends upon many factors. Although heredity plays a part in physical fitness, the environment in which an individual lives and the personal daily regimen which he follows play more significant roles.

Physical fitness is acquired to a large degree. Most persons can contribute immeasurably to their own well-being. The food they eat, the rest they get, the exercise in which they engage and similar factors will determine the degree to which they will achieve and maintain physical fitness. The American Medical Association, for example, has listed seven paths to physical fitness: proper medical care, good nutrition, dental services, exercise, satisfying work, healthy play and recreation, and adequate amounts of rest and relaxation.

To understand the meaning of physical fitness and how it is achieved and maintained is an important responsibility for any teacher in the schools as well as any youth leader in the community. Unless the many-faceted sides of fitness are known, educational programs may become distorted and physical fitness may never be developed in the children.

The President's Council on Physical Fitness

The President's Council on Youth Fitness, now called the President's Council on Physical Fitness, was initiated by executive order under President Dwight D. Eisenhower on July 16, 1956. It was continued under the following administrations.

The President's Council, with the cooperation of 19 leading national educational and medical organizations, has developed a basic physical fitness program for schools. This recommended program is called the Blue Book[2] and can be obtained from the Superintendent of Documents, Washington 25, D.C. The basic recommendations of this program are as follows:

1. A health appraisal for each child to discover remedial defects and determine his capacity for exercise.

2. A screening process to identify underdeveloped children.

3. At least 15 minutes of vigorous activity as part of a daily physical education program.

4. Periodic achievement tests to measure progress and provide incentive.

The President's Council strongly urges every school to adopt the basic philosophy expressed in these four points.

The President's Council has put forth a noteworthy effort to enhance the physical fitness of the nation's children and youth. In general, the publicity that has been given by the Council has had a salutary impact on the schools. Parent-teacher associations have held meetings, schools that have not had programs have instituted them, and provisions have been made for facilities and equipment to implement the Council's recommendations.

THE ROLE OF THE SCHOOL IN FITNESS

The school program that best contributes to physical fitness must take into consideration not only exercise but also the various health habits that a child is forming. The school can help in great measure by determining pupil needs through such means as health appraisal by medical personnel, identification of pupils with special health problems, screening of children to ascertain those who are physically underdeveloped, identification of posture problems, use of health surveys, and evaluation in physical education to determine status in regard to physical fitness, skills, knowledge, and attitudes. After this job has been ac-

[2] President's Council on Youth Fitness, *Youth Physical Fitness—Suggested Elements of a School-Centered Program,* Washington, D.C., President's Council on Youth Fitness, 1961.

complished, the school can provide a very well-rounded physical education and health education program that meets the needs of its students, grade by grade.

The best way to meet the recommendations of the President's Council on Physical Fitness is to provide a well-rounded physical education and health program. Through such a program the physical fitness of the children will be enhanced. But, equally and perhaps more important from an educational point of view, many other positive physical, mental, and social results will be achieved.

Education in its broadest sense means preparation for life. It should help each individual to become all he is capable of being. Therefore, it is inexorably tied in, not only with physical fitness, but total fitness.

Education and physical education must be concerned with developing in each individual optimum organic health, vitality, emotional stability, social consciousness, knowledge, wholesome attitudes, and spiritual and moral qualities.

Schools have the responsibility for providing many opportunities for understanding and developing fitness. The school programs should provide experiences and services that contribute to fitness. This means that health knowledge, attitudes, and practices are stressed; protective health services are provided; physical activities are available to, and engaged in, by all, not just the few who are skilled; necessary facilities are provided; the environment is conducive to proper growth and development; and experiences in every area stress proper social and ethical behavior.

School leadership should exemplify fitness and all disciplines in the school should be concerned with this quality. It should permeate the entire program and all persons associated with it. It is not the responsibility of only one area and just a few people.

Schools should provide community leadership in this area. They should work closely with, and play a leading role in, the utilization of the entire resources of each community to do the job.

The American Association of Health, Physical Education and Recreation has listed the following goals as "What the Public Schools Hope to Achieve for Your Child Through Fitness Programs":

1. Excellent health, through knowledge of the human body and its needs.
2. Self-protection, through knowledge about safety, alcohol, narcotics, wise purchase of products.
3. Sufficient strength, vitality, and coordination to meet emergencies as well as the requirements of daily living.
4. Emotional stability to meet the stresses and strains of modern life.

5. Skill in meeting the requirements of group living.
6. Attitudes, values, and skills which help achieve and maintain fitness.
7. Spiritual and moral qualities that make for personal maturity.[3]

The elementary school in particular has an important function to play in the development of fit children. Attitudes toward physical activity and education essentials are being formed, knowledge is being imparted, and habits which will contribute to or detract from good health are being developed. An educational program is needed which takes into consideration the fact that physical fitness is the foundation of intellectual fitness and is an area where the child recognizes the importance of all phases of his growth.

Physical Fitness Testing

Physical fitness testing has become the vogue in many of the nation's schools. Children are tested periodically and reports are posted and in many cases sent home to parents. On the basis of these tests many youngsters are declared to be strong and healthy or weak and unhealthy. Sometimes the tests used are good, sometimes poor; sometimes the analysis of the results of physical fitness tests are used in the right way, sometimes they are misused. Because of the confusion that exists in regards to physical fitness testing, a short discussion of them is included here.

Physical fitness tests include such activities as running, pull-ups, sit-ups, throwing, and jumping. On the basis of individual performance in these items, conclusions are

[3] American Association of Health, Physical Education and Recreation, "Your Child Can't Sit and Keep Fit," Washington, D.C., Division of Press and Radio Relations in cooperation with the American Association of Health, Physical Education and Recreation, National Education Association.

reached as to whether or not a person is physically fit. In a strict sense, however, such tests are merely indexes of physical performance in these particular activities. Many other measurements are needed— medical examinations, for example—to get at the child's total physical fitness.

Physical fitness tests vary in respect to the number and type of items that are included. Some of the components of physical fitness commonly tested are muscular strength, tested when the child has his hand grip checked; cardiorespiratory endurance, tested when the child is asked to run for a certain period of time; muscular power, tested when the child is required to broad jump; and muscular endurance, tested when the child is required to do push-ups.

A good test is one that meets certain criteria. Some of the more important criteria are validity, reliability, administrative economy, and norms. The *validity* criterion means that test must measure what it is supposed to measure—for example, if a test is to measure strength, then it should measure strength and not endurance. *Reliability* means that a test must give the same results to different teachers or administrators. *Administrative economy* means that the time, equipment, and other technical essentials of the test must be reasonable and practicable for the situation in which they are used. *Norms* means that performance standards must be established for the tests so that a measure of comparison exists between students. The test set up by the American Association for Health, Physical Education and Recreation, for example, has national norms for boys and girls, so that students in a New York class may be compared with those in a California class.

Several physical fitness tests are widely available today. In addition, some teachers make up their own tests. Many of these tests do not have objective evidence of validity. Furthermore, not all physical fitness tests measure the same kind of physical fitness. Therefore, when selecting a fitness test it is necessary to select one that has validity and measures the kind of fitness the program is aiming to achieve.

In spite of the many limitations of physical fitness tests, they can be utilized to advantage in the elementary school physical education program. They can be used for purposes of motivation. When a student sees his score and compares it with those of his classmates and with others in other parts of the country it motivates him to make a commendable showing and spurs him on to develop the strength and other qualities essential to such an accomplishment. Physical fitness test scores show the progress a student or class is making in regard to such qualities as muscular strength, endurance, and power. Test results offer information which can be used as a guide to group a class for special work in areas of physical performance that need improvement. Test results can be utilized as one consideration when giving grades in physical education. Tests can help identify strengths and weaknesses of pupils and aid in curriculum planning. Tests also can give direction and help to supply information for guidance purposes.

One important point should be brought out, however. The test results must never be used as the final and absolute analysis of a child's physical fitness. The results are only a guide to be utilized in conjunction with other evidence and information.

The American Association for Health, Physical Education and Recreation has developed its own physical fitness test[4] for national use. It consists of seven basic items (see Appendix E) plus a swimming test.

[4] American Association of Health, Physical Education and Recreation, *AAHPER Youth Fitness Test Manual,* Washington, D.C., American Association for Health, Physical Education and Recreation, 1961.

1. Pull-ups (modified for girls): to test arm and shoulder girdle strength.

2. Shuttle run: to test speed and change of direction.

3. 50-yard dash: to test speed.

4. Sit-ups: to test strength of abdominal muscles and hip flexors.

5. Standing broad jump: to test explosive power of leg extensors.

6. Softball throw for distance: to test skill and coordination.

7. 600-yard walk or run: to test cardiovascular system.

8. Swimming test (jumping into water, resting, and swimming 15 yards): to test protective powers in the water.

The first seven tests are included in Appendix E, along with tables of percentile rankings for ages ten through seventeen for boys and for girls. The Appendix begins on page 432.

Physical Fitness Guides for the Elementary School Teacher

Some guides for the teacher in developing physical fitness in elementary school children are as follows:

1. *Periodically appraise the health and physical fitness of each child through a medical examination.*

A complete medical examination should be given to each child by either the family physician or the school doctor at least once a year. The family physician is best suited for this because of his knowledge of the child and his health history.

2. *Provide for a variety of vigorous physical activities in the program.*

The regular program of physical education activities will provide a core of experiences which will develop the necessary strength, speed, agility, balance, coordination, flexibility, muscular endurance, good posture, and organic efficiency essential to

the development of optimum physical fitness. Special groups of games and sports are not needed.

3. *Adapt activities to the individual pupil.*

A blanket program cannot be prescribed for all students. Instead, each child should have a program adapted to his needs, interests, and capacities. It is especially important to identify pupils who have a low level of muscular strength and other components of physical fitness and plan a developmental program in light of their needs.

4. *Be alert to teachable moments.*

There are many teachable moments in the life of a child. It may be when he is curious about his physical makeup, when he is trying to compare his physical performance with that of another pupil, or when someone in the class is sick. These are the times when the teacher can get across important information which will have much meaning for the child.

5. *Motivate pupils to be physically fit.*

Through discussion with pupils in class and individually, test results, audio-visual aids, performance charts, and other techniques, boys and girls can be motivated to become physically fit.

6. *Provide for a sound testing program.*

Each teacher should determine what he or she wants to measure in the area of physical fitness, and what test will provide the most valid results. After the test has been selected and administered, the results should be utilized in a meaningful manner.

7. *Establish a guidance program.*

The teaching program should provide an opportunity for individual guidance of students in the area of physical fitness. Individual conferences could be held, for example, after a physical fitness test has been given. Personal problems and weaknesses could be discussed in light of test results. When a teacher is able to offer this personal attention to each student and can suggest methods of improvement, the boy or girl will benefit considerably.

8. *Provide instruction in health and safety education.*

Concentrated instruction relative to specific health concepts and problems should be provided at each grade level. Such topics as cleanliness, nutrition, sleep, rest, and exercise, if taught effectively, will contribute to the physical fitness of boys and girls.

Additional Guides

The American Association for Health, Physical Education and Recreation lists some suggestions for further promoting physical fitness.[5] A few are presented here in adapted form.

1. Establish a system for parental reporting and counseling on the health and physical fitness of the school's children.

2. Install and maintain a bulletin board devoted to health and physical fitness. Keep it attractive and current with stimulating ideas, announcements, posters and flyers.

3. Make prominent use of such slogans as "Think Fit—Look Fit—Be Fit," "You Can't Sit and Be Fit," and, "Shape Up or Ship Out."

4. Plan demonstrations and exhibitions of fitness and involve as many children as possible in a program for the public.

5. Plan a school assembly program with a physical fitness theme.

6. Develop a homework program for physical fitness. Require some activities to be engaged in during out-of-school hours.

7. Plan and conduct occasional week-

end hikes and bicycle treks to points of interest, with packed lunches.

8. Plan a special school fitness club and establish standards for membership. Provide membership cards and public recognition.

Working with Parents for the Physical Fitness of School Children[6]

At a recent parent-teachers association meeting an impetuous mother jumped to her feet and wanted to know why the school permitted her child to remain a physical weakling. "Roger can't run without puffing, push-up without grunting, and he looks like a girl every time he throws a ball." She continued in a dejected tone of voice, "My boy is pale, frail, and lacks vitality. Our school has a physical education program, yet Roger is soft." As the confused woman sat down her last words were "I can't understand it."

If the physical education department had been represented at the meeting, the staff could have pointed out that Roger is a physically underdeveloped youngster, but that a program with only two 45 minute periods a week, 75 youngsters in the class, and 15 minutes out of each period devoted to dressing and showering makes such a bodybuilding task difficult to accomplish.

It is also important to realize that physical fitness is the responsibility of the home as well as of the school. Parents should conceive of themselves as half the team. After all, the child is in school only 180 or so days a year, 5 days a week, from 8:30 A.M. until 4:00 P.M. He is at home much more than this—or should be. The control that is

---

[5] American Association for Health, Physical Fitness and Recreation, *Operation Fitness—U.S.A., 1963,* "The Year of Cooperation, Coordination, and Concerted Action in the Nation," Washington, D.C., American Association for Health, Physical Education and Recreation, 1963.

[6] Adapted from an article by Charles A. Bucher entitled, "What Can Parents Do? (About Their Child's Health and Fitness)," *National Education Association Journal,* February, 1962.

exercised by an understanding mother and father is also important.

Physical educators need public support for a daily class program that has no more than thirty-five to forty pupils in a class, support that is readily given to English, science, and mathematics teachers. Parents must develop values concerning physical fitness in their children so that when their youngsters are in class they will want to work hard to be physically fit. The author once heard a father remark that he would rather have a soggy body than a soggy mind. His children look at it the same way and try to skip physical education class everytime they can. But it isn't an either/or proposition. The late John F. Kennedy's words ". . . the foundation of intellectual fitness is physical fitness" have deep meaning for all parents.

Studies have shown that a child is more likely to smoke if his parents smoke and that he is more likely to use alcohol if his mother and father do. The same thing is probably true where physical fitness is concerned. If parents take pride in their bodies and keep them in good physical shape, the child is likely to follow suit. Whenever you see an obese girl or boy, take a look at the parent—the old block may give off fat chips.

Too many parents think of physical fitness in terms of stereotypes, such as a Charles Atlas or Miss Universe strolling up and down Muscle Beach. Or their minds turn to Kyle Rote, Rafer Johnson, or the high school football or basketball star. Because a boy or girl doesn't know which end of a tennis racquet to hold, mothers and fathers may assume that fitness is a quality far removed from their youngsters. Such erroneous and misleading beliefs make it imperative that each parent know what physical fitness is, how important it is, and how it is acquired and maintained.

It is important for grown-ups, by example and precept, to create in the minds of youngsters the feeling that to be a good American one must be physically fit. This is a responsibility that each of us has if our democratic way of life is to be preserved and our national purposes accomplished. Democracy is not a spectator sport, it is a game in which all are participants. In this life and death struggle we must have a total effort on the part of all. This means total fitness—emotional, mental, and physical.

A recent newspaper article stated that Russia, instead of having the American coffee break twice a day, allotted time for required calisthenics for all employees. In a democracy this regimentation is out of place; yet in America, where physical fitness is a voluntary thing, we must motivate our young to recognize that their own physical development is important to them as individuals and also to the nation. Each person has the responsibility to be in good physical condition and not to detract from our national power and strength.

More specifically, here are some practical suggestions that parents can follow to promote their children's physical fitness:

1. See that their children get proper rest, medical care, nutrition, and the other essentials to physical fitness.

2. Buy toys that give children a good physical workout as well as fun. Instead of an electric train, buy a horizontal bar that fits in the doorway that each child has to chin on before passing through.

3. Construct a gymnasium in the basement or backyard complete with climbing ropes, trapeze, badminton court, swings, and other equipment.

4. Provide a meaningful work schedule around the house which includes mowing the lawn, shoveling snow, and other jobs which provide healthful physical activity.

5. Arrange for more total family participation in physical activities, where mother and father and all the children go camping,

bowling, square dancing, ice skating, or engage in other appropriate physical activity.

6. Insist that the older children walk or ride their bicycles to school and other places if the distance is not more than one or two miles.

QUESTIONS AND PRACTICAL PROBLEMS

1. Write an essay on the relation of physical fitness to the fitness and health of the elementary school child.

2. Your school principal has asked you to make recommendations for a broad and comprehensive physical education program that will achieve the recommendations of the President's Council on Physical Fitness. Outline such a program for the elementary school.

3. Prepare a list of five outstanding physical fitness tests found by research and prepare a table showing the validity, reliability, availability of norms, and administrative feasibility of each.

4. Develop a newsletter that you could send to parents to acquaint them with the responsibilities they have and the role they can play in the physical fitness of their children.

5. What is the relation of the physical fitness objective to all of the objectives of physical education.

6. Prepare a file of materials on physical fitness which would be of value to the classroom teacher.

SELECTED REFERENCES

Many of the materials needed on physical fitness can be obtained in pamphlet form in individual or economy lots through the American Association for Health, Physical Education and Recreation, 1201 Sixteenth Street, N.W., Washington 6, D.C. Some of these materials are listed below:

AAHPER Youth Fitness Test Manual. Directions for administration of the AAHPER Youth Fitness Test, with test descriptions, percentile scores, and norms for fifth grade through college. (See Appendix E.)

Children and Fitness. Report of the National Conference on Fitness of Children of Elementary School Age.

Exercise and Fitness. Joint statement by the American Medical Association and American Association for Health, Physical Education and Recreation.

Selected Fitness Articles. Packet of 25 articles on fitness.

Your Child's Health and Fitness. A series of articles reprinted from the *National Education Association Journal*, February, 1962.

Youth Physical Fitness—Suggested Elements of a School-Centered Program, President's Council on Youth Fitness, 1961. This pamphlet is available from the United States Government Printing Office, Washington 25, D.C.

CHAPTER 5

Current Trends in Elementary Physical Education

Trends may be defined as movements or changes in educational thinking or practices that have or take a particular direction or that turn in a specified or implied direction.

Trends in education do not just happen. They are the result of historical developments. Trends may be difficult to trace, however, because they usually result from many different influences. The advancements in science and research techniques and the rise or decline of a culture are among the factors which produce changes and directly or indirectly cause various trends.

After World War I there were defin-able trends in citizenship education, health education, curriculum studies, and more liberal education in elementary schools.

Educational trends today continue to reflect such factors as the national income, a greater understanding of child behavior, recent findings in child growth and development, a saner understanding of mental health, and an increased emphasis on school planning and development.

Trends which will be discussed in this chapter have direct bearing on and offer specific challenges to programs of physical education. They show needs in the over-all structure in content, planning, and organization.

GENERAL TRENDS IN THE WORLD OF TODAY AND THEIR CHALLENGE TO PHYSICAL EDUCATION

The major trend of our era is automation. Automation is greeted with joy by some people, yet others receive it with consternation and fear. Some feel it represents a new utopia where electronic tapes, push buttons, and giant brains will do all the work while humans live a life of ideal perfection. To others it represents the vehicle which will carry the world into the worst depression in history, characterized by unemployment and degradation of the human spirit.

The result of automation probably will not be as drastic as either of these two extremes. However, it will, according to most experts, result in a new way of life for millions of Americans with many new problems to challenge their thinking.

The automation era, with its ability to perform work which formerly took hundreds and thousands of man hours, is giving mankind more and more free time. The worker in the United States today produces as much in a 40-hour week as three men did in 1870 in a 70-hour week. In 1850, approximately 66 per cent of all power was produced by man or animal muscle, while 100 years later it had dropped to only 2 per cent. If the trend continues for another 100 years, a 7-hour work day will produce as much as a 40-hour work week does today. In 1800, the average work week in industrial establishments consisted of 84 hours; in 1900, it averaged 60 hours; and today, 40 hours. Experts predict that with the application of atomic energy to industry the day of the 30-hour work week is not far off. This means there will be twice as many hours for leisure-time activities as there are hours devoted to work.

If one wants to be pessimistic about the future, a pathetic picture can be painted for the years ahead. Workmen by the thousands can be displaced by machines faster than they can be absorbed into other occupations. The factor of monotony and wearisome repetition in mechanical work can dampen man's mental powers. A new ruling class can be established based on profits. The machine can deprive human beings of many useful skills which provide a feeling of accomplishment and belonging. The machine can create so much leisure time, that although it may be used wisely by some people it can act as a destructive force for others. There is danger that mental illness will continue to take a greater toll of human lives. The mental health problem has already become a major concern of the medical profession. Some mental illnesses are brought on by pressures, competition, lack of worthwhile hobbies, inability to get release from tension, and a futile search for happiness. Howard Mumford Jones, an outstanding writer, refers to the present age as a century of increasing horror. Others have called it the "aspirin age." Robert Hutchins, formerly Chancellor of the University of Chicago, in referring to the atomic age says, "If we survive, the leisure which the atomic age will bring may make peace more horrible than war. We face the dreadful prospect of hour after hour, even day after day, with nothing to do. After we have read all the comic books, traveled all the miles, seen all the movies, and drunk all the liquor we can stand, what shall we do then?"

However, it is also possible to paint a very bright picture of the future. If atomic power, man's ingenuity, and good judgment combine to guide the nation and world in the years ahead, it can be an age of prosperity, happiness, and health such as the earth has never seen and has scarcely dared dream to be possible.

William Engle, a writer discussing automation in a lighter vein in one of the nation's weeklies, points out some of the possible advantages. These include living in push-button homes, driving jet cars and helicopters to work, flying to Europe in an hour, taking ray-shooting atomic pills to trace and treat disease, having more time for sports and travel, and seeing the world in 3-D and color on portable television.

With electronics and an abundance of energy to drive machines, there definitely should be higher productivity, more consumer goods produced at lower prices, and a shorter work week. This will allow more time for cultural interests and a wide assortment of hobbies. In addition, this country's inventive genius should result in great medical advances, luxuries, and conveniences hitherto undreamed of and a higher standard of living for a larger percentage of the population.

Benjamin Franklin once said, "Leisure is a time for doing something useful, and this leisure the diligent man will obtain, but the lazy man never, for the life of leisure and a life of laziness are two things." Horace Mann, a great educator, also pointed out the problem when he said, "Lost yesterday, somewhere between sunrise and sunset, two golden hours—each set with sixty diamond minutes. No reward is offered, for they are gone forever."

It has long been the task of education to prepare for those hours spent in work. For years the schools have trained the mind and body for earning a living and accomplishing the many daily tasks. This was its main challenge when everyone was faced with long hours of hard work and no opportunity for relaxation and recreation. But now, education must adjust its goals if it is to fit in with modern living. Surely it should be of utmost importance to prepare for those hours which will soon take up twice as much time as work. There should be thinking and planning for those many leisure hours so that they may be used to greatest advantage—to help develop the human body and mind, to enhance one's total fitness. Another noted educator has said, "Education also consists in knowing what to do when you have nothing to do." If education is truly preparation for life, then surely this important responsibility cannot be ignored.

1. Correct Attitudes Toward Leisure Are Essential

If education accepts the challenge of the automation era, then teachers and other leaders should be interested in developing in the pupil a proper attitude toward leisure. A child should not grow up thinking that free time is something to waste, to get rid of recklessly or foolishly. He should not feel that the purpose of leisure is to kill time, but rather to use time wisely, every golden minute of it. It should be viewed as an opportunity for self-development, for achieving many of those worthwhile things which cannot be accomplished during hours of work —a time for travel, for engaging in refreshing physical activity to meet bodily needs, and as a main spoke in the wheel of balanced living where work, play, rest, and recreation must all contribute.

Each young person should have as his or her objective the development of an integrated personality where the mental, physical, social, and emotional are in harmony and both supplement and complement each other. If such an attitude can be instilled in each young mind, the misuse of leisure will not exist. According to Henry Thoreau, students should develop the attitude that the new age of leisure affords new avenues for plucking the "finer fruits of life."

2. Leisure Skills Are Needed

Another important responsibility of teachers in preparing students for worthy use of leisure is to see that a wide variety of skills which can be utilized in leisure hours is developed in each boy and girl. These skills can be a source of health and happiness during youth and also in the adult years. Possession of these skills will greatly determine the pleasures that attract youngsters, the types of amusements they want during their free time, and the luxuries they consume. Dr. Nash, a leader in the fields of physical education and recreation, says that the early years of life are the crucial ones for the child in regard to skill learning. He conducted a study which showed that skills and hobbies learned by children under twelve years of age constituted 78 per cent of their hobby interest when they became adults, and those skills and hobbies learned under ten years of age made up 62 per cent of the leisure-time pursuits during their middle and later years.

Dr. Nash comments further on this subject:

An educated man is a man who is a master in a skill, regardless of the form of the skill. . . . We are short-circuiting education by moving the child into word symbols without going through an activity program to give meaning to these words. The child needs hand skills, not just in games and sports, but across the board in crafts, in music, in painting and the entire range of nature. If we are going to get people to enjoy life, if we are going to get them to contribute to society, if we are going to get them to be valuable members of the family, they are going to have something to do beyond sitting for six or seven hours a day, listening to radio or looking at television.[1]

Physical education must be concerned with developing a wide range of skills which will serve as a motivating force for insuring the worthy use of leisure time.

3. Physical Development Is a Requirement

Another important implication of the automation era for elementary school teachers and other educators is the growing concern regarding the fitness of youth. Today's children and youth are threatened with physical and moral bankruptcy as a result of modern push-button technology and materialism.

Today's children ride to school instead of walking. Even in situations when they are close enough to walk, many times they are transported.

Home chores once necessary and which gave excellent muscular development are diminishing. Instead of lawn mowers being pushed, they are ridden, power snow plows are replacing the man-powered shovel; walking is replaced by the auto and, in most other cases, by the bicycle. Climbing trees is a lost art because of urbanization. Few trees exist in the densely populated areas or in the new developments in semirural sections. The opportunities to run across

fields, jump brooks, and chase butterflies are being slowly but surely lost.

Homes are being built today on small lots with no special space set aside for play areas. Yet real estate statistics tell us we may expect two and one-half children per house. Why do we not require all building areas to set aside two acres of playground for every 250 children? Children are not allowed to play in one neighbor's yard because of damage to the flowers, in another a window was broken by a fly ball. In still another the swimming pool is interesting, yet dangerous unless supervised, so they must leave there. Where will they play? How will they use up their abundance of energy and how will they become physically strong if denied the place and opportunity for play and big-muscle activity?

Is it any wonder then why they sit hour after hour in front of television sets, munching potato chips and drinking soda?

Because of these factors it is an increasing challenge to educators to educate children and parents to the need of activity, so that they will find places for it and plan programs which will be usable in smaller areas than were formerly available.

A former Vice-President of the United States in voicing concern about the automation era focused his remarks particularly on the physical aspects of fitness:

We are not a nation of softies but we could become one, if proper attention is not given to the trend of our time which is toward the invention of all sorts of gadgetry to make life easy and in so doing to reduce the opportunity for normal physical, health giving exercises. . . .

The objectives of an adequate physical fitness program can be summed up in one word, participation—participation on the part of every boy and girl in America in some form of health, recreational, and physical activity. . . . Everyone agrees that the person who has physical fitness enjoys a healthful mental outlook and a general feeling of bodily well-being. Physical activity relieves emotional strain under

[1] Jay B. Nash, "Leisure and the Advance or Decline of Our Culture," *The Reporter,* New Jersey Association for Health and Physical Education (Spring 1956), p. 6.

which we live and relieves the pressure of our highly productive lives.

Education can help by providing experiences for children which will give them an understanding of the human body—its needs and limitations—the ability to discriminate fad from scientific fact, the interest and desire to be physically fit, the resources for spending leisure hours in a manner that contributes to fitness, and skill in activities which provide release from strains and tensions associated with modern-day living. They should also be provided with experiences that contribute to wholesome personal and group adjustments and opportunities for creative expression. These are only a few of the contributions that the schools can make. If total fitness is to be within the reach of a larger number of children and youth in this nation, schools and teachers must be aware of and take active steps to fulfill the many contributions they can make.

4. The Need for Extracurricular Programs Is Evident

The school's job does not end when the three o'clock bell rings. Its influence extends into the child's life throughout the school day and is also reflected in those activities in which he engages after regular school hours. How the child spends his free time after school, on Saturdays, Sundays, and holidays will influence his health and also his success in life.

The out-of-school part of the child's daily life is entirely his own, to get the most fun and satisfaction from. This period of the day is especially important to mental health and well-being. During this time he can find outlets for aggressive drives, he can create, and he can learn. Activities engaged in during this period can meet his physical

needs and also play a part in meeting his social needs. Through play with other children he has an opportunity to satisfy the need for recognition. This time can also offer opportunities for developing hobbies. The interests developed will carry over into adult life and will supply many happy and profitable hours.

The elementary school teacher can help guide youngsters in the selection of their activities during out-of-school hours. By taking an interest which extends beyond the school day, she will be helping to pave the way to a satisfying future for each of her students. Here are some suggestions of things the teacher can do:

1. Develop an intramural program for out-of-school hours in various sports, games, and other physical activities.

2. Through the regular class program, draw attention to activities which will be an extension of the curricular program.

3. Have those youngsters who have special talent or skill in selected activities put on a demonstration for the rest of the class.

4. Arrange clinics for certain activities where experts are brought in to work with children.

5. Form clubs which have as their primary purpose the exchange of ideas and the development of skills and interests in special activities.

6. Encourage parents to devote some time to family recreation where such interest can be explored more thoroughly.

7. Utilize parent-teacher asociations as a medium for promoting recreational interests.

8. Set aside special days for sports days and play days where all children can demonstrate their choice of activities.

9. Help parents obtain and/or evaluate outside instruction for children in recreational activities—dancing, singing, swimming, and so on.

A few of the activities related to physical education that teachers should encourage pupils to explore as possible leisure-time pursuits shown in Table 5–1.

should allow opportunity to improve these essential items rather than detract from them.

7. Does the activity compensate for

TABLE 5–1. *Possible Leisure-Time Activities*

Camping	Ice skating	Bowling
Bicycling	Sailing	Golf
Fishing	Mountain climbing	Archery
Dancing	Tennis	Hiking
Horseback riding	Table tennis	Softball
Badminton	Swimming	

In selecting recreational activities it is important to use some guide. Here are some points the teacher should have each child consider:

1. Is he interested in the activity? One of the main considerations for selection is an interest in the activity. The choice is his. Do not select an activity for him; he should not participate in one unless he has an inner desire to do so.

2. Are facilities available for pursuing the activity? He shouldn't select swimming as an activity when there are no pools, beaches, or other accommodations.

3. Is the activity within his financial means? Some activities, such as photography, require expensive equipment. He must ask himself (and his parents) if he can afford such an expense.

4. Will the activity be useful later in life? All other things being equal, activities should be selected in which he can participate throughout life.

5. Will the activity enhance his social relationships? If possible, leisure-time pursuits should enable him to develop his social self. Therefore, it may be wise for him to choose group activities in preference to those done alone.

6. Does the activity interfere with such important phases of his life as his work, religion, and home life? Activities selected

some of the shortages of schoolwork? Activities should help meet emotional and physical needs that sometimes fail to be achieved in regular required activities.

8. Does he have time for the activity? The time needed for participation should be considered in light of his required daily responsibilities.

The teacher can make an important contribution to the education of her youngsters by taking an interest in what they do out of school. Although the daily class work is very important, the after-school activities of children should not be left to chance. By having an understanding of the place of recreation in balanced living and a desire to have her children recreationally educated, she can do much to guide their energies and interests into channels which will be constructive and will further their self-development.

5. Water Sports Make Swimming Essential

The ease of travel today, the numbers of national and state lakes, and the rise in the amount of leisure time has seen an increase in boating, canoeing, water skiing, skating, fishing, and home pools.

Today, boating is enjoyed by more than

Figure 5-1. Instruction in swimming and diving is important.

40 million people. These boaters either pull skiers, haul fishermen, or try for the best speed from their powerful motors. From these boats many swimmers dive into unknown waters, some never to return. Many of the people riding in boats and canoes do not know how to swim. Over seven thousand drownings occur each year. While many may say this is a small number compared with the number engaged in these water sports, most of them could have been saved if they had been taught swimming in their physical education programs or in Red Cross classes conducted at Y.M.C.A.'s, Y.W.C.A.'s, Y.M.H.A.'s, or Boy Scout or Girl Scout organizations, because 50 per cent of these seven thousand drownings involve nonswimmers.

Companies constructing permanent pools in the yards of home owners predicted that over 50,000 would be completed in 1963. Conservative estimates for the purchase of portable or temporary plastic pools ranging in size from the very small to those of 40 foot diameter and 5 foot depth indicate that nearly one million are bought annually.

Drownings rank third among causes of death of people between the ages of fif-teen and twenty-four and second in cause among children between the ages of five and fourteen. There is great need for increased instruction in swimming and safety in water sports. More schools should be able to include swimming as part of their program of physical education. When pools are not available in schools it is possible many times to use community facilities for this excellent program. This challenge should be met by all educators.

CURRENT TRENDS IN ELEMENTARY EDUCATION THAT DIRECTLY CONCERN PHYSICAL EDUCATION

1. The "Whole Child" Learns

Teachers must be prepared to educate the "whole child" in his infinite variations of behavior and reactions to his environment. This means that the teacher is responsible for the development of the emotional, social, intellectual, and physical learning and well-being of each child.

Dr. Robert Krogman states:

Child growth and development is bio-social and none shall deny that the strands of both inter-twine inextricably to give design and pattern. There emerges the "whole child" as a nucleus of research and as the focus of integrative analysis.[2]

Story, an administrator in elementary education, believes the responsibility of the school is to

. . . administer a program of activities for chil-dren developed in relation to the achievement purposes of the school, activities that reflect teacher understanding of a student's needs, abil-ities and interests, activities which in their scope and sequence indicate a knowledge and sensitive-ness to the total development of the "whole child."[3]

It is impossible to separate the various parts of the child and teach each part sepa-rately. Each part is interrelated and the child learns as a whole indiidual. This whole is important and the individual elements alone are unimportant except as parts of the whole.

The Schools' Challenge

The elementary schools must serve the child, the community, and the nation. They will serve the community and nation to the greatest degree by serving the individual child to the best of his ability.

The dualist notion of a separate mind in a separate body is not acceptable today. The whole child goes to school and there he

[2] Robert Krogman, "Factors of Physical Growth as They Apply to Children," *Proceedings,* 1954 National Convention, American Association for Health, Physical Education and Recreation, p. 54.

[3] Bascum H. Story, "The Good Life in the Elementary School," *Thirty-first Yearbook, Associ-*ation of Department of Elementary School Princi-pals, National Education Association, p. 22.

learns skills, techniques, knowledges, and appreciations. This necessarily challenges the school to assist him in his physical, mental, social, and emotional growth and development.

It is agreed among educators that physical education is an integral part of the program and will assist in the development of the whole child.

Our machine age has made great changes in the lives of children, and the school must accept the responsibility to substitute activities once believed unnecessary because of the physical activity necessary for mere survival. Man is by nature active. Physical activity today is becoming less and less necessary for maintaining a livelihood and consequently the needs must be met in other ways.

Physical Education as an Aid in Total Development

Because of our changing world the need for physical education as an integral phase in the development of the whole child becomes apparent. Each individual needs activity for biological growth and development. Physical education exists as a good constructive social force to guarantee all youth the fulfillment of these needs.

Thus it appears that to educate the whole child, the school must assume many jobs and these are in a great part the responsibility of the elementary classroom teacher. Each classroom teacher must understand the ways in which physical education contributes to the development of the whole child and must be prepared to plan and administer an adequate program. Much learning may be gained through a program of physical education and motor activities because these cannot be isolated from the mental, social, and emotional learnings of the child.

2. Consolidation of Districts Gives Challenge

There are now 37,000 school districts as reported by the U.S. Bureau of Census' "Public School Systems in 1961–1962." In 1942 the same Bureau reported 108,579 school districts. Thus, in 20 years 71,000 school districts have been abolished through reorganization. During the last 25 years the number of one-teacher schools has dropped from 148,000 to 39,000. Some of the reasons for this trend are as follows.

1. The shift of population from farms to cities is reducing enrollments in rural areas and making it increasingly difficult for the population in these areas to finance good schools.

2. Consolidation of districts makes it easier to provide better schools and more services.

3. With cost of education rising, consolidation is essential to make the best possible use of financial resources.

4. Recruitment of good teachers is easier in consolidated districts than in small, poorly managed ones.

A recent commission on school district organization of the American Association of School Administrators pointed out that in general any district that contains less than 1,200 pupils or fewer than 40 teachers is too small to operate efficiently. This commission pointed out some of the limitations of small districts. They provide meager high school programs; they are unable to construct needed school plants; the cost per pupil is unreasonably high; and their low pupil-teacher ratio results in a loss of manpower.

This trend toward consolidation of school districts offers a direct challenge to physical education to plan and administer adequate recreation programs during the noon hour because there are many children transported by bus to these schools who must remain there all day. The need for planned activity is great.

In addition to the challenge of the noon hour program early morning programs are also advisable. Because the same buses are often used to transport two or three different groups of children, causing many to arrive at school long before the actual beginning of the school day, some planned worthy activities should be available then, also. Opportunities for these children to secure equipment and supplies in order to participate in a safe and organized program of activities during this time is a responsibility of educators. A similar plan to that of the noon hour has been used with great success in many schools.

Additional time for similar programs is again prevalent at the close of school when the same buses must make two or three trips to transport all the children home. The opportunity for worthy use of leisure is again the responsibility of leaders in these elementary schools.

Chapter 15 devotes more space to the consideration of ways and means that teachers may organize and administer worthy programs of recreational activities before school, during the noon hour, and after school to meet a great desire and need for children to be busy in worthy and educationally sound activities.

3. Acceptance of Camping Education Is Vital

Various educational agencies and associations recommended in May 1948 that camping be a part of every child's education. Such associations included the American Association for Health, Physical Education and Recreation, the United States Office of Education, the National Secondary Principal's Association, the American Association of School Administrators, and the American Council on Education.

Many educators believe that camping education is an integral part of the child's education. Mehl and her associates, all outstanding educators in the field of elementary education, state that "Camping experience should be provided for every child as a part of a well-rounded educational program,"[4] Frank Irwin comments:

Increasingly camping and outing activities become an integral part of the total school program. Ideally these activities may be best stressed in grades four through twelve, although some may be begun at any time in the first three grades. Crowded classrooms and gymnasiums often create a problem, yet every school in America, whether located in a village or teeming city, has access to wide-open spaces, city parks or even school grounds, where a camping program might be initiated. Thirty-three cities operate public school camps on a year-round basis. Over 500 more provide some kind of over-night, day or week-end camping experiences for their students.[5]

Use of National Parks from 1960 to 1962 shows a 63.4 per cent increase, according to statistics compiled by the U.S. Department of the Interior, National Park Service, Washington, D.C. These figures are very small compared with those for the use of of our state parks for family outings and camping activities. There are in addition, of course, thousands of individuals who, during their vacations, camp on land owned by friends.

Camping education offers an opportunity to further the democratic living relations between teachers and children. These relationships have great carry-over value into adult life. All phases of education benefit

[4] Marie Mehl, Hubert H. Mills, and Harl R. Douglass, *Teaching in Elementary School,* New York, The Ronald Press Company, 1950, p. 108.
[5] Frank Irwin, *The Theory of Camping,* New York, A. S. Barnes and Company, 1950, p. 153.

from camping education. No subject or part of the curriculum is apart from it. It is a fine chance for integration of the total education of the whole child.

The trend toward camping education is well established and will show great strides within the next decade. This movement may well be directed and coordinated by physical education departments.[6]

4. Team Teaching Assists

The integration and correlation of sub-jects today make team teaching possible, and the challenge is given to teachers in all areas to assist. The physical education specialist teams with the music and art specialists who in turn work directly with the classroom teacher to make the unit in social studies much more meaningful to the students. Dances of the countries studied, their games, songs, types of music and musical instruments, costumes, colors, and drawings change words in a text into living experiences that bring home to children the reality of life in strange and far-off lands around the world.

CURRENT TRENDS IN PHYSICAL EDUCATION IN
ELEMENTARY SCHOOLS

There are specific trends in physical education which directly affect the educational offerings of our schools. These trends make necessary demands on programs both internally and externally and may not be disregarded if physical education is to be an integral part of the education of each child. Understanding and awareness of them assist in program planning, administering, and evaluating. Those considered the most important are discussed.

1. Classroom Teachers *Must* Teach Physical Education

The elementary classroom teacher is one of the most important educators in our society. He or she is the person who has contact with and guidance of more children than almost any other one person in the field of education. He or she has the child during his

impressionable growing years. The child can be considered a work of art to be fashioned by the teacher into something wonderful. Furthermore, many children receive their only formal educational guidance from the classroom teacher because of drop-outs. The number of drop-outs per thousand children from grade five through high school is 364, according to the United States Department of Health, Education and Welfare, Office of Education, Bureau of Educational Statistics. The Department's study began with fifth grade children in 1954–1955 and concluded in 1962 when the children were—or should have been—graduated from the twelfth grade.

Highlights of a report, *Physical Education in Urban Elementary Schools*, based on 532 school systems and published in 1959 by the U.S. Department of Health, Education and Welfare, Office of Education, show that 26 per cent of the classroom teachers in grades one to three do not have the help of specialized personnel in physical educa-

[6] Chapter 20 is devoted entirely to camping and outdoor education.

tion. Sixteen per cent of the teachers in grades four to six also teach entirely alone.

The classroom teacher needs to be prepared to teach physical education to the children. The aid of specialists and consultants is desirable, but this help is often lacking.

Elementary educators believe the classroom teacher should teach physical education to the children. As Gans, an outstanding authority in elementary education, so ably writes:

In general, children can be more efficiently taught by the classroom teacher than by the physical education specalist. The teacher knows the best ways for the groups to organize and can see the vigorous activity program in relation to each child's total day. However, she may need the help of a specialist in demonstrating the most efficient use of a particular piece of equipment; in analyzing where a specific child needs help and how that help should be given; and in seeing that the program maintains an adequate variety of games, self-testing activities, and stunts as well as free play and rhythms.[7]

The self-contained classroom with consultants on call is popular.

2. Individual Differences Must Be Stressed

Good results in schoolwork are accomplished only when the teacher has a thorough knowledge of the children being taught. The outstanding work being achieved in the kindergarten and primary fields of education is attributed to this knowledge and understanding.

In education today, leaders stress the understanding of growth, development, and behavior characteristics of children as basic requirements for the professional preparation of teachers.

The growth processes of children are uneven in physical, organic, and psychological aspects as well as in mental, social, and emotional development. Therefore, programs of physical education should be based on these findings and be attuned to meet the needs of the individual child. Children possess different physical abilities in the same chronological age group and these must be considered in planning and administering programs.[8]

3. Development of Leisure Activities Is Essential

Today's work week of 40 hours will gradually be reduced. But even when people work an eight-hour day and a five-day work week, much time is available for leisure. Today there are more people, more goods, more money, more workers, more paid vacations, more cars, more places to go—all of which add up to the need for more leisure-time activities and facilities.

Physical education must broaden its offerings for leisure-time activities to meet some of these needs by teaching an appreciation of sports and by adding more recreational activities, which are valuable for leisure-time use now and in later life. Worthy use of leisure time may tend to lessen juvenile delinquency and promote good mental and emotional health. This challenge to physical education is very important. Programs must also be changed to offer instruction in activities suitable to be carried on in smaller areas because of urbanization.

---

[7] Roma Gans *et al., Teaching Young Children,* New York, World Book Company, 1952, p. 337.

[8] Chapter 7 is devoted to a discussion of the program of physical education attuned to meet needs found in growth and development studies and research.

4. Physical Education Is a Means of Developing Democratic Living

Democracy derives its strength from the worth of each individual. In turn, each individual must learn to live in a democracy and value himself, his status, and his fellow man. He must learn to live in harmony with the conflicts in and about him which he cannot change. He must learn respect for all people.

Physical education has an opportunity to aid in democratic living because it is primarily concerned with the qualitative aspects of human behavior. It does not have as its only aim mere strength, endurance, and motor skills. These are not ends in themselves. They are only means toward and end and are aimed at assisting the child in his total development by giving him the ability to cooperate and succeed in a complex society.

Youth may be taught to reach mutual understandings through a program of physical education. They may be taught to play with others, to win and lose, to give and take, and, whatever the outcome may be, not to give up.

Hurlock, a well-known authority and author on child growth and development, believes:

By no means the least important value of play is its socialization influences. Through their play activities children learn to get along with other children, to share their possessions, to be fair and play the rules of the game, to cooperate, to wait their turn. Learning to be a good sport and a good loser in childhood will fit the child for many difficult social adjustments he will have to make as he reaches maturity.[9]

The gymnasium, playground, and athletic field are laboratories wherein attitudes and ideals are developed into worthy patterns of socially acceptable conduct and behavior for our democracy. Fair play, respect for the rights of others, willingness to abide by rules and regulations and accept an official's decision, the development of leadership and followership, the place and value of self-sacrifice for the sake of the team, loyalty and respect for oneself and one's team mates may all be taught in the program of physical education. From the situation on the play-field, true tolerance and the democratic way of life may be won or lost.

One of the most important contributions of physical education is the insight it provides into human nature. Games are intensive social experiences. Participation in them aids children in forming ideals, habits of judgment, and the basic social organization needed now and in adulthood in a democracy.

In the physical education program, teams and squads give vent to the gang instinct. Lee believes the gang may be one of the greatest educative factors in a child's life.[10]

There must, however, be a differentiation between childhood gang and gangsterism. Team play correctly planned and guided will fill the needs children gain from belonging to gangs. *Gang* need not be a word with bad connotations. Gangs can be good as well as evil.

The Educational Policies Commission[11] recognizes physical education as a part of the curriculum having value beyond mere physical performance. They believe an adequate program develops socializing oppor-

[9] By permission from *Child Growth and Development,* by Elizabeth Hurlock, Copyright, 1949, McGraw-Hill Book Company, Inc., p. 260.

[10] J. Murray Lee and Doris Lee, *The Child and His Curriculum* (Second edition), New York, Appleton-Century-Crofts, Inc., 1950, p. 75.

[11] Educational Policies Commission, "Health and Physical Fitness," Washington, D.C., Educational Policies Commission, American Association for Health, Physical Education and Recreation, 1954, p. 12.

tunities, builds character, and provides opportunities for developing leadership and followership so urgently needed in a democracy. Physical education may be a laboratory for aiding the development of harmonious teamwork, a democratic spirit, and the ability of the child to accept his place in sharing and belonging to the group.

5. Physical Education Programs Are Evaluated

Much is claimed for physical education, but how can teachers know what they are accomplishing unless they evaluate their programs? Effectiveness and efficiency should be developed and maintained in planning and administering programs of physical education.

Evaluation is a process. It is not accomplished by one test or one measuring device. Most parts of the curriculum may be evaluated. The physical education program should be also. This is a responsibility of the teacher.[12]

6. Special Developmental Activities Are Included

Today, the trend to use gymnastic equipment in all schools, including the elementary school, is gaining ground. Whether or not the poor results of the Kraus-Weber tests created this interest is hard to determine. Elementary playgrounds throughout the nation are being equipped with more climbing apparatus such as jungle gyms, horizontal ladders, and horizontal bars. In a report made by the U.S. Department of Health, Education and Welfare concerning physical education in 12,217 urban elementary schools, we find that one third of the

schools have a climbing apparatus, 20 per cent have horizontal ladders, and 21 per cent have horizontal bars. Indoor facilities for elementary schools are also being eqiupped with climbing ropes and poles and combination pieces of apparatus such as the "Physical Educator"[13] and the "Challenger[14] which include the horizontal ladder, vertical ladder, ropes, and rings.

Several companies are now manufacturing pieces of apparatus in smaller sizes especially for use in elementary schools.

This trend in physical education in the elementary schools is very popular among children where it is being taught because it meets their needs for climbing, hanging, and testing themselves, needs which used to be satisfied in their own yards and the out-of-doors by ropes attached to tree limbs, by climbing trees, and skinning the cat over tree limbs.

Such a development is indeed worthy of a place in our programs.

7. Intramural Sports and Play Days Are Increasing

Interest among children in participating in activities during the noon-hour and after school has increased the number of intramural sports, play days, and sports days in our elementary schools. In a recent survey of over 12,000 urban elementary schools, 57 per cent were busily engaged in intramural programs as part of their activities. Play days were popular in 58 per cent of these same schools.

Because many children remain at school during the noon-hour, this is an opportune time to carry out intramural programs in grades five through eight, using

---

[12] Chapter 18 discusses evaluation needs and techniques.

[13] See the Nissen-Medart catalogue; the address is given in Appendix D.

[14] See the Paneltrol, Inc. catalogue; the address is given in Appendix D.

activities taught in the regular physical education program. Many who must wait for late buses or who walk to school may engage in such programs after school and gain much value from participation.

Intramurals, play days, and sports days must be well planned and correctly administered to be of value. If children of different grades are to play together they must be mixed. Do not challenge the fifth graders against the sixth graders or the seventh graders against the eighth graders.

Play days usually include many children participating in many different activities, all being administered simultaneously. For example, while one group participates in dodge ball, another is playing kick ball, another softball, and as many other activities as interest warrants and space will permit.

In summary, trends give challenge and direction to physical education programs. If there is not to be an educational lag, these challenges in all of our educational processes must be met. Physical education is no exception if it is to be justified as an integral part of the program of education for elementary children. All programs should be planned to meet the needs shown through the trends of the times. To be successful, education must meet the challenges of the day and because trends do not remain static, we must expect, accept and plan for changes.

QUESTIONS AND PRACTICAL PROBLEMS

1. Trace the history of physical education and show how trends have directed its development.

2. Did trends have any influence on changing the physical training programs to physical education? Substantiate your position.

3. Predict trends and their influences on our educational program in the next decade. Be specific in explaining how these trends will challenge the program of physical education.

4. Read several educational articles. Summarize them and show either how present trends influenced the philosophy of the author or how the author is proposing to meet educational needs caused by new trends.

5. What do we mean by cultural lag? educational lag? Give examples of each.

6. Divide into committees with each group doing further reading and research on the trends mentioned in this chapter. Be prepared to share your findings with the class.

7. Define the word *trend*. Why is it important to consider trends in physical education?

8. What are some current trends in the field of education in general?

9. What are some current trends in elementary education which directly concern physical education?

10. What is meant by the phrase "the whole child goes to school?"

11. How does physical education contribute to the development of the "whole child?"

12. What is the relationship between physical education programs and the consolidation of school districts?

13. Trace the development of camping education as a worthy educational medium from 1948 until the present. What were some of the factors that contributed to camping becoming a trend in elementary education?

14. Discuss five trends in physical education in elementary schools.

15. What is the role of the classroom teacher in physical education in the modern elementary school?

16. To what degree does an emphasis on individual differences represent a trend in physical education today?

17. What trend is being developed in physical education as a result of the "push-button age?"

18. Develop a bibliography of outstanding references which discuss trends in physical education.

SELECTED REFERENCES

AINSWORTH, DOROTHY, "Contributions of Physical Education to the Social Service Agency," *Journal of Health, Physical Education and Recreation,* **21:**325 (June 1950).

AMERICAN ASSOCIATION FOR HEALTH, PHYSICAL EDUCATION AND RECREATION, "Education For Leisure (A Conference Report)," Washington, D.C., American Association for Health, Physical Education and Recreation, 1957.

————, "Athletics in Education, Platform Statement by the DMA," Washington, D.C., American Association for Health, Physical Education and Recreation, 1961.

BROWNELL, C. L., "Role of Health, Physical Education and Recreation in the Space Age," *National Association of Secondary School Principals Bulletin,* **44:**3–9 (May 1960).

BUCHER, CHARLES A., "Athletics in Education," *Journal of Educational Sociology,* **28:**241 (February 1955).

BUTLER, GEORGE D., *Introduction to Community Recreation,* New York, McGraw-Hill Book Company, Inc., 1959.

COMMISSION STUDY REPORT 26, "Prospective Demand for Outdoor Recreation," *Outdoor Recreation Resources Review,* Washington, D.C., Superintendent of Documents, U.S. Government Printing Office, 1962.

COWELL, CHARLES, and HELEN W. HAZELTON, *Curriculum Designs in Physical Education,* Englewood Cliffs, N.J., Prentice-Hall, Inc., 1955.

DAUBERT, R. D., "Evaluating the Recreation Camp Program," *Recreation,* **51:**76 (March 1958).

DAVIS, ELWOOD C., and GENE LOGAN, *Biophysical Values of Muscular Activity,* Dubuque, Iowa, W. C. Brown and Company, 1961.

DECKER, JOHN K., "Can We Predict Recreation's Future?" *Journal of Health, Physical Education and Recreation,* **26:**31 (March 1955).

GREEN, LEON, "The P.T.A. Believes in Recreation for American Youth," *Journal of Health, Physical Education and Recreation,* **30:**5 (May–June 1959).

HUNSICKER, PAUL, *Physical Fitness,* Washington, D.C., Department of Classroom Teachers, National Education Association, 1963.

MARSHALL, R. M., "Toughening Our Soft Generation," edited by W. Gill, *Saturday Evening Post,* **235:**13–17 (June 23, 1962).

METHENY, E., "Physical Education Has Changed," *National Education Association Journal,* **49:**45–6 (May 1960).

NASH, J. B., "The Contributions of Physical Education to Recreation," *Journal of Health, Physical Education and Recreation,* **22:**53 (October 1951).

NOLAN, JAMES B., "Athletics and Juvenile Delinquency," *Journal of Educational Sociology,* **28:**241 (February 1955).

SPOCK, B. M., "Are Our Children Getting Enough Exercise?" *Ladies Home Journal,* **77:**30+ (June 1960).

STERN, E. M., "There's No Place Like Camp," *Parents' Magazine,* **35:**58–9+ (March 1960).

WILKINSON, C. B., "RX for Physical Fitness," *P.T.A. Magazine,* **56:**7–9 (September 1961).

————, "In a Dangerous World, Is American Youth Too Soft?" (interview with fitness tests), *U.S. News,* **51:**75–7 (August 21, 1961).

CHAPTER 6

Basic Principles of Physical Education for Elementary Schools

Webster's defines the word *principle* as a fundamental truth; that which is an essential or characteristic econstituent; and that which gives a substance its essential properties. For general understanding, principles may be considered as beliefs, based on facts, which are used as guides or criteria. They are needed to form judgments and to determine actions. Discussion of some basic principles as they apply to physical education in the elementary school and which may act as guideposts in developing programs is the purpose of this chapter. Complete textbooks have been written on principles of physical education. The authors have in no way endeavored to include all of them in this chap-ter. They will discuss only those which they believe to be absolutely necessary in planning and administering worthy programs of physical education in elementary schools.

Through the years, educational leaders have deemed physical education an important enough part of the educational program for almost all states to pass laws making it a mandatory part of the public school curriculum. The remainder have passed permissive laws for the inclusion of it in their program. This shows that its importance is realized by educators and legislators and challenges the planning and administration of worthy programs. Such programs must be based on sound principles.

TYPES OF PRINCIPLES

Educators believe that programs of physical education should be based on physiological, psychological, and sociological principles. Each principle, in turn, should be related to the needs, interests, and abilities of the individual child in the program of each school.

Physiological principles stress opportunities for a wide range of physical movement and activity as essential to organic development. Psychological principles stress the learning situation in the teaching of skills and activities based on natural play activities. Sociological principles urge the selection of activities that are adaptable to leisure-time participation and which contribute to education for citizenship and to accepted character development.

Education for the immediate present and the future may be either good or bad, depending on the teacher or leader, the environment, and all interactions. Although

70

children are primarily concerned with the present, some thought must be given to preparation for adulthood. Hence, the principles on which a program of physical education is based must endeavor to meet the immediate needs of childhood as well as help prepare the child to meet the future needs of adulthood. Bearing these criteria in mind, the authors believe that the following basic principles are essential and must be carefully considered in planning and administering a worthy program.

BASIC PRINCIPLES

1. Physical Education Must Consider Needs, Interests, and Abilities of the Child

Needs Must Be Met

Today the needs of children have been well defined according to various age groups through studies of child growth and development. Some of the needs of children which may be met through a program of physical education have previously been discussed. The following specific needs and supporting reasons give challenge to programs of physical education:

1. Programs of physical education should include activity to satisfy biological needs for growth because (a) physical activity is essential to good health and a satisfying and vigorous life; (b) today many children are deprived of outdoor farmwork, fishing, hunting, and similar activities; (c) out-of-school time is curtailed because of wide and varied interests and opportunities for instruction in music, art, and dramatics; (d) the failure to provide appropriate play facilities in many areas, both urban and suburban, is a problem; (e) the television fad encourages inactivity.

2. Programs of physical education should include activities to aid organic health and emotional stability needs because (a) modern competitions and stresses sometimes prove disastrous to those who are unfit; (b) labor-saving inventions result in less need for large-muscle activity; (c) the incidence of strain, illness, and fatigue decreases with physical fitness; (d) a strong body, well cared for, may lessen emotional instability.

3. Physical education programs should increase skills, responses, and coordinations essential for a productive, active life. There should be a direct correlation between accident prevention and the possession of these skills. Hazardous conditions are ever present and accident prevention may be aided through good mind and muscle coordination, good reflexes, and quick mental reactions.

Interest Must Be Considered

On the subject of interest William Burton makes the following statement:

The problem is not whether children are to learn with interest or without it. They never learn without it. The real problem is to determine what kind of interest it shall be and from what it shall be derived. No competent and responsible educational leader has ever said anywhere at any time that the pupil is to do what he wants to do. It has been said, however, that the pupil should want to do what he does if he is to learn.[1]

Children learn best when they have a purpose and interest. If activities in physical

[1] William Burton, *The Guidance of Learning Activities,* New York, Appleton-Century-Crofts, Inc., 1944, p. 101.

education are selected according to their interests and needs, and the teaching is based on sound philosophy, they will be of educational value to the child.

Anything for which children see an immediate purpose is easier to teach than that which is planned to help them only later in life. Play is a fundamental part of the life of each child. Most children are more interested in play than in anything else. Because of this interest, they throw themselves wholeheartedly into it. With programs based on these interests, it is possible to direct them into proper growth channels through this phase of education.

If interest is lacking, children learn less rapidly and may acquire a dislike for the activity and for the leader who is forcing them to participate. Because of these factors they may develop bad habits.

It has been said by educators that motivation plays the leading role in education. The interest drive in play is the motivation from which we direct it into useful channels through properly planned programs of physical education. Play interests change with age, and for this reason programs must also change.

Abilities Must Guide

Children's abilities change as they grow. Boys and girls differ in ability as they mature. The best programs of physical education should be flexible enough to be adapted to a wide range of activities at different levels of abilities, often within the same grade as well as in different age groups. This principle also implies that activities will be planned for the exceptional child, who will be discussed in Chapter 8.

Chapters 9 and 10 will discuss the types of activities, time elements, and other program factors based on the needs, interests, and abilities of the child to further assist the teacher in the application of this principle.

2. Programs of Physical Education Must Plan for Large-Muscle, Social, and Emotional Development

The Need for Planning

Unless a program of physical education activities is planned, it will be slipshod and relatively unimportant. Many teachers do not see the necessity of planning for their physical education but look at it only as an energy-release device. Good planning avoids mistakes, confusion, needless and boring repetition, and meets the needs, interests, and abilities of the children.[2]

Once a program is planned it is easier to administer. The therapeutic value received by the child from the play situation in physical education often depends on the provisions made for the activity, *i.e.*, planning and the way it is administered. All teaching principles used in education apply to the physical education program.

Large-Muscle Development

Activities necessary for large-muscle development are based on the needs of the individuals within the program. Types of equipment and facilities are factors which have some bearing on the physical education program. Various play apparatus such as jungle gyms, horizontal ladders, merry-go-rounds, and ropes for climbing are excellent for developing the muscles in the arms and chest. Self-testing activities and stunts as well as games will also aid in big-muscle development.

Social and Emotional Development

Participation in games should create an atmosphere conducive to acceptable and de-

[2] Refer to Chapter 13 for further discussion on planning.

sirable social development. Activities taught in the program which have carry-over value for leisure time aid in the social development of the child. Social qualities of play may provide suitable relationships between the child and his playmates and develop constructive behavior patterns of helpfulness, kindness, truthfulness, justice, and sociability. If these experiences through play are adequate and properly guided, they should assist him at the time and also aid him to take his place as a better-adjusted adult.

A child learns self-discipline through his play in physical education. The experiences he gains through the program must be honest, give him satisfactions, present cooperative social experiences, and emphasize the group ideal. Children who play fair learn to get along with others, become good sports, and learn to give and take, to win and lose, to accept decisions made by the majority and those made by the elected captain or official. All of these assist in teaching him the democratic way of life. He knows no distinction between color or creed. His teammates and he are striving for the same goals of success and fun. Barriers do not exist.

3. Providing Necessary Equipment, Facilities, and Leadership Is the Responsibility of Every School

How well a teacher teaches depends on education, love for the work and the children,

Figure 6–1. Exercises contribute to organic development. (Courtesy of Panetrol, Inc.)

teaching conditions, facilities, equipment, administration, and a happy, cooperative, democratic environment. Each of these factors is important no matter what field or branch of specialization one prefers. To plan, administer, and execute a program of physical education that will meet the needs of individuals requires varied personal as well as physical equipment; equipment, facilities, and leadership are all essential.

Recommended Equipment

Recommended equipment and supplies for elementary schools are listed in Tables 6–1 and 6–2.

TABLE 6–1. *Equipment and Supplies for 30 Elementary-Age Children*[3]

Activities	Primary	Intermediate
Individual activities		
Balls—rubber—		
10″		
8½″	30	
6½″		15
Bean bags	30	6
Bowling sets	1	2
Croquet sets		2
Hoops	30	15
Indian clubs	12	12
Pogo sticks	6	6
Ropes—		
Jump (various lengths)	30	30
Long (8′ to 10′)	6	6
Stilts	8	8
Targets—bean bag	6	3
Group activities		
Aerial tennis—		
Birdies		12
Paddles		12
Nets		2
Baseball—		
Balls		10
Bases		2 sets
Bats		10
Gloves—fielder		3
Masks		2
Mitts—baseman		3
—catcher		3
Plates—pitcher		1

[3] The Athletic Institute, *Equipment and Supplies for Athletics, Physical Education, and Recreation,* Chicago, The Athletic Institute, 1960, p. 7.

Activities	Primary	Intermediate
Basketball—		
Balls—junior size—28″ cir.		6
Official		4
Croquet sets		3
Deck tennis—		
Rings		15
Nets		2
Football—		
Balls—junior size—10½″		3
Paddle tennis—		
Balls	30	12
Paddles		6
Nets		1
Portable basketball goals		2
Quoits		4 sets
Shuffleboard		4 sets
Soccer balls	6	6
Softball—		
Balls—official		6
—soft—12″		15
—supersoft—12″	15	6
Bats—28″ to 31″	6	12
Mitts—catcher		2
—first base		2
Masks		2
Bases, sets	2	2
Batting tees		2
Tetherball—		
Poles		3
Balls		3
Volleyball—		
Balls	6	6
Nets		2
Standards		2

Quiet games such as Checkers, Flinch, Lotto, Scrabble, Chinese Checkers, Monopoly, and the like are recommended for classroom use.

The proper care and distribution of equipment is essential. If it is kept in a central equipment room, a systematic way of checking it out and in must be planned so that each person using it will be responsible for it. If it is possible to keep some in each classroom, it will undoubtedly be used more and there will be less conflict. Naturally the amount of equipment needed varies according to the number of students. One ball for each four to six students is suggested. Rubber balls which may be inflated the same as

TABLE 6–2. Apparatus, Playground Equipment, and Rhythmic Materials for 30 Elementary-Age Children[4]

Materials	Primary	Intermediate
Apparatus and playground equipment		
Balance beams	6	6
Benches, 18" high, 12" wide, 4' long	6	6
Climbing structures		
Rope ladders	2	2
Metal or wood, maximum height 9'	2	
Giant blocks	6	
Horizontal ladders	2	2
Jumping standards	2	2
Bamboo crossbars	4	4
Mats 4' $\times$ 7' (lightweight and washable)	6	6
Merry-go-round	1	
Multiple horizontal bars	3	3
Oblique ladders	1	1
Sand box	1	
Scramble nets	2	2
Slides		
Maximum height 6'	1	
Maximum height 8'		1
Swings		
Maximum height 8' (safety seats)	6	
Maximum height 10'		6
Trampoline, junior	1	1
Travel rings	1	1
Vertical ladders	1	1
Vertical ropes	4	4
Walking boards		
8' long, 10" wide, 1½" thick	6	
Rhythmic materials		
Blocks, pairs	2	2
Cymbals	2	2
Drums	2	2
Gongs	2	2
Gourds	2	2
Sticks	2	2
Tambourines	2	2
Triangles	2	2
Pianos	1	1
Record players	1	1
Records (variety)	many	many
Record carrying cases	1	1
Table, with wheels	1	1

[4] The Athletic Institute, *Equipment and Supplies for Athletics, Physical Education, and Recreation*, Chicago, The Athletic Institute, 1960, p. 8.

leather ones are recommended. They are less costly as it is possible to buy two or three for the cost of one leather ball. Also, they last longer when used on wet playgrounds. When leather gets wet, unless it is carefully cared for, which is time-consuming, it becomes very hard and rough, the stitches break, and the balls are then short-lived.

Safety equipment should include eye guards for those who must wear glasses, safe markers for sectioning play areas, safe bases for games, and protective equipment such as body protectors, masks, and gloves for catchers in softball games.

Apparatus or permanent playground equipment is essential for large-muscle activity and social pleasure. The most popular and useful pieces include jungle gyms, horizontal ladders and bars, swings, seesaws, slides, merry-go-rounds, and sand boxes. Care and inspection of this apparatus and equipment are essential for safety. Further discussion of equipment inspection is included in Chapter 19. Proper instruction in the use of all apparatus is necessary. Planned and organized periods need to be worked out so that each group will have an opportunity to use it with a minimum of conflict or hard feelings. Properly supervised play apparatus provides excellent opportunities for big-muscle activity and teaches safety and respect for individual rights.

Recommended Facilities

The recommended space for play areas is a minimum of 10 acres for each 500 students. This is, of course, not possible in many schools already functioning. However, when purchasing land for new buildings, administrators are keeping this recommendation in mind and are preparing for large playground areas. The minimum recommended area for outdoor play is 100 square feet per child. In a recent issue of *Educational Summary*, it is stated that new sites for elementary schools average 10 to 15 acres. Facilities in the community may also be used by the school to good advantage and the community should be encouraged to share and make use of the school's recreational facilities. Community facilities are always great assets. This is especially true for the school that is already functioning with a small playground area and little opportunity for expansion.

Minimum indoor facilities recommended include a playroom or gymnasium 50 by 80 feet with a 20-foot ceiling. More is desirable if possible. It is natural to suppose that the play area both indoors and outdoors will be one factor which determines the types of activities in which children may engage.

Adequate locker and shower rooms should be available for children in the intermediate grades. Children from eight years of age and up are ready for showering. It seems only educationally sound when we endeavor to teach children good grooming and healthful living that we continue this teaching during our physical education programs. We should make it possible for students to have facilities where they may leave their street clothes and dress appropriately for their physical activity program. After 30 to 50 minutes of vigorous activity, showers should be available and be used. Surely, each teacher who has used these facilities knows children feel more like continuing their classroom work after showering and dressing that they do when they return to their classroom without that privilege.

Lockers should be provided for all children who will be changing clothes. Storage lockers for gym clothes should equal the number of children changing clothing. Street clothes lockers should equal the greatest number using the area at any one time.

Showers should be mostly group type. A few individual showers may be desirable in the girls' area. One shower head for each four users during the peak load period is recommended. Shower heads should be placed at varying heights so that they may be used without getting the hair wet.

Qualifications of Leaders

A report of the National Conference on Physical Education for Children of Elementary School Age suggests the following necessary qualifications for leaders:

1. A genuine liking for children.
2. Good health, physical vitality, sound mental attitude, emotional balance, and social adjustment.
3. Physical skills, efficient posture and body mechanics, and ability in a variety of recreational activities.
4. Ability to get along with pupils.
5. Understandings and interests that stem from a broad cultural background.
6. Knowledge of how children grow and learn and skill in using that knowledge in practical situations.
7. Competence in teaching and guiding elementary school children.[5]

Since the classroom teacher is the person responsible for most of the physical education in each grade, he or she also should possess these qualifications.

4. There Should Be Progression in All Programs

Maintaining interest in any area of education is essential if learning is to be successful, adequate, and challenging. It is also necessary to remember the individual differences of children, the differences between boys' and girls' interests in the intermediate level, and differences in interest span, abilities, and needs in general.

A well-planned program will include specific materials for the grade level so that each teacher will know when she receives a

[5] National Conference on Physical Education for School Children of Elementary Age, *Physical Education for Children,* Washington, D.C., National Conference on Physical Education for School Children of Elementary Age, 1951, p. 29.

new class what they have had in their physical education program, in addition to how they score in reading and other parts of the curriculum. Forms for keeping these records may be found in Chapter 18. Too much repetition in the same activity is often boring. Children tire of the same activity year after year in the elementary grades. They like new activities and new challenges. Each new experience is a learning situation for them. The lack of planning for progression may lead to a program of activities either too hard or too easy for the group. Either is dangerous.

Little children need plenty of big-muscle activity such as running, climbing, throwing, and chasing. This may be gained through play that is not too highly organized. Creative rhythms and dances give free expression and are fun. As children grow older, they need more difficult types of activity. They are less interested in games of low organization, such as circle and running and tagging games. Advancement should include team games which give them more challenge and require more skills and techniques to provide the needed physical activity as well as the social and psychological development suitable to their needs and abilities.

The teacher who does not know the correct materials for her children and who does not plan a progressive program will find that interest lags, the children may grow to dislike the physical education period, and there are many problems to settle.[6]

5. Programs Must Develop Free-Time and Recreational Skills

The physical education program should meet the play desires of children and teach them activities which they may use in their

[6] Further discussion of progression may be found in Chapters 9 and 10.

leisure time when they are not at school. These needs challenge the program to include activities which may be used in homes, back yards, basements, or sand lots. Children are often in groups of two, three, or four when out of school. Activities must be taught which may be enjoyed by a few as well as larger groups.

A good program should include activities usable for parties or picnics and on trips with the family. Games suitable for small areas, the beaches, and picnics are necessary if the recreational needs of children are to be met. Participation in wisely selected activities under proper guidance is needed and should aid the development of character and citizenship because:

1. There is an increased amount of leisure time.

2. There is a rise in reported juvenile crimes and delinquency.

3. Older pupils are interested in the social or gang stage and physical activities can be a constructive outlet.

4. Home conditions are changing in many instances and are creating greater needs and responsibilities for outside organizations, including the schools.

5. Facilities and adequate provisions for wholesome leisure time activities are many times not provided by society.

Activities for leisure are needed to develop skills and techniques and a love of wholesome recreation because:

1. The shorter work day and week results in more free time.

2. There is need for recreation to assist in a well-balanced life to preserve good mental and emotional health.

3. Youth has much freedom and the number of questionable modern commercial attractions is great.

4. Outdoor recreation is good for the many sedentary workers in our society.

5. Modern conveniences have given housewives more time for leisure.

Figure 6–2. Fun in a pool. (Courtesy of Seaboard Pools, Inc.)

Nash[7] stresses the fact that the early years are crucial and that 78 per cent of all hobby interests are developed before the age of 12 years. This would surely challenge activities of a recreational type to be included in elementary school programs.

Undesirable commercial recreation may well replace that of the desirable wholesome type if programs are inadequate. Brace, an outstanding author and educational leader, sums up the challenge for physical education very well with this statement:

Thus physical education has become that phase of education particularly assigned the function of guiding youth in developing skills in forms of physical education, recreation and attitudes favorable towards continuing in leisure recreation which will be mentally sound and emotionally satisfying and which will contribute to the maintenance of physical fitness.[8]

[7] Jay B. Nash, "The Skill-Learning Years," *Children in Focus,* Washington, D.C., 1954 Yearbook of the American Association for Health, Physical Education and Recreation, 1955, p. 65.

[8] David K. Brace, "Contributions of Physical Education to Total Education," *Journal of Health, Physical Education and Recreation,* **20:**635 (December 1949).

6. Interscholastic Sports Are Not Acceptable in Grades One Through Six

Interscholastic competition means competition of team games or individual and dual activities between two or more schools or outside groups. Highly organized, high-pressured competitive athletics have no place in the elementary schools.

Interscholastic competition places too much stress on winning and permits too few children to participate. Facilities, equipment, and leadership are often used for the approximate 10 per cent who have already developed the greatest skills and techniques and who show the greatest potentiality. The remaining 90 per cent are supposed to be satisfied as passive observers rather than active participants. Such competition lacks group focus by isolating many from participation and impedes the desired outcomes for children.

Children are not developed emotionally, physically, or psychologically to stand the stress and strain of interscholastic competition. Programs should be planned on a wide basis to include the participation of all children.

Many important educational organizations, such as the American Association for Health, Physical Education and Recreation, the Department of Elementary School Principals of the National Education Association, the National Council of State Consultants in Elementary Education, the National Recreation Association, the National Federation of High School Athletic Associations, and the American Association of School Administrators emphasize no interscholastic competition in elementary schools because it may be physically, emotionally, sociologically, and educationally harmful.

For a better understanding of competition for elementary school children, the Joint Committee on Athletic Competitions for Children of Elementary School and Junior School Age has published a report entitled *Desirable Athletic Competition for Children*. Every educator should read this report. The reader's attention is also called to "The Report of the Committee on School Health of the American Academy of Pediatrics."

7. Awards Are Not Recommended Incentives

Each child should engage in a program of physical education for the enjoyment and benefit he gains from it, not for the awards he may be given.

Motivation in the teaching process has often emphasized the external or incentive aspect of the program at the neglect of internal factors of readiness based on growth, needs, and interests. Studies prove that educators cannot expect as much positive behavior from children who are competing for individual awards, prizes, and similar incentives as when they are working and playing together. Competition usually creates out-group hostility and anti-social behavior patterns. At best, awards are artificial incentives. They should be ruled out in favor of the real goals of participation. These should be sufficient reward.

Educators frown on awards which are impossible to be achieved by all, as they tend to point out individual differences. An example of this is the abolishment of the awards for perfect attendence which were so popular at one time. These have been found to be educationally unsound because children who were physically unfit at times came to school merely for that award. Many children in the physical education program might overindulge to gain an award and thus, instead of benefiting from participation, would be harmed by it. Prizes and awards are artificial and questionable ways to stimulate participation and learning and may create a false standard of value.

8. Physical Education Programs Must Meet Community and Family Needs

Emphasis is being placed on getting parents and members of the community into the schools and teachers out into the community. The needs of each community should aid in determining the organization, procedures, and method of education. For the best programs, the maximum support of all concerned persons is needed.

Interests in a given community are guides for programs of physical education. Facilities present in the area should be used. Surely, if the community boasts of swimming, fishing, and boating areas, they should be a part of the program of physical education, and planned and administered in joint cooperation with the school, the home, and the community.

It is generally agreed that the best success in the educational process emerges when the school and the parents who make up the community share common goals. In this way, parents may learn the true value of play for their children.

Play days, May days, and sports days serve to acquaint the public with the physical education program. Through this medium it is often possible to interest the parents in coming to school to see programs in action. These special programs should be an honest outgrowth of the physical education program and not be planned only for publicity and public entertainment.

Physical education may serve the school and community by providing recreational and leisure activities for children, families, and adults. Civic groups and organizations, both for adults and for children, such as 4-H Clubs, Boy Scouts, Girl Scouts, Rotarians, Kiwanians, Lions, women's clubs, and the like may play an important part in the cooperative planning of physical education programs in community and school.

Wylie[9] in his study of 504 families found that many feel they have very unsatisfactory recreational programs. There was greater family unity among the families where good recreation habits were practiced. It would appear wise for the school to act as the leader, if necessary, and gain the cooperation of the homes in all programs of physical education and recreation. Parents are willing to aid and cooperate under wise guidance and leadership, especially when they understand the purposes and needs.

The next four principles, discussed in separate chapters throughout the text, are only listed here. Reference to their discussion may be found in Chapters 12, 14, and 19, respectively. A chapter has been devoted to each because of their importance.

9. Provision for the Exceptional Child Must Be a Part of Each Program

10. Physical Education Should Be Coordinated with the Whole Curriculum

11. Facilities, Equipment, and Leadership Should Be Available Before School, at Noon, and After School

12. Evaluating Physical Education in Terms of Pupil Growth Is Essential

[9] James A. Wylie, "A Survey of 504 Families to Determine the Relationship Between Certain Factors and the Nature of Recreation Program," *The Research Quarterly*, 24:229 (May 1953).

QUESTIONS AND PRACTICAL PROBLEMS

1. Organize a planning committee for the development of the physical education program in a school of grades one through six. Organize this group in committees and assign each a task to plan the program, its administration, and evaluation based on the principles discussed in this chapter.

2. Write a paper to be used as a talk before the citizens of your town relating to the ways the school and community may cooperate for the betterment of the physical education and recreational programs within the area. Present your talk to your class. Discussion following your presentation will indicate whether you have aroused sufficient interest by showing the needs and values necessary to accomplish your objectives.

3. You do not have sufficient equipment for the physical education program in your school. Discuss ways in which you could approach the administrator of your school to convince him of the need for your requisitioned equipment. Be specific in what you need and why you need it.

4. Choose the grade you wish to teach, or are teaching, and plan ways in which you can correlate physical education with units of work in various parts of the curriculum appropriate for the grade.

5. What characteristics do you possess which you believe make you a good teacher? What are your weaknesses? How will these either aid or hinder you in teaching physical education? How can you further develop your strengths? How can you correct or compensate for your weaknesses?

6. Discuss the pros and cons of awards for achievement in the program of physical education.

7. You are hired to teach in an elementary school where there has been interscholastic competition. The grade you are assigned to teach is one from which children enter this competition. Plan approaches and ways you would use to delete this competition.

8. Prepare an additional list of principles of physical education. Show how these apply to the profession and to the programs.

SELECTED REFERENCES

ABERNATHY, RUTH, "Implications for Physical Education in the Current Re-examination of American Education," *Journal of Health, Physical Education and Recreation,* **32:**19 (January 1961).

BACMEISTER, RHODA W., "Games That Teach Fair Play," *Parents' Magazine* (December 1962).

BRINLEY, ELDON D., "Interschool Athletics for Elementary School Youngsters," *Journal of School Health,* **33:**209–215 (September 1953).

BUCHER, CHARLES A., *Administration of School Health and Physical Education Programs* (Third edition), St. Louis, The C. V. Mosby Company, 1963.

————, *Methods and Materials in Physical Education and Recreation,* St. Louis, The C. V. Mosby Company, 1954.

DAVIS, ELWOOD C., *Philosophic Process in Physical Education,* Philadelphia, Lea and Febiger, 1961, Chapters 2, 3, and 4.

DAVIS, ELWOOD C., and GENE LOGAN, *Biophysical Values of Muscular Activity,* Dubuque, Iowa, W. C. Brown and Company, 1961.

ERICKSON, KENNETH A., "The Principal's Physical Education Principles," *The Bulletin of the National Association of Secondary School Principals,* **44,** No. 256 (May 1960).

FITZWATER, IVAN, "Developing Responsible Citizens," *Journal of Health, Physical Education and Recreation,* **31:**26 (May–June 1960).

HALL, V. L., "Physical Education: Why Children Need It," *National Elementary Principals,* **39:**8–11 (April 1960).

HAYES, ANNA H., "Planning and Working with Parents and Children," *Children in Focus,* 1954 Yearbook of the American Association for Health, Physical Education and Recreation, Washington, D.C., American Association for Health, Physical Education and Recreation, 1955, pp. 74–84.

HUTCHINSON, DORIS, "Tailored to Fit the Child," *N.E.A. Journal,* **52**:27 (February 1963).

JOINT COMMITTEE ON ATHLETIC COMPETITION FOR CHILDREN OF ELEMENTARY AND JUNIOR HIGH SCHOOL AGES, *Desirable Athletic Competition for Children,* Washington, D.C., American Association for Health, Physical Education and Recreation, 1952.

JOINT CONFERENCE OF THE D.G.W.S. AND D.M.A., *Values in Sports,* Washington, D.C., American Association for Health, Physical Education and Recreation, 1963.

MANLEY, HELEN, "Who Shall Teach?" *Children in Focus,* 1954 Yearbook of the American Association for Health, Physical Education and Recreation, Washington, D.C., American

Association for Health, Physical Education and Recreation, 1955, pp. 235–238.

OBERTEUFFER, DELBERT O., *Physical Education—A Textbook of Principles,* New York, Harper and Brothers, 1951.

PRICE, HARTLEY D., *The Establishment of Principles Which Are Essential for the Realization of the Objectives of Physical Education,* Doctoral Dissertation, School of Education, New York University, 1946.

VANNIER, MARYHELEN, "Toward Better Physical Education," *The Instructor,* **72**:5 (February 1963).

WILLGOOSE, C. E., "Don't Just Turn Them Loose; Elementary Physical Education Program," *National Education Association Journal,* **49**:13–14 (April 1960).

WILLIAMS, JESSIE F., *Principles of Physical Education* (Seventh edition), Philadelphia, W. B. Saunders Company, 1960.

THE CHILD

CHAPTER 7

Child Growth and Development Factors

It has been an established practice for many years for teachers to accept individual differences in children. The organization of two or three reading groups within the same grade is not uncommon. This is a good educational procedure because it accepts individual differences. We know that all children do not learn at the same rate of speed.

To select meaningful activities in elementary physical education programs, all known facts relating to child growth and development must also be applied. Differences in ability within a given age group must be accepted. All children do not develop alike at the same rate nor do they all grow alike in size and stature. Children do not all have the same start in life. Some are ill at birth and in early childhood, the home atmosphere makes a difference, and actual mental abilities differ. How shall these facts in child growth and development be used to aid a physical education program?

In addition to applying general facts gained from her knowledge of child growth and development, each teacher should secure data from all sources relating to each individual child. These data may come from medical records, tests and examinations, conferences with former teachers, parent conferences, and individual discussions with the child. The teacher should spend some time trying out recommended activities for her class and note through careful observation the range of abilities and interests among the students. Specific patterns of maturation will perhaps fit the majority of children at a given age level, but provisions should be made in the program to provide experiences in physical education which will meet individual differences and which will aid each child. If this is accomplished a teacher will be presenting meaningful activities because she has selected those which are within the child's range of ability and meet his needs and his interests.

A study of the physical, social, and emotional development of the child may aid the teacher in understanding why John is afraid of a ball, why Mary fears the swings, and why Jack seems to gain the most pleasure from not sharing anything with anyone. What causes these fears and the lack of cooperation and sharing? Is it something related to home and play experiences? These are questions which must be answered before the teacher can succeed in helping the individual child. Was John hit by a ball and injured? Did Mary fall from a swing or have an unpleasant experience with swings? Is Jack an only child or is he not permitted to share his toys with neighbors at home? Children are sensitive to their peers. Why isn't Jane accepted? Why won't the children hold Jimmie's hand in a circle game? The teacher must recognize the motivating forces behind these actions and correct them accordingly. She must respect all individual differences and needs. She must have a thorough understanding of the children for whom she is planning the program.

GROWTH AND DEVELOPMENT CHARACTERISTICS AND
NEEDS OF CHILDREN

The following list[1] of needs of children in the age group of from five to thirteen should assist the teacher in understanding the needs of children in various age groups and present a challenge to the program of physical education.

[1] From "Growth and Development Characteristics and Needs" (Chart), *Organizing the Elementary School for Living and Learning,* Association for Supervision and Curriculum Development, Washington, D.C., The National Education Association, 1947.

I. *Needs of Age Group Five, Six, Seven*

1. Expression through movement is necessary for growth.

2. It is part of the child's development to play in mud, wade in puddles, fall in snow, walk in fallen leaves and roll down hills. He may approximate rock and tree climbing activities on playground climbing apparatus. Playing animals (walking on all fours) will develop muscles of the back and abdomen. Use of the

Figure 7–1. Sharing and learning are fun.

walking board (balance beam) will help correct pronation (flat feet). Scooters and coaster wagons develop the leg muscles and fulfill a need for speed.

3. There must be opportunity to organize simple group play, to skip and dance in small groups. Half a dozen children are capable of playing together for a fifteen minute period or longer. All demand attention from one another and demand their own "turns."

4. Dramatic activities and rhythmic activities are essential.

5. The withdrawn child must be encouraged gradually to find his place in the group.

6. Since the attention span is short the periods should be short.

7. The child should sleep about eleven hours.

8. Although the child from time to time may reject certain foods because of texture and strong taste, variety in the menu will provide the full protection.

9. The child needs training both at home and in school in habits of personal hygiene; covering coughs and sneezes, using the handkerchief, keeping fingers away from the mouth and nose, etc. He needs training in the choice of clothing appropriate to weather.

II. *Needs of Age Group Eight, Nine, Ten*

1. The child needs an assured position in a social group. Membership in a gang or secret club fills this need. At this period children need a certain amount of freedom in setting up their own standards and rules, yet strongly desire understanding and sympathy from adults. Participation in family affairs is important.

2. There must be full opportunity to develop body control, strength and endurance. The child of 8, 9 or 10 years needs activities involving use of the whole body; stunts, throwing and ctaching, running "it" games, with their accompanying noise, etc. Seasonal play is important; kites, marbles and the like.

3. He needs organized team play. He is willing to practice in order to become adequate in skills for games; others gain self-confidence by excelling in some one thing.

4. It is as important for children to learn good followership as it is to learn good leadership.

5. Encouragement to exercise creatively in rhythms should be given.

6. Activities such as playing in caves and brooks, gathering nuts, and making campfires are needed. Bicycles and skates are enjoyed.

7. The child should sleep about ten hours. He usually does not get enough rest. A quiet period in the afternoon, not necessarily bed, may prevent overfatigue.

8. The child's increased interests in foods provide a basis for better understanding of the seven basic foods in maintaining good health.

9. The teacher must see that pupils having visual or aural defects always be seated in strategic positions in the classroom.

10. Close supervision is required to assure properly adjusted furniture and to prevent slumping over desks. Creation of an awareness that good posture is a comfortable posture is important.

III. *Needs of Age Group Eleven, Twelve, Thirteen*

1. There must be careful supervision in order that children of these ages may choose games proportionate to their strength and appropriate for their development needs.

2. Skill is essential for successful group participation. The child is willing to practice skills in order to gain proficiency, but needs informed guidance.

3. Games of increased organization such as softball, kick-ball, modified soccer, etc., are needed. The sedentary or self-protective child may need encouragement to play out of doors. Differentiation of activities for boys and girls may begin at these ages.

4. Special provision must be made for the child who is reaching his literate capacity and may be able to gain his chief satisfactions from muscular activities.

5. It is as important for children to develop good spectatorship as it is for them to develop good sportsmanship.

6. More mature interests must be met by more mature programs. There must be oppor-

tunities for many types of social contact. Club programs, church groups, Boy and Girl Scouts, Y.M.C.A., Campfire Girls, camping and the like fill the need for guidance.

7. Provision must be made for a growing interest in social dancing.

8. The rest needs are about eight or nine hours or longer.

9. The child's increasing desire to improve his personal appearance provides excellent opportunity to remedy habitual postural defects and to establish a balanced diet.

These needs challenge the physical education programs to provide activities which are significant and meaningful to children; which meet and satisfy the needs, ages, development, and abilities of children; and which are adaptable to the areas and places available for children to engage in play. Participation in activities which give opportunity for vigorous physical activity to aid in organic growth and development and which develop specific skills and techniques are musts. Challenging experiences and activities which assist in developing attitudes of pride in success and accomplishments and those which have definite carry-over values for future use help spell out the criteria to be used in the selection of activities to meet the needs of children.

CHARACTERISTICS AND NEEDS OF CHILDREN AND THEIR MEANING FOR PHYSICAL EDUCATION

Ray Duncan, a leader in the field of physical education, has very ably used certain characteristics and needs of children in various age groups and has shown specifically the role of physical education in helping to meet them.

The following tables are of assistance in understanding the implications of the physical education program based on the characteristics and needs of children in the early childhood grades of one, two, and three and the middle childhood grades of four, five, and six. Item-by-item comparison, where possible, will prove valuable.

TABLE 7–1. *Characteristics and Needs of Children in Grades One, Two, and Three (Early Childhood)*[2]

Characteristics	Needs	Meaning for Physical Education Programs
1. Full of energy but easily fatigued. Heart growing rapidly. Growth steady and slow. Eager to learn but restless—attention span short.	1. Physical activity. Frequent rest periods. Adequate rest. 10–12 hours of sleep.	1. Daily physical education. Short periods, 15–30 minutes. Relaxation activities (deflated balloon, rag doll, sack of sawdust, etc.).
2. Like to play together.	2. Large space for play. Need to feel they belong to their peer group.	2. Boys and girls together.

[2] Ray O. Duncan, "The Growth and Development Approach," *Journal of Health, Physical Education and Recreation*, **22**:364 (March 1951).

Characteristics	Needs	Meaning for Physical Education Programs
3. Not particularly interested in team games.	3. Active running and climbing activities.	3. Group games of low organization involving running and chasing which require little instruction and involve big muscles.
4. Large muscles better developed than small ones. Like to use hands. Learn best through active participation. Enjoy songs and rhythms.	4. Motor activities instead of abstract learning.	4. Stunts and self-testing activities, mimetics and story plays. Rhythms consisting of fundamental movements of skipping, running, walking, hopping, singing games, and folk dances.
5. Anxious to do things well. Sensitive to feelings of peers and adults.	5. Approval of teachers, assurance. Avoidance of humiliation. Affection from adults, praise, encouragement, love.	5. Show an interest in each pupil's progress. Give encouragement and praise for accomplishment. Select activities which permit all children to participate and achieve some measure of success and satisfaction.
6. Poor posture may develop.	6. To learn health precautions, health habits, and safety.	6. Posture exercises.
7. A period of fun-fantasy-fear.	7. Activities requiring some responsibility—no pressure.	7. Stress participation and fun—not winning. Assign pupils some responsibility for equipment, etc. Rotate so each pupil has an apportunity to be responsible.

TABLE 7–2. *Characteristics and Needs of Children in Grades Four, Five, and Six (Middle Childhood)*[3]

Characteristics	Needs	Meaning for Physical Education Programs
1. Extremely active, easily fatigued; rapid growth. Capable of prolonged interest.	1. Physical activity. Active rough and tumble play (safe and supervised). Adequate rest, 10–11 hours a day. Training in physical skills.	1. Daily physical activity. May increase periods to 20–30 minutes.

[3] *Ibid.*, p. 364.

Characteristics	Needs	Meaning for Physical Education Programs
2. Girls "tomboyish." Boys and girls changing interests—separate for play.	2. Creativity in rhythms (girls) and activities.	2. Separate boys and girls where desirable (fifth or sixth grade). Some coeducational activities necessary and popular.
3. Interest in active competitive games.	3. Team games—no pressure.	3. Group games of higher organization, relays, team games, folk and square dancing, mimetics (of games and sport activities).
4. Alignment with peer groups—seek group approval. 5. Development of self-reliability to achieve.	4. Friends and membership in a group. 5. For opportunity and stimulation to improve and display motor abilities. Recognition of individual shortcomings and adjustment to them.	4. Stress good sportsmanship. 5. Increase responsibilities (student leaders, team captains, squad leaders). Adapt program to individual needs. Stress development of individual skills.
6. Receive satisfaction from ability to achieve.	6. Understanding and sympathy from adults.	6. Deal with each pupil as an important person and show affectionate and sympathetic understanding of shortcomings. Give praise for accomplishments.
7. Careless of personal appearance.	7. Correction of posture.	7. Posture exercises. Stress development of posture, poise and personality.

RECOMMENDED PHYSICAL EDUCATION ACTIVITIES

Early Childhood Activities

Recommended types of activities for the physical education program of children in early childhood are as follows:

1. Dance and rhythmic activities.

2. Developmental activities using equipment and other specific types with no equipment.

3. Games of low organization.

4. Individual and dual activities.

5. Self-testing activities and stunts.

6. Story plays.

Additional activities for consideration:

7. Classroom games (to be used when other indoor facilities are not available).

8. Aquatics (to be used if facilities and qualified teachers are available).

Middle Childhood Activities

Those types of physical education activities recommended for the middle childhood grades (four, five, and six) may be listed as follows:

1. Dance and rhythmic activities.
2. Developmental activities (specific).
3. Games of low organization.
4. Individual and dual activities.
5. Preliminary and lead-up games and activities.
6. Self-testing activities and stunts.
7. Team games.
8. Track and field events.

Additional activities for consideration:

9. Classroom games (to be used if other indoor facilities are not available).
10. Aquatics (to be used if facilities and qualified teachers are available).[4]

GROWTH THROUGH PHYSICAL ACTIVITY

If the physical education program is planned, based on the knowledge of child growth and development, it will be guided by the needs, interests, and abilities of each child. If it is then correctly administered, one may readily expect that it will aid the child in organic development, neuromuscular skill development, and grace in movement. It should also continue to guide natural play instincts so a child may gain pleasure through participation in games and develop a carry-over interest in activities to be used in leisure time.

A child learns through play, and learning is synonymous with living. Joseph Lee says, "Play to a child is growth—the gaining of life; to the adult recreation."[5]

To gain the most from physical education each child should be assisted in his natural growth patterns without force. Each one may need this assistance by different processes, but every process should supply an acceptable social pattern and achievement. How physical education may help meet a child's needs is ably summarized in *Physical Education for Children*.

Every child needs sufficient muscular strength to maintain good posture at rest and in motion and to do with ease the tasks of each day. He attains this strength through vigorous physical activities. Strength coupled with a flexible body gives him ability to move quickly and effectively. He needs the stamina and endurance that depend on well-developed heart and lungs to persist in work and play without undue fatigue. Strength, agility, and endurance come from play that is long and intense enough to tax the body beyond the ordinary.

A child's ability to use his body skillfully in work and play requires coordination of brain and muscles that comes only from purposeful practice. Skills learned in a variety of rhythmic activities, dances, games, and stunts, will remain through life. . . .[6]

Physical education must involve guidance to be educational. Children learn certain activities such as creeping, standing, walking, and the like which are not greatly affected by teaching. However, the game situation, learning to play with others, and developing certain needed skills and techniques are all acquired faster and improve through good teaching. These game situa-

[4] A discussion with definitions, aims, and objectives and examples of each type of activity may be found in Chapters 9 and 10.

[5] Joseph Lee, *Play in Education*, New York, The Macmillan Company, 1915, p. 174.

[6] National Conference in Physical Education for School Children of Elementary Age, *Physical Education for Children*, Washington, D.C., National Conference in Physical Education for School Children of Elementary Age, 1951, pp. 9–10.

Figure 7–2. Playtime starts at an early age. (Photo by Carl Purcell, National Education Association)

tions aid a child in meeting his organic and social needs, are interesting, and should influence his life. Anderson believes a child is aided through play in the following ways:

A game or contest has rigid rules which are well-defined and well-administered . . . probably more so than are rules of conduct in any other area of human affairs, even including government. As a result, the child acquires not only the skills needed for a game or sport, but also knowledge of the activity and its rules. Although the process is gradual and largely informal, its completeness causes some wonder as to what would happen if similar methods could be used for regular school work.[7]

Each person should bear in mind the fact that no program of physical education activities may be justified unless all the facts available in child growth and development have been applied in its planning and administration.

QUESTIONS AND PRACTICAL PROBLEMS

1. Using books on child growth and development and psychology, list the social, physical, mental, and emotional characteristics of children in the early and middle childhood grades. Show how each must be considered in planning a program of physical education.

2. Show specifically how each recommended type of activity will help meet the specific and general needs of the children in each of the six grades.

3. Give examples of types of children who may challenge the teacher to meet their needs through a program of activities which differs from the one you plan for the group in general. How will you be guided in planning such a program? What will be your difficulties in administering it?

4. What challenge do you meet in evaluating your program in relation to child growth and development? Be specific and concrete.

5. Discuss pertinent factors which influence children's behavior. Apply the various behavior patterns to a program of physical education and show how you will attempt to assist the child.

6. How may many of the physical, social, and emotional tensions of children be removed? How may physical education aid? May it cause more tensions and strains if not planned and administered according to principles and knowledge of child growth and development?

7. What are the basic changes in skeletal, muscular, and organic development in children in the six-, seven-, and eight-year age levels compared with those in the nine-, ten-, eleven-year-old child? What significance do these changes have to the program of physical education?

SELECTED REFERENCES

AMERICAN ASSOCIATION FOR HEALTH, PHYSICAL EDUCATION AND RECREATION, "Developing Democratic Human Relations Through Health Education, Physical Education, and Recreation," *First Yearbook,* Washington, D.C., American Association for Health, Physical Education and Recreation, 1951.

ASSOCIATION FOR SUPERVISION AND CURRICULUM DEVELOPMENT, "Growing Up in an Anxious Age," Washington, D.C., Association for Supervision and Curriculum Development, 1952.

AUSUBEL, DAVID P., *Theory and Problems of Child Development,* New York, Grune and Stratton, Inc., 1957.

BALLER, WARREN R., *Readings in the Psychology of Human Behavior and Development,* New York, Holt, Rinehart and Winston, 1962.

BRECKENRIDGE, MARIE E., and E. LEE VINCENT, *Child Development: Physical and Psychological Growth Through the Years* (Fourth edition), Philadelphia, W. B. Saunders Company, 1960.

COMBS, ARTHUR W., and DONALD SNYGG, *Individual Behavior* (Revised edition), New York, Harper and Brothers, 1959.

CROW, LESTER D., and ALICE CROW, *Child Development and Adjustment,* The Macmillan Company, New York, 1962.

ELSBREE, WILLARD, *Pupil Progress in the Elementary School,* New York, Bureau of Publications, Teachers College, Columbia University, 1951.

ENGLISH, HORACE G., *Dynamics of Child Development,* New York, Holt, Rinehart and Winston, 1961.

[7] John Anderson, *The Psychology of Development and Personal Adjustment,* New York, Henry Holt and Company, 1949, p. 375.

HURLOCK, ELIZABETH B., *Child Development* (Third edition), New York, McGraw-Hill Book Company, Inc., 1956.

LANE, HOWARD, and MARY BEAUCHAMP, *Understanding Human Development*, Englewood Cliffs, N.J., Prentice-Hall, Inc., 1959.

LEE, J. MURRAY, and DORIS MAY LEE, *The Child and His Development*, New York, Appleton-Century-Crofts, Inc., 1958.

MILLARD, CECIL V., *Child Growth and Development in the Elementary School Years*, Boston, D. C. Heath and Company, 1951.

SARTAIN, AARON Q., *et al., Understanding Human Behavior*, New York, McGraw-Hill Book Co., Inc., 1962.

STEFFENS, ADA DAWSON, *Providing Developmental Experiences for Young Children*, New York, Bureau of Publications, Teachers College, Columbia University, 1952.

CHAPTER 8

The Exceptional Child

The seriousness of the problem of the exceptional child is very well expressed in the following statement by Mehl, Mills, and Douglass, authors and educators:

Studies of children enrolled in our schools reveal that at least one-third of them are handicapped by serious defect or illness and that another third have minor defects. . . . Many problems of learning and behavior can be traced directly to the child's physical handicaps. A feeling of inadequacy often results in social maladjustments and acts of overcompensation. This is especially true if the handicap is serious enough to prevent the child from participating in games and sports.[1]

For years educators have taken the individual needs and differences of children into consideration in many parts of the school curriculum. They have established within a given grade or class several different reading groups and have given work according to the abilities of children. There has, however, been too little planning for the exceptional child in physical education. The whole range of exceptional individuals, from the highly skilled to the mentally and orthopedically handicapped, needs attention. The handicapped should not be completely by-passed and left in the classroom during each period of physical education. Harvey was an example of this until grade four,

[1] Marie Mehl, Hubert Mills, and Harl Douglass, *Teaching in Elementary School,* New York, The Ronald Press Company, 1950, p. 104.

when he came to the attention of a wise teacher.

Harvey was a polio victim. Large, heavy steel braces on both legs from his hips down were fastened around his waist to his knees and down his legs to specially built shoes. His face was pale, his eyes were haunting. He needed fresh air, sunshine, friends, and a feeling of being needed. Instead, as each play period rolled around, Harvey was left in the classroom to do as he wished in the belief that it was too strenuous for him to travel out-of-doors or to the gymnasium. That was the teacher's opinion only. Harvey had not been asked. No excuse had come from the doctor requesting that he remain indoors. In fact, when the case was discussed with the school physician and the boy's own doctor, they both wanted him to be given incentives and encouragement to walk. They felt it would tend to aid and strengthen his legs.

One day the physical education teacher purposely permitted the class to go to the playground without the equipment she needed for the planned program. She started getting it ready to carry outside and found she needed some help. Harvey sat in the room watching her get the equipment from the closet. After finding she could not carry all of it she said, "Harvey, I surely need your help. Would you please carry this ball out to the playground for me?" His eyes lit up. He got up from his desk and slowly came to the closet. There was a slight smile on his face and he said, "Do you think I can get there fast enough?" Assured he could, he started out after the teacher. It was a beautiful, sunny, fall day. The class was busily engaged in the activities they had chosen before they left the classroom, and were playing happily under the guidance of their squad leaders and classroom teacher. Haste was not necessary so the teacher walked and talked with Harvey in an attempt to break some of the three-year formation of ice. This was the start of Harvey's part in the physical education program.

Daily he went to the playground. He was asked to assist in scoring the squads' accomplishments for the day. This interested him greatly and at home one evening he made a score pad. It was fastened together with colored yarn his mother gave him, and he was as pleased as one could be when he showed it to his teacher and classmates. His daily trips to the playground gave him some needed physical activity. He got sunshine and fresh air. He learned the rules of games rapidly. He was then asked to umpire and act as a judge in relays. He felt he was needed and wanted. The class accepted him wholeheartedly through the fine work of the teacher. He was equipment manager, score keeper, umpire, judge, or referee as the activity demanded. Then another happy occasion came into his life. The class wanted to learn to play the game of batball. In the

process, they decided Harvey had arms as good as theirs. "Why can't he have his turn up at bat and we'll take turns running for him?" The look on Harvey's face was worth a million dollars. His classmates had found another place for him in the physical education program. He could play with them. He hesitated because he said he had never hit a ball with his hand. They offered to help him, and so it was that he entered into every activity which required no running on his part and many where his peers took turns running for him.

The doctors were very pleased with the progress of his physical condition. He was happy and lost the haunted look, his paleness disappeared, and his legs seemed to grow stronger. His mother said his appetite was much improved and he was happier at home. He was now *a part of* his group and not *apart from* it during the play period and the physical education program. He went outside during the noon hour, also, and was the most popular official in the school. All of this participation gave him physical activity, social and psychological growth, satisfaction, and an interest in games and activities. This illustration gives an example of how a child with a physical handicap was aided by working with his regular class in the physical education program. This child was classified as an exceptional child due to a locomotion handicap. Other handicaps are discussed below.

DEFINING THE EXCEPTIONAL

The exceptional child is so classified because of a variety of factors. These may be physical, mental, emotional, or social in nature.

Included under the classification of physical deviations are those of a postural nature, heart malfunction, nutritional diffi-

culties, locomotive problems, speech impediments, vision and hearing defects.

Emotional deviations may include those of mental retardation and the many emotional maladjustments such as aggressiveness, antisocial behavior, withdrawal, or depression. These maladjustments will not be helped by programs which are not adapted to the physical and mental abilities of the child and which fail to insure him satisfactory emotional and social development.

The mentally exceptional child could be a genius or one who is mentally retarded. Socially exceptional children include those who have specific deviations in their human relations with others.

THE RESPONSIBILITY AND NEEDS

Emphasis on the democratic ideal means a realization of the full responsibility due these children in growing and developing to their fullest potentialities. "The Recommendations on Children and Youth"[2] from the White House Conference states that a program for children and youth with handicaps must be expanded to provide for their physical, mental, emotional, and occupational needs.

Most exceptional children may gain many educational experiences through associations with other children. Unless these children are so handicapped that they require the services of teachers especially educated to care for them alone, they should be permitted to remain with the regular class.

In every 1000 children the estimated number with physical handicaps which require special school adjustment is 59. In the same group there will be about 40 who deviate from average mental ability.[3] They are subdivided as shown in Table 8–1.

The deviations from normal create serious problems for children. Such problems are at times made more serious by adults who do not understand them and who leave children out of learning situations because of overprotection, fear, or indifference.

[2] The White House Conference, "Recommendations on Children and Youth—The White House Conference," *Journal of Health, Physical Education and Recreation,* **22:**48 (April 1951).

[3] Charles C. Wilson (Editor), *School Health Services,* Washington, D.C., National Education Association and American Medical Association, 1953.

TABLE 8–1.
Deviations per Thousand Children

Deviations	Number
Blind or partially seeing	2
Deaf or hard of hearing	15
Speech defects	15
Crippled	10
Lowered vitality	15
Epileptic	2
Mentally retarded	20
Mentally gifted	20

These children challenge the teachers and parents to help them with all the skills they can master and to substitute for those they cannot.

Play releases frustration and pent-up energies. The exceptional child needs to learn to use swings, slides, jungle gyms, and the like and to be a part of the regular group so he may learn from contact and experiences with other children.

The exceptional child is one who has all the desires and ambitions of a physically normal child. These are intensified and thwarted by some abnormal condition. Such children, too, need an outlet for their desires. A well-planned program of physical education with the approval of the school and the family physician is a good way to help them in the physical, emotional, and social phases of their life.

It is the duty of educators to stress in

great measure the similarities of children—not the differences. The handicapped child must be helped to accept himself, to find ways in which he may substitute activities and gain satisfaction from these substitutions. To permit him to take part in a physical education program gives him a chance to be accepted socially and an opportunity to be a part of the group.

The National Committee on School Health Policies recommends that:

. . . all pupils be enrolled in physical education classes; those who by reason of illness or disability are unable to participate in the more vigorous forms of activities should be assigned to modified activities.[4]

A corrective program for the exceptional child is not a complete program. While it is true that some children require much special help, it is just as true that many will gain from social contacts with children in their group. In any case, where the program of games and other activities will meet some of the desired objectives, the child should be permitted to participate rather than assigned to a class to take only special exercises. Harvey was an example of this. It is true that he needed special exercises for his legs, apart from his regular class, but if he had that alone he would have missed the other essential part of his living. Many times special activities are needed to supplement what the child can do in the regular physical education program with his classmates, but it is the belief of the authors that exceptional children should in every possible case be permitted to remain a part of their group and take part in whatever ways they can in addition to special activity recommended by the doctor.

WAYS THE PROGRAM SHOULD SERVE

The philosophy being accepted by educators is that if a child is well enough to be in school, he is well enough to participate in a program of physical education, even though it must be adapted to meet his individual needs. This is the responsibility of the school.

The physical education program should make an honest attempt to improve the health status of the child. This can only be accomplished if individual needs and abilities are taken into consideration. Programs of physical education have too long been based solely on the physically gifted child and have neglected those who are under par. The physical education program should in-

clude a gamut of activities such as correctives, body mechanics, active sports, quiet games, vigorous exercises to increase strength and endurance—all based to fit the needs of the child.

In a report of the National Conference on Physical Education for Children of Elementary School Age, it was found that every child received more benefit from physical education when the programs were planned for individual needs. A majority of children can take part in all activities, some need a modified program and can take part in only certain phases, while others can participate only in quiet games and activities.

A National Committee on Adapted Physical Education believes their specialty has much to offer each individual who faces the combined problems of seeking an education and overcoming a handicap. This

[4] National Conference for Cooperation in Health Education, *Suggested School Health Policies* (Second edition), Washington, D.C., National Education Association, 1946, pp. 33–34.

adapted program should serve the individual in each of the following four ways if the program is to be successful:

1. Aiding and discovering deviations from normal and making proper referrals where such conditions are noted.

2. Guiding students in the avoidance of situations which would aggravate new conditions or subject them to undue risk or injury.

3. Improving general strength and endurance of individuals who are poorly developed and those returning to school after illness or injury.

4. Providing opportunities for needed social and psychological adjustment.

No teacher or administrator should feel that his or her job is well done unless physical education is planned to meet the needs of each child in the school with an adapted program. As one educator expresses it, "We must be as interested in the handicapped child as the potential All-American halfback."

GUIDANCE IN MEETING THE NEEDS

The teacher must naturally be guided in the programs of physical education for the exceptional child by the school doctor and the family physician. Many times the first referral comes from them in the form of a blanket excuse stating that a certain child must not take any physical education. To take the path of least resistance this excuse could be accepted and no program would then be attempted for the child.

On the other hand, in order to be fair to the child, a prepared form giving all of the types of activity in the physical education program should be sent to the doctor asking him to check the activities in which the child may participate and to recommend the amount of time advisable for each.

Many times physicians do not know that the school is willing to offer activities other than the usual program mapped to fit the needs, interests, and abilities of the greatest number of children within the given group, activities which are many times too strenuous for the handicapped child, and hence these physicians send the school the blanket excuse.

A letter to a physician in reply to a blanket excuse might read:

Dear Doctor ———,

We have just received your excuse stating that ——— should not participate in any physical education activities.

May we, through this letter, acquaint you with the types of activity we are capable of rendering in our program and ask you if there are some which would be beneficial to ———?

If you note any in which it would be possible for him (her) to participate, would you be kind enough to check them? It would be helpful to us if you would also suggest the length of time you believe would be best for participation.

We have the interest of each individual in mind and endeavor to plan our programs to fit the needs, interests, and abilities of each child in our school.

Sincerely yours,

———————————

Enclosed with this letter should be a form giving all the types of activities offered in the program. Such a form may be planned as on the next page. It should be checked and signed by the family and school physicians and returned to the teacher in charge of the child.

Dear M———,

I have checked the activities you are offering in your program of physical education and the time I believe it would be beneficial for ——— to participate in them. The diagnosis of my patient's condition requires a special program as follows:

Type of Activity	Recommended Time for Participation
1. Special conditioning activities	
2. Special developmental exercises for:	
a. Arms	
b. Legs	
c. Feet	
d. Back	
3. Quiet table games	
4. Swimming	
5. Boating	
6. Hiking	
7. Biking	
8. Individual and dual activities:	
a. Shuffleboard	
b. Marbles	
c. Croquet	
d. Archery	
e. Hopscotch	
9. Rhythmic work	
10. Less-strenuous circle games and relays	

Signed ———————, M.D.

In following this procedure, the teacher is working with the exceptional child directly under the guidance of a medical person and is not taking any chances. Without the help of a physician, what she believes may benefit the child may be harmful to him.

Regardless of whether the teacher working with the child is a specially trained physical education major or an elementary classroom teacher, it must be stressed that neither is qualified to plan and/or administer an adapted program without the direction and guidance of a medical authority. Even a physical therapist works under a physician's recommendation and supervision. This point cannot be too strongly emphasized.

Teachers have been known to conduct programs, especially those of a corrective nature, which could definitely injure the child rather than help him. At the same time, there is the possibility of a legal liability suit if harm results to the child.

An example of the need for caution is shown in postural defects. These defects may be symptoms of fatigue caused by poor nutrition or skeletal disease such as bone tuberculosis and osteomyelitis. They may be caused by nervous and muscular disorders such as polio or cerebral palsy. Unless one knows the cause of a postural defect, great injustice may result in overstressing mechanical correction through exercises. Proper attention must be given to each individual child through the health services department to determine the underlying cause before one may safely endeavor to aid the child through a special program of corrective work.

The close cooperation of the home is also needed in aiding the exceptional child. This may be partially accomplished by inviting the parents to be present at the annual medical examination of their child and through the home visits of the nurse, the classroom teacher, and/or the special teacher of physical education. The parent-teacher conferences, which are so popular today, may serve as the necessary link for close cooperation of the parent and the school in their endeavors to assist the exceptional child.

SUGGESTED ACTIVITIES FOR THE EXCEPTIONAL CHILD

Activities suitable for the exceptional child may advance from those of very little physical activity to those with vigorous exercise, especially for some parts of the body or limbs.

Quiet games may be needed such as card and table games. Darts, horseshoes, quoits, and such types of activities are often suitable. Croquet, marbles, and archery answer many needs. Bowling, shuffleboard, ring toss and quiet circle games, bicycling, hiking, simple rhythms, simple stunts, and quiet relays requiring no running but which include catching and passing balls, beanbags, and rings will aid many. Camping, fishing, swimming, and boating are both interesting and helpful if it is possible to include them in the regular program.

It should always be remembered that the exceptional child has the same basic needs as the normal child and must be helped to meet these needs. The challenge is always present to include something in an adapted program of physical education which will aid him in making the necessary adjustment and make him a happier, better integrated, emotionally and socially happier individual. The physical education program may help the exceptional child in many ways, though it is not the claim that it will be able to aid all handicapped children to the same degree.

It is the belief of the authors that the physical education program which stresses only corrective work is not meeting the needs of the child since it neglects the other phases and objectives of providing opportunities for needed social and emotional adjustment.

Figure 8–1. Driving a golf ball, an activity here being enjoyed by a normal boy at camp, can also be suitable for some exceptional children.

EVALUATION OF THE PROGRAM

The progress and accomplishment of the exceptional child in the program of physical education is especially important. Some means of evaluation are necessary; some will be subjective and others objective in their nature.

Conferences with the child; observation of his social behavior exhibited in various informal play situations; the results of certain skill achievement and knowledge tests planned specifically to show the progress he has made—all will aid in evaluating the program of activities in which he is engaged.

These children, in many cases, should be carefully examined by the school physician every two or three months to ascertain whether the planned program is meeting the physical needs of the child and to recommend necessary changes for his benefit. Teachers usually can help the child by assisting him to prepare an evaluation sheet for himself on which he records what he desires to accomplish and how he is succeeding. As in all cases of evaluation, if it is to be meaningful to him, the child must know his goals and his growth.

SUGGESTIONS FOR THE TEACHER

1. Each child may benefit from some phase of the physical education program if it is carried out with his needs, interests, and abilities in mind and planned under the close guidance of the medical profession.

2. The corrective program is *not* the complete answer. Many children will not be able to have their handicap removed, and it is the teacher's responsibility to help them to adjust and enjoy themselves in spite of it.

3. The exceptional child gains needed social adjustment, fun, fresh air, sunshine, and emotional help through participating and being with his peers.

4. Physical education can help the child in many ways other than physical development.

5. All children need not participate in the same activity during the physical education period any more than all will participate in the same activities in the other parts of the school curriculum. Several activities may be enjoyed at one time during the period with one class or group.

6. Do not attempt to do the impossible.

7. Accept the situation and do your best for the child.

8. At times you will meet children who are unable to participate in the regular program. These students should be referred to the school physician for guidance. This may be necessary when a new child enters a school and is assigned to a class prior to the annual school medical examinations. It is the classroom teacher's responsibility to bring each case to the attention of the health services department so that the examination and recommendations may be made during the first days of school.

9. The teacher should familiarize herself with the complete physical records of all

new children admitted to her room each September and at other times during the year.

10. Refer to the health service department a child who has returned from a prolonged illness or accident and develop his program based on its recommendations. These children will need, in most cases, only a temporary adapted program.

11. Keep an individual record of each child's daily activities and the length of time he spent in each.

QUESTIONS AND PRACTICAL PROBLEMS

1. Plan a meeting with the school nurse and doctor regarding some exceptional child. Be specific. Know what you wish to discuss and what help you need.

2. Use hypothetical cases, if you know of no real ones, of children with specific handicaps. Plan activities which are generally accepted for handicapped children.

3. Set up an evaluation chart for the teacher to use in her work with the exceptional child.

4. Organize an evaluation chart for each exceptional child to use in his physical education program. Devise a rating rule or guide easy enough for him to understand and use.

5. In connection with your health and physical education, plan a unit on posture for the grade of your choice.

6. Can you justify giving a child a mark on posture?

7. What is your stand on the planning and administration of a corrective program for children by a physical education specialist? By a classroom teacher? Your class may be interested in debating the negative and positive sides of this question.

8. Ask the personnel of the health services department in your school to speak to your class about the exceptional child and the physical education program.

SELECTED REFERENCES

ASSOCIATION FOR SUPERVISION AND CURRICULUM DEVELOPMENT, *Learning More About Learning,* Washington, D.C., Association for Supervision and Curriculum Development, 1959.

COWELL, CHARLES, and HELEN W. HAZELTON, *Curriculum Designs in Physical Education,* Englewood Cliffs, N.J., Prentice-Hall, Inc., 1955, pp. 150, 178, 198.

DANIELS, ARTHUR, *Adapted Physical Education,* New York, Harper and Brothers, 1954.

———, "What Provision for the Handicapped?" *Children in Focus,* 1954 Yearbook of the American Association for Health, Physical Education and Recreation, 1955, p. 134.

DAVIES, E. A., "Physical Education for Handicapped Rehabilitation in the Schools," *Teacher's College Record,* **56:**92–97 (November 1954).

HARTLEY, RUTH E., LAURENCE K. FRANK, and

ROBERT M. GOLDENSON, *Understanding Children's Play,* New York, Columbia University Press, 1952.

HEINRICH, EUNICE L., "The Handicapped Child in the Main Stream," *The Volta Review,* **57:**164 (April 1955).

MARTMER, E. E., *The Child with a Handicap,* Springfield, Ill., Charles C. Thomas, Publisher, 1959.

MEHL, MARIE, HUBERT MILLS, and HARL DOUGLASS, *Teaching in Elementary School,* New York, The Ronald Press, 1950, p. 104.

NATIONAL CONFERENCE FOR COOPERATION IN HEALTH EDUCATION, NATIONAL COMMITTEE ON SCHOOL HEALTH POLICIES, *Suggested School Health Policies* (Second edition), Washington, D.C., National Education Association, 1946, pp. 33–34.

NATIONAL CONFERENCE IN PHYSICAL EDUCATION FOR SCHOOL CHILDREN OF ELEMENTARY AGE, *Physical Education for Children,*

Washington, D.C., National Conference in Physical Education for School Children of Elementary Age, 1951, p. 11.

OBERTEUFFER, DELBERT O., *Physical Education—A Textbook of Principles,* New York, Harper and Brothers, 1956.

PRESCOTT, D. A., *Child in the Educative Process,* New York, McGraw-Hill Book Co., Inc., 1959.

SNYDER, RAYMOND A., "The Gifted Student and Physical Education," *Journal of Health, Physical Education and Recreation,* **33**:18 (January 1962).

STAFFORD, GEORGE T., and E. D. KELLY, *Preventive and Corrective Physical Education* (Third edition), New York, The Ronald Press, 1958.

STONE, ELEANOR, "The Physically Handicapped Children in Our Schools," *Journal of Health, Physical Education and Recreation,* **18**:67 (February 1947).

WHITE HOUSE CONFERENCE, "Recommendations on Children and Youth—White House Conference," *Journal of Health, Physical Education and Recreation,* **22**:48 (April 1951).

WOODWARD, EVERETT W., "Camping Motivation in Communication Skills for Speech Impaired Children," *Journal of Health, Physical Education and Recreation,* **32**:26 (May–June 1961).

THE PROGRAM

CHAPTER 9

Types of Activities for Early Childhood and Examples of Progression

Children differ in their needs, interests, and abilities in physical education just as they do in all areas of education. Certain types of activities have been found to be desirable to meet these needs in early childhood. During this period of growth and development children need plenty of big-muscle activity. They may receive it through play which is not too highly organized but which is planned to meet their interests and abilities.

Recommended types of activities for this group with definitions, objectives, and examples of each will be discussed in this chapter. New materials and more of each type may be found in Chapter 21 and 22.

TYPES OF ACTIVITIES AND SUGGESTED TIME FOR EACH

The types of activities recommended for children in grades one, two, and three are shown in Table 9–1.

The suggested time for each type of activity in the over-all physical education program is given only as a rough guide. All

TABLE 9–1. *Activities and Times Recommended for Grades One Through Three*

Types of Activities	Suggested Time for Each (Per Cent)
1. Dances and rhythms	30
2. Developmental activities using equipment	10
3. Games of low organization	30
4. Individual and dual activities	10
5. Self-testing activities and stunts	10
6. Story plays	10
7. Classroom games (to be used during inclement weather if other indoor facilities are not available)	
8. Aquatics (to be used if facilities and qualified leaders are available)	

children differ, and the teacher must use her judgment in the use of the activities. The percentage of time recommended here is in agreement with leaders in the field of physical education. The program should not consist of only one type of activity. For example, a program of games alone is not justified. Aquatics should be included when facilities and qualified leaders permit. Because so many areas do not have these facilities, the suggested time tallied 100 per cent without aquatics. If facilities make their use possible, one could easily justify 10 per cent or more of the total program time for swimming.

Classroom games are listed because many times in the elementary schools there are no other indoor facilities for use during inclement weather. Hence, if a program is offered it must be carried on in the classroom. There are various types of activities suitable for use in classrooms which should be used when the weather will not permit children to go out-of-doors and when there are no gymnasiums, playrooms, or other indoor facilities.

Dances and Rhythms

Definition and Types

Rhythms are activities in which a child responds to music, percussion instruments, or singing. His response includes physical, mental, and social reactions. Rhythmic activities may include:

1. *Fundamental Rhythms.* The fundamental rhythms are concerned with basic natural movements. These include running, hopping, jumping, and leaping. Combinations of the movements include skipping, galloping, and sliding.

2. *Dramatized Rhythms.* Dramatized rhythms include the rhythmic dramatization of nursery rhymes, poems, or stories, such as Hickory Dickory Dock, Humpty Dumpty, and Jack-be-nimble.

3. *Folk Dances and Singing Games.* Many times folk dances are traditional dances which characterize different groups or races. They involved definite group relationships. Examples of these would include "The Shoemakers' Dance," "Chimes of Dunkirk," "Looby Loo," and "The Farmer in the Dell."

4. *Creative or Interpretive Dance.* The child develops his own movements and patterns of design as he interprets the musical composition.

5. *Mimetics.* The child poses himself in his imaginary world and interprets a *suggested* subject, such as bicycles, dolls, tops, animals, or clocks.

Objectives

The objectives of dances and rhythms are as follows:

1. To develop a sense of rhythmic coordination.

2. To develop a sense of grace.

3. To teach an interest in and love of rhythmic and dance activities.

4. To develop desirable social attitudes and courtesies through group activity.

5. To develop a strong, well-coordinated body.

6. To develop a means of expressing onself through rhythmic movement.

Teaching Hints

Introductions are important means of motivation. Tell something about the dance and the country from which it comes, show pictures of people and dance, bring in personal group experiences, or correlate it with other subjects in the school. These are only a few methods.

1. Be sure the children know the beat of the music. Have them listen to the music and then clap out the beat.

2. Demonstrate the step to be used (i.e., skip, slide, polka).

3. Let each child try the step alone in an informal organization, not in the set formation called for in the dance.

4. Give individual help.

5. Organize the children in the formation called for in the dance.

6. Teach a small part without music and let the children practice it.

7. Next try it with music.

8. Teach the next part; practice this.

9. Combine parts one and two; continue with each part until the dance is complete.

10. If there are words which may be sung, break the rhythm up in parts and teach a part at a time. Do not try to teach the entire dance at once. Words may be taught in music class.

11. For more enjoyment leave enough time so the entire rhythm or dance may be gone through once or twice after the teaching situation.

12. Do not expect all children to do it equally well.

13. Commend for work well done and also for improvement.

14. Never humiliate one child before the class. An example of this was seen after a teacher had spent several parts of periods on the fundamental rhythm of skipping. All children had mastered it but John. He skipped on his right foot and walked on the left. Finally the teacher asked all the class to sit down while she "hammered away" at John. Naturally, he was worse, much embarrassment was created, all learning ceased as did everyone's fun.

15. Stop the rhythm or dance while the children still like it. Do not bore them with it.

16. If a rhythm gives certain children in the circle a chance to be more active than others, make certain that each child has a good opportunity for activity before stopping it. This is readily accomplished by placing more than one child in the center to start an activity. In this way, the rhythm or dance will be completed faster and the children will not be bored by repeating it too many times nor will they be discouraged and disappointed because each one did not get a chance. An example of this is shown in the singing game of "Here Comes a Bluebird through My Window." Directions for this game and one suggested way to get more activity will be discussed.

HERE COMES A BLUEBIRD THROUGH MY WINDOW

FORMATION

Children form a circle, which represents a large imaginary house. The directions call for one child to be chosen as a bluebird and to take his place in the center of the circle or house. Change this. Choose more than one. If there are 24 or 32 in your class, choose three or four bluebirds. Select one for the leader of the birds, and have the others follow him to avoid confusion.

FIRST VERSE (TUNE,"LONDON BRIDGE")
Here come some bluebirds through our windows,
Through our windows, through our windows.
Here come some bluebirds through our windows,
My fair lady.

TEACHING DIRECTIONS

1. Teach the words and have class sing it and clap to the rhythm. (Words could be taught in a music class before going out for physical education.)

2. Children hold hands and raise arms upward opening imaginary windows.

3. Bluebirds skip, with arms extended for wings, through the windows in time to the words sung by the class. All birds follow the leader.

4. When the music stops, each bluebird should stand directly behind the person nearest him in the circle.

SECOND VERSE

Take a little partner and tap her on the shoulder,
Tap her on the shoulder, tap her on the shoulder.
Take a little partner and tap her on the shoulder,
My fair lady.

TEACHING DIRECTIONS

1. Teach the words and have the class sing them.

2. Each bluebird taps the shoulders of the partner behind whom he is standing. He taps in rhythm with the music. (Make certain that the children understand the meaning of *tap*.)

3. Children in the circle clap their hands in rhythm as they sing.

THIRD VERSE

Take a little partner for a hip-skip-scholar,
A hip-skip-scholar, a hip-skip-scholar.
Take a little partner for a hip-skip-scholar,
My fair lady.

TEACHING DIRECTIONS

1. Teach the words and have the class sing them.

2. Each bluebird takes the hand of the person he tapped and skips around the outside of the circle in rhythm to the singing of the group.

3. All children remaining in the circle hold hands and swing their arms forward and backward keeping in rhythm with the music. The circle is now much smaller. Repeat the entire rhythm with all partners as bluebirds. If the activity started with only one bluebird, after the completion of the song there would be only two skipping and it would take a long time before each child had a chance to do the skipping and be either a bluebird or a partner. Children could tire of the activity, and problems might result. Hence, if it is started with three bluebirds, six are busily engaged as partners at the completion of the song. The second time it is played, there would be twelve bluebirds going in and out windows tapping partners. By playing and singing it three times, a starting circle of thirty-six children would be completely used. In this way each child has a chance to participate in some part of the activity and is happy.

Developmental Activities Using Equipment

Definition and Examples

The specific category of developmental activities using equipment refers to activities offering more use of big muscles than the other categories. Included here are activities on playground and indoor equipment such as climbing bars and jungle gyms, horizontal ladders, horizontal bars, ropes and climbing poles, large tiles for crawling in and out, swings, seesaws, slides, merry-go-rounds, and various new kinds of equipment made by creative leaders. Creative Playthings, Inc., is one company with excellent creative playground equipment. (See Appendix D for a list of suppliers and addresses.)

It must be understood that all classifications of activities by their very nature offer big-muscle activity. However, the category here under consideration creates the opportunity for muscles to be used in ways and combinations different from those of many other categories.

The pieces of equipment mentioned above give exploratory experiences to children. Learning the safe and best way to walk on balance beams, to climb jungle gyms, to use swings, and to ride merry-go-rounds gives children confidence and courage. It helps them to continue to have fun without injury while they develop strong muscles.

Objectives

The objectives of developmental activities are as follows:

1. To give opportunity for vigorous

Figure 9–1. Developmental activities on the "Challenger." (Courtesy of Panetrol, Inc.)

activity developing strength, agility, and dexterity.

2. To teach children the safe way to use the various pieces of equipment.

3. To teach courtesy and respect for others.

4. To provide the fun and delight that accompany free movement and development of control.

5. To help children discern many different ways of movement.

6. To develop independence.

7. To help children become skillful in movement.

Teaching Hints

1. Teach respect for each piece of equipment.

2. Teach respect for each individual child.

3. Teach safe ways to use the equipment—for example, to always hold with at least one hand.

4. Teach certain children first and permit them to demonstrate to others.

5. Organize groups so that after the proper instruction much activity is possible for all without too long an interval between turns. A class of 25 may be split in four groups (after instruction) and may be assigned to play on four different pieces of equipment. Rotation may be used so each will have the opportunity to use each piece.

6. Check each piece of equipment daily to ascertain its safety (for example, check for worn chains or ropes on swings).

7. Do not use these pieces of playground equipment on rainy or snowy days or when they are wet or icy because of the dangers involved.

Games of Low Organization

Definition and Types

Games of low organization refer to activities which have few rules and involve relatively simple skills and techniques so that children may learn them fast and progress quickly from the learning stage to that of enjoyment. This is necessary because of the relatively short interest span of the children in grades one, two, and three. These games can be adapted to varying conditions such as facilities and sizes of the group. There are various types of games included under this category. They are classified in Table 9–2 and examples of each are given.

TABLE 9–2. Games of Low Organization

Classification	Examples
1. Games with equipment	Teacher Ball
	Call Ball
2. Circle games without equipment	Three Deep
	Run for Your Supper
3. Fleeing and tagging games	Red Rover
	Bear in the Pit
4. Relays (not below third grade)	Running and Jumping Relay
	Ball-Passing Relay

Objectives

The objectives of low-organization games are as follows:

1. To provide vigorous physical activity.

2. To teach children to play together.

3. To teach activities which have a carry-over value for leisure-time use.

4. To develop mind and muscle coordination.

5. To teach specific skills and techniques.

6. To provide good fun and lessen emotional stress.

Teaching Hints

1. Analyze the game before you teach it and know the skills and techniques needed.

2. Be sure all necessary equipment and facilities are available including marked areas.

3. Introduce the game in an interesting way.

4. Use as little time as possible to explain and demonstrate the games.

5. Get children into the activity fast.

6. Give children a chance to ask questions.

7. Permit children to use their own suggestions.

8. Teach as the game progresses by giving hints and help to the children.

9. Encourage each child to try.

10. If possible, participate in the games with your children.

11. Stress sportsmanship and fair play at all times.

12. If tagging is a part of the game, teach the proper way to tag so that a child is not too rough and does not tear clothing or push another child down.

13. If a game is started and the children appear to lose interest, stop it. Analyze it later. It may have been too hard or too easy, or it may have been presented in a way the children did not understand.

14. Have an adequate ending for the game. Review the name, objective, winners, if any, and why they won. Do not overemphasize winning.

15. Evaluate the activity: (a) What did the class learn? (b) How did they respond? Why? (c) What needs to be taught and prac-

ticed to make the game better? (d) How will you practice the skills and techniques needed? (e) Were all children playing? (f) Was there bickering and poor sportsmanship? If yes, why? (g) What can you do to help them avoid this?

16. Provide chances for repetition of the activity to improve skills and techniques.

17. Many games of low organization, after being taught to the class as a whole, should then be played by several groups to increase student participation.

Individual and Dual Activities

Definition and Types

Individual and dual activities are activities which may be enjoyed by one, two, or four individuals. They are perhaps best known for their recreational value.

Children of this age group need to work many times in twos or fours to help develop needed skills such as tossing and catching a ball at different distances. Tossing bean bags through special boards such as the clown's mouth develops skill in accuracy. Various rope-jumping games, marbles, hopscotch, and jacks are additional examples of this type of activity.

Objectives

The objectives of individual and dual activities are as follows:

1. To give opportunity for children to improve certain skills.

2. To teach activities that have great carry-over value for use at home in leisure time.

3. To teach activities that may be used in small areas.

4. To give opportunity for each child to sense his own growth and feel a satisfactory sense of accomplishment.

5. To provide social experiences that develop desirable behavior patterns.

Teaching Hints

1. Teach activities to the entire group and then give them the opportunity to participate with different individuals and couples.

2. Plan necessary areas for participation.

3. Be sure sufficient equipment is available.

4. Give individual help to those in special need.

5. Encourage those who are better skilled to assist others.

6. Do not plan for competition!

Self-testing Activities and Stunts

Definition and Types

Self-testing activities and stunts entail big-muscle activity. They may use imagination by imitating certain actions of animals or fowls, such as the bear walk, kangaroo hop, or duck walk. They provide opportunities for children to frolic in such activities as barrel rolls and forward or backward rolls. They may include activities in which one may work individually or with a partner. Examples of each type include:

1. *Individual activities:* Seal Slap, Kangaroo Hop, Inch Worm, Duck Walk, Seal Crawl, Bunny Hop.

2. *Couple activities:* Sit-Ups, Wheelbarrow, Churn the Butter, Wring the Dish Rag.

Objectives

The objectives of self-testing activities are as follows:

1. To afford an opportunity for big-muscle activity.

2. To develop fine muscle coordination, flexibility, balance, and timing.

3. To develop individual skills.

4. To give children a chance to use their imagination and to mimic actions.

5. To give children an opportunity to work individually and to see success in accomplishment.

6. To develop strength, body control, and agility.

7. To provide opportunities for genuine fun and the release of emotional tension.

Teaching Hints

1. Create an interest in the activity through the proper introduction.

2. Teach one or two children the activity before presenting it to the class so they may demonstrate it, or demonstrate it yourself.

3. Permit each child to work at his own rate of speed.

4. Give individual help and encouragement by analyzing what the child is doing wrong and how he may correct it.

5. Never use these activities for races or in relays. For example, teachers have used the duck walk as a race for children. Naturally, when done correctly it is a slow pace. The children who win are always the ones who do not stoop correctly and who do not walk as a duck. These activities are not for speed, but should be taught for skill and fun.

6. Watch for safety. Racing will tend to cause danger.

7. Do not pit one child against another. Some can never do certain stunts.

8. Use a wide variety of activities so that each child may accomplish some. Do not expect all children to be able to do each stunt.

9. Use each activity for a short time in any given period of physical education. Do not expect the children to practice it for long periods at one time.

Story Plays

Definition

Story plays give the child a chance to use his vivid imagination and play in the land of make believe. Often little girls dress up in their mothers' clothes, including shoes, hats, handbag, and gloves, really being the "lady of the hour." Boys pretend they are cowboys, Indians, robbers, and policemen. All have seen boys and girls playing fathers and mothers with dolls as their children, or playing school, with one child acting as the teacher and the others acting as the pupils.

Story plays are dramatizations of activities which are interesting to children. They may be taken from stories children read or they may be planned to show the use of citizens in communities, such as policemen and firemen. They may also be made up and may very interestingly portray various leaders in history, or holidays and seasons of the year.

Objectives

The objectives of story plays are as follows:

1. To give big-muscle activity.

2. To give the child a chance to use his imagination.

3. To teach him to play with others.

4. To help him relax and have fun.

5. To provide opportunities for children to act and play in informal situations.

6. To teach cooperation.

7. To teach leadership and followership to each child.

≥≤

AN EXAMPLE OF A STORY PLAY

An example of a story play entitled "The Firemen" is used to illustrate the steps in planning and progression, because the teacher will find very little help available where story plays are concerned.

The selection of this title may arise from a true incident following a fire in the area the night prior to the presentation. Perhaps most of the children heard the siren and knew about the fire. Some of their parents may have gone to the fire. Thus it provides a true situation from which children may gain the desired objectives. It also affords an excellent opportunity for teaching about community and civic helpers and may develop great respect for a fireman. Safety hints for the prevention of fires may be outgrowths of this story play. One way to proceed and use such an incident as a story play in the physical education class is as follows.

INTRODUCTION—SETTING THE STAGE

Certain lead questions may be used to start the children's discussion and to motivate their interest. Some might be as follows:

"How many of you heard the fire siren last night?"

"Do you know where the fire was?"

"Was anyone hurt?"

"Who put the fire out?"

The teacher may now wish to make a definite suggestion in a very enthusiastic manner and say, "Today let's play we are firemen and we are called to a fire." To gain suggestions from the children certain lead questions may again be asked. In this story play the teacher may ask the children, "What will we need to play firemen?" Their answers may start with trucks, a fire chief, drivers, sirens, and so on. After the necessary pieces of equipment and personnel have been suggested, the teacher will permit the children to decide in a demo-cratic manner who will act each part and drive each piece of equipment. From this point the activities begin.

LOGICAL ACTIVITIES SEQUENCE

1. Let's pretend we are firemen and asleep at the fire house when the siren blows. (Ascertain whether children know the difference between *paid* and *volunteer* firemen. Later, have children check in their home town to learn which they have.)

2. Put your hands up and your face on them and pretend you are asleep.

3. Blow an imaginary siren.

4. Hop out of bed. Stretch way up high.

5. Get dressed. Reach high for clothes; bend low for shoes. (Use various types of physical activity.)

6. Pretend to slide down poles or go down stairs.

7. Get in your trucks.

8. Fire chief goes first.

9. Start motors. (Children make sounds of running motors.)

10. Follow the fire chief. Clang bells, blow sirens to warn all traffic. Drive carefully.

11. Stop at the area designated for the fire.

12. All choose a job to aid in putting the fire out and rescue work: (a) Put up ladders. (b) Attach hoses to hydrants. (c) Go in house, if possible, to rescue people. (d) Climb ladders, rescue people. (e) Direct hoses on the fire, make hissing noise of water on fire.

13. Finally, declare the fire out.

14. All work to get ready to return to the fire house: (a) Take ladders down and put them on trucks. (b) Roll up hoses on trucks. (c) Climb back in trucks. (d) Start trucks.

15. Follow the fire chief back to the fire house.

16. Jump out of trucks—off with boots, raincoats, and fire clothes. Hang them up to dry.

17. "Aren't you hungry? I am. All right, let's pretend it's time for breakfast. What makes a good breakfast?" (Health correlation.) While

eating, talk over how the fire might have happened and how we may prevent fires.

18. Breakfast is over. Now it's time for the new firemen to come to work and we may go home.

19. Stress safety while going home (lights green before crossing street, and so on).

20. "Good-by. I'll see you at the next shift of duty."

Note: Physical activities included bending and reaching while dressing, bending to slide down imaginary pole, climbing in and out of trucks and up and down ladders, running while driving trucks, and so on.

TEACHING HINTS

1. Make story plays interesting to children by getting them ready with a good introduction.

2. Guide the suggestions for the activities so they move quickly.

3. Get the children into the activity quickly.

4. The entire activity should not last longer than ten minutes.

5. Do not tell the whole story first and then have them act it out. They will remember the first and last parts only.

6. Never repeat a story play because it did not go well. Check why it was not successful. It is usually the fault of the teacher.

7. Use every available chance to teach; for example, in the firemen story play teach respect for the fireman, show the responsibility of his job, how he risks his life to help others, and so on.

8. Make the story complete. If you do not, the children will tell you about it. Have a logical beginning and ending.

9. Get suggestions from your children for the activities to be included.

10. Take part yourself or at least go with them so you may talk to them at the areas designated for specific actions. Do not stand still and shout to them.

11. Evaluate when you are through. Did the children have fun? Why? Did the action include big-muscle activities? Were all the chil-

dren active? If not, why? Ask the children what they learned? Did all children cooperate with each other; for example, were they willing to select a chief, drivers, and so on, in a democratic way or were some sulky and did they refuse to play because they could not be the driver? How can you help them?

12. Use every opportunity for carry-over in the classroom. In the firemen story play, for example, children could draw pictures of any part of the equipment used, write about the firemen, draw pictures of clothes worn by firemen, learn new words and terms, write and discuss safety rules for preventing fires, learn how to report a fire on their phones, and learn how to use fire alarms. Emphasize respect for alarms, so no false alarms are spread. Visit the fire house and have a fireman come and talk to the children at school. Each of these offers excellent teaching situations.

Suggested Topics for Story Plays

Make use of the seasons of the year, all holidays, and special occasions in addition to stories the class enjoys reading.

Classroom Games

Definition

Classroom games are informal activities which usually permit little vigorous activity but offer fun, relaxation, and group cooperation in an educational situation in the classroom. They are usually appropriate for various recreational situations.

Some examples of classroom games are Lost Child; Seven-Up; Huckle Buckle Beanstalk; Coffee, Tea, and Milk; Bean Bag Toss; and Cat and Mice.

Objectives

The objectives of classroom games are as follows:

Figure 9–2. Learning to kick so we can swim.

1. To help children relax after the constant mental work of the school day when the weather does not permit physical education to be held out-of doors and there are no other indoor facilities.

2. To help children have fun.

3. To provide some physical activity.

4. To teach the social qualities of play and cooperation.

5. To teach indoor activities which will have carry-over value at home, parties, or other social gatherings.

6. To develop sportsmanship and respect for the rights of others through the proper respect for playmates and through gaining cooperation in quiet play so individuals in other rooms are not disturbed.

7. To develop the ability to play with others.

8. To aid in the all-round development of social and emotional qualities.

Teaching Hints

1. Be sure the children understand why they must be quiet when playing these games in the classroom (respect for the other teachers and pupils.)

2. Do not use much running (safety). Have children walk with giant steps or skip if games call for running.

3. Ventilate your room as well as possible during this play period.

4. Use rhythms and mimetics to advantage while in the classroom.

5. Where games call for balls use bean bags, yarn balls, or clean blackboard erasers instead.

6. Many classroom games are of an elimination type. Change the rules of these so that all children may play and need not sit and watch others.

7. Do not permit children to use walls for goals. Make all goals a safe distance away from them.

8. Choose activities which will permit all children to play in the given space. Do not expect some to be happy while watching others.

9. Have fun with your children.

10. Teach them to be good sports and to have fun in spite of the weather, little space, and other handicaps.

Aquatics

If facilities and qualified instructors are available, swimming should be taught as a part of the physical education program. As is true with many other activities, younger children may be taught to respect and enjoy the water. Floating, doggie paddle, and basic strokes are teachable to a child of this age group.

THE NEED FOR PROGRESSION IN PHYSICAL EDUCATION

Children tire of the same activities day in and day out, and they also tire of the same ones in each grade. The same principle of progression used in other parts of our curricula needs definite application to physical education.

New things are challenging to all. They also provide new learning experiences. No child likes to know that he must participate in a certain activity each day in physical education. He grows bored, endeavors to find excuses to stay away from the class, or creates a problem.

There should be progression in the programs of physical education from very easy to more difficult activities within each grade. Provision should also be made to assure progression in activities from grade to grade.

At first a child learns certain fundamentals like running, tossing a ball, and catching. As these fundamentals progress they are put in simple game formation using only one skill or fundamental at first. Later activities include more than one skill and become more difficult.

Example

An example of progression in games of low organization would be to teach first the game named Teacher Ball, then advance to Call Ball, and then to Ball Stand.

TEACHER BALL

In the game of Teacher Ball one child acts as the teacher and stands a few feet in front of his squad of from four to seven other children.

The distance from the teacher to the squad members depends on the capabilities of the children. Each teacher must judge this according to the children. The teacher tosses the ball to child number one, who tries to catch it, and then toss it back to the teacher. Next the teacher tosses the ball to child two, and so on, until each child has received the ball from the teacher and returned it to the teacher. The teacher may then go to the end of the line if the children are interested in playing it again.

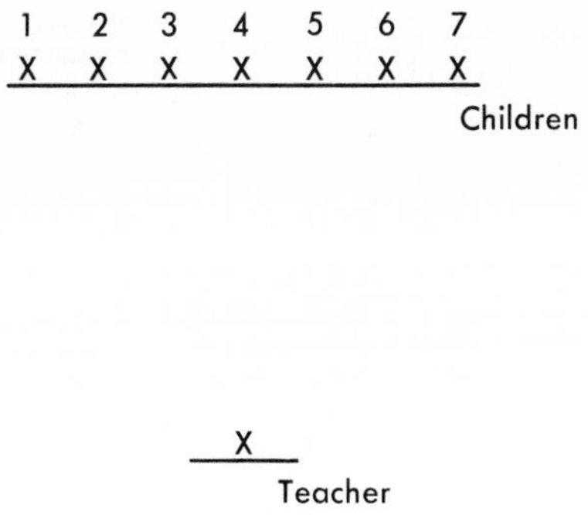

```
1   2   3   4   5   6   7
X   X   X   X   X   X   X
                    Children
```

```
      X
   Teacher
```

Figure 9–3. Teacher Ball.

Child *two* would become the new teacher. This game may progress until each child has had a chance to be the teacher if interest warrants. The interest of the children will determine how long it should be played.

The skills involved are tossing and catching. Attitudes involve sharing equipment and playing together. From Teacher Ball we may progress to Call Ball.

≈≈

CALL BALL

Call Ball starts with the children in a circle position. One child is chosen to be the "thrower" and stands in the center of the circle. He tosses

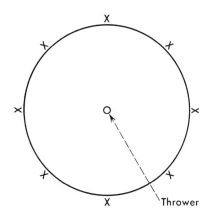

Figure 9–4. Call Ball.

the ball straight up in the air and as he does calls the name of one child out loud. The child whose name is called runs to the center of the circle and endeavors to catch the ball before it hits the ground. If this is impossible, he recovers it on the first bounce. Although the rules of this game call for the first thrower to remain in the circle until a player called successfully catches the ball, the game is better if that rule is deleted. This will afford more opportunities for each child to practice tossing the ball straight in the air as well as endeavoring to run and catch it. Some children who wish to remain "It" for a longer period may purposely toss the ball so it cannot be caught.

Notice the added progression in relation to skills involved. *Throwing* and *running* to catch the ball are necessary instead of *standing* to catch it as in Teacher Ball. This calls for greater skill and is more difficult to accomplish than when a child is standing and the ball is tossed directly to him. After this game has been taught to the entire class, it should be played by squads so that there is more chance for each child to play in the same amount of time. The next game used in the progression is called Ball Stand.

≈≈

BALL STAND

Ball Stand, like Call Ball, starts with the group in a circle. A thrower is chosen. He throws or tosses the ball straight up in the air and at the same time calls the name of a player out loud. The player whose name is called runs forward and tries to catch the ball before it hits the ground. If he misses it, he hurries to get his hands on the ball as soon as possible. All other players in the circle including the thrower run away from the ball. When the player called to catch the ball has his hands on it, he calls "Stand." Players who are running must stop

TABLE 9–3. *Suggested One Month's Progression in Physical Education for Grade One, 30 Minute Period*

	Monday	Tuesday	Wednesday	Thursday	Friday
First week:	New story play—10 min. New game—15–20 min., running and tagging type.	Review game learned Monday—10–15 min. New rhythm—15–20 min.	Review rhythm learned Tuesday—10–15 min. Teach two self-testing activities (new).	Choice of activities by squads. Each squad will choose one activity, get equipment, and be designated a play area. Rotate once.	Review testing activities taught on Wednesday—10 min. Teach new Jump Rope verse and jump.
Second week:	New rhythmic dramatization—10–15 min. Teach new game of Hopscotch—15 min.	Choice by class of two activities. Use each one for one-half period.	New story play—10 min. Play on and give instructions on safe and courteous use of playground equipment—15–20 min.	Review self-testing activities learned last week. Teach one new—10–15 min.	New game using equipment—15–20 min. Choice of action by class—10 min.
Third week:	Review game learned Friday of last week—15 min. Review rhythm—10–15 min.	Use entire period for individual and dual activities such as Hopscotch, Jump Rope, activity on playground equipment.	Review any game using equipment—15–20 mins. One or two new self-testing activities.	New circle game—10–15 min. Review any rhythm.	Choice of activities by squads, four different activities being played at one time. Rotate activities once.
Fourth week:	Review two games using equipment. Teacher selects, based on skills needed.	Review one rhythm based on teacher's judgment of steps needed—15–20 min.	New game with equipment—15 min. Choice by class—10–15 min.	Review game taught Wednesday—15–20 min. Review individual and dual activities including playground equipment.	Permit choice of activities by the four different squads. Rotate once (each plays two activities).

The amount of new activities taught will depend on various factors, such as: (a) What repertoire of activities does class already know? (b) What is their learning speed? Some classes will naturally demand more in new activities because of their quickness to comprehend and their eagerness for new experiences. (c) The time of year. (d) Weather governs choice as to the necessity of very active types of games or dances for colder days and the quieter type for very warm days.

and stand where they are. The player with the ball may advance three steps in any direction. He then endevors to hit a player, below the waist, with the ball. If he succeeds, the player whom he hits is "It" and tosses the ball up the next time. If the thrower misses, he remains "It" and all children return to the original circle formation.

The progression of these three games shows more skills involved in each. The skills in Ball Stand are as follows:

1. Tossing or throwing a ball straight up in the air.
2. Running to catch a ball.
3. Running away from a ball.
4. Throwing at a target.
5. Dodging a thrown ball.

Thus progression provides more skills and techniques, more rules in the game, and a greater challenge to think. This same idea of progression is valid in all other types of activities, both within a given grade and from grade to grade.

RECORDING ACTIVITIES

To assist teachers during the year and the teachers in the succeeding grade who receive the children, a complete record of all activities taught should be kept and filed with the records of the class.

A suggested form which can be easily mimeographed is shown in Table 9–4. Teachers may wish to change the form completely. The important point is to develop a form, use it, and pass it along.

TABLE 9–4. *Physical Education Record of Activities*

Year: _____

Grade: _____   Teacher: _____

Activities Taught	Response of Children	Rating of Group
I. Games: Teacher Ball	Excellent.	Excellent—good skills in catching and tossing. Good group relations.
II. Self-testing activities: Seal Slap	Fair—not too thoroughly enjoyed. Response only warm.	Fair—many could not accomplish this. Appeared too difficult.
III. Rhythms and dances: Lobby Loo	Fair.	Fair—children do not have a good sense of rhythmic coordination.
IV. Classroom games: Huckle Buckle Beanstalk	Excellent.	Very good—children cooperate well in respecting rights of other classes by being quiet. They were generous in sharing turns and thoroughly enjoyed the game.
V. Story plays: Fireman Santa's Helpers A Trip to the Zoo	Excellent.	Excellent—vivid imagination, very interested, asked to repeat activity.

With such a record and evaluation, though brief, the teacher throughout the year may examine the progress in her class, may note that she has had a good variety of activities, and may determine the response of her class. The next teacher who receives the children will know exactly what they have had in their physical education experience and may plan her program accordingly. Her plans should include review work, progression for maintaining interest and challenge, and opportunities to enlarge the repertoire of activities children may engage in during school and leisure time.

QUESTIONS AND PRACTICAL PROBLEMS

1. Make up two complete story plays. Plan exactly how you would teach them, including the introduction. Plan and illustrate ways you may correlate them with other parts of the curriculum. Be certain the story plays include good physical activities.

2. Plan a program of physical education for a ten-week period for the grade of your choice.

3. Show two weeks' progression in daily plans for this same class using the activities you have chosen.

4. Choose several self-testing activities you wish to teach your class. Plan how you will teach them. Show progression from very easy activities to more difficult ones.

5. Use your originality and make up two classroom games suitable for the early childhood grades.

6. Your second grade insists on playing softball, perhaps because your community is very baseball minded. Will you permit this? If so, justify it. If you will discourage it, be specific and show how you would do it and what activities you might substitute.

7. Mary will not enter any activities on the playground with her classmates. She does not show this attitude in the classroom. What will you do? Will you ignore it? If so, why? If not, how will you endeavor to gain her confidence and interest?

8. You have a jungle gym, a merry-go-round, slides, swings, and seesaws on your playground. How may they be used for your class?

SELECTED REFERENCES

BAKER, GERTRUDE, *A Guide for Teaching Health and Physical Education in the Elementary School,* New York, Bureau of Publications, Teachers College, Columbia University, 1946.

BAUER, LOIS M., and BARBARA A. REED, *Dance and Play Activities for the Elementary Grades* (Vol. I), New York, Chartwell House, Inc., 1954.

BUCHER, CHARLES A., *Methods and Materials in Physical Education and Recreation,* St. Louis, The C. V. Mosby Company, 1954.

COWELL, CHARLES C., and HELEN W. HAZELTON, *Curriculum Designs in Physical Education,* Englewood Cliffs, N.J., Prentice-Hall, Inc., 1955, Chapters 12 and 13.

JOINT COMMITTEE (EDITOR), *Administrative Problems in Health Education, Physical Education, and Recreation,* Washington, D.C., American Association for Health, Physical Education and Recreation, 1953, Chapters 11, 12, 13, 14.

LASALLE, DOROTHY, *Physical Education for the Classroom Teacher,* New York, A. S. Barnes and Company, 1947.

O'KEEFE, PATTRIC RUTH, and ANITA ALDRICH, *Education Through Physical Activities* (Second edition), St. Louis, The C. V. Mosby Company, 1955, Part II.

VAN HAGEN, WINIFRED, GENEVIEVE DEXTER, and JESSE F. WILLIAMS, *Physical Education in the Elementary School,* Sacramento, Department of Education, 1951.

VANNIER, MARYHELEN, and MILDRED FOSTER, *Teaching Physical Education in Elementary Schools* (Third edition), Philadelphia, W. B. Saunders Company, 1963.

CHAPTER **10**

Types of Activities for Middle Childhood and Examples of Progression

Children in the middle childhood grades need a great deal of physical activity and are capable of gaining it through activities which are more difficult to accomplish than those listed in the previous chapter. Activities with more difficult skills and techniques and complicated rules meet their challenge. These children have a longer interest span and will practice to be successful in activities they like and are motivated to accomplish. They are very interested in team games and group activities. The social and gang stages are present. Team games will aid in meeting some of these needs, in addition to providing vigorous activity.

The types of activities recommended for this age group, definitions, objectives, examples, and specific teaching hints for each will be discussed in this chapter. New materials and some of each recommended type may be found in Chapters 23 and 24, starting on page 306.

TYPES OF ACTIVITIES AND SUGGESTED TIME FOR EACH

The types of activities found suitable and recommended to meet the needs, interests, and abilities of the children of this age and grade level are listed in Table 10–1. It is hoped that interests developed through the years in school and experience in activities of various types will be of value to the child as he grows older and needs more of a recreational type of program.

The suggested time element is for guidance purposes only. The total of 100 per cent of time is suggested without classroom games and aquatics. If other indoor facilities are not available for use during inclement weather, the classroom activities might necessarily be 10 per cent. Rhythms, certain self-testing activities, and some developmental activities may be used to advantage in the classroom. The main point for teachers to remember is that it requires each of the types listed to present a well-balanced and ineresting program in order to meet the needs and interests of all children. The allotment of time for aquatics is not included in arriving at 100 per cent of the time since few elementary schools have available facilities. The teacher will use her judgment in the total amount of time for each activity to meet the factors of facilities, space, and equipment.

TABLE 10–1. *Activities and Times Recommended for Middle Childhood Grades*

Types of Activities	Suggested Time for Each (Per Cent)
1. Dance and rhythms	25–30
2. Developmental activities (specific)	5–10
3. Games of low organization	5–10
4. Individual and dual activities	10–15
5. Preliminary and lead-up games	5–10
6. Self-testing activities and stunts	10–15
7. Team games	35–40
8. Track and field events	5–10
9. Classroom activities (for use during inclement weather when playground or gymnasium is not available)	
10. Aquatics (if facilities and qualified personnel are available)	

Dances and Rhythms

Definition and Types

The actual definition of rhythms is, of course, the same for any grade level. In the middle childhood grades, dances are more highly organized and require more difficult and completed steps and patterns to challenge the participants.

The recommended types differ. They include more folk dancing, including the American square dance. More creative and interpretive dancing may be offered, particularly to the girls. Boys enjoy strenuous athletic types of dances. The social dance for coeducational groups is often recommended for the fifth or sixth grades. The success of it will depend largely on whether the children are interested in it and the social needs of the children in the area.

Objectives

Children in the middle childhood grades should have a good start in accomplishing the basic objectives of rhythms and dance through participation in them while in grades one, two, and three. It is hoped they will be further developed in the middle childhood grades. Objectives, in addition to those listed in Chapter 9, include:

1. To develop skills which will not only provide present enjoyment, but also those which will meet possible future needs and interests.

2. To develop a wholesome social relationship between boys and girls.

3. To develop an understanding of socially acceptable standards and courtesies of individuals and groups in dancing situations.

4. To aid in learning and appreciating the characteristics and activities of people in other countries.

5. To develop the desire and ability to create rhythmic and dance patterns and movements.

6. To develop skill, grace, balance, and agility in body movements.

7. To overcome awkwardness.

8. To establish fun and happy recreational experiences that decrease nervous tension.

9. To increase poise.

Teaching Hints

1. Create an interest in the dance

Figure 10–1. Developing strong bodies. (Courtesy of Panetrol, Inc.)

through a proper introduction. In addition to the name and derivation, the correct atmosphere may be developed by the use of pictures and costumes of the people of its origin and by making it a part of a unit of work.

2. Permit the group to hear the music before endeavoring to teach the dance. This usually creates interest.

3. Assist them in getting the beat of the rhythm.

4. Describe and demonstrate the first step and permit them to do it in an informal grouping.

5. After they have practiced, try it with the music. If it is a couple dance, have them try it next with a partner.

6. Teach the dance in parts. Add a new part to those already practiced, and continue to the completion.

7. Do not force children to be partners. It is much wiser to permit them to select.

Many times boys of this age wish to work out the steps with boys, and girls with girl partners. Usually, when they are at the enjoyment stage of the dance, they will volunteer to mix partners.

8. Give them encouragment and individual assistance without embarrassing them before their group.

9. In the social dance situation, boys may wish to have some classes apart from the girls until they gain some confidence.

10. Create social situations where folk, square, or social dancing may be enjoyed to achieve their value.

Developmental Activities

Definition

This category of activities is very vigorous and includes specific movements in a planned sequence to increase the efficiency of body use, strength, and agility. They are planned appropriately for each grade and age level with care being noted for individual differences in relation to body structure and build. In these activities it is usually best to have each child challenge himself to increase his record as he increases his strength, movement coordination and ability. They include activities such as sit-ups, push-ups, squat thrusts, jumping, climbing, flexing and bending. The use of equipment for climbing, hanging, and jumping is also very popular in their grade levels.

Objectives

The objectives of developmental activities are as follows:

1. To increase the strength of all muscles of the body.

2. To increase endurance.

3. To improve total physical fitness.

4. To show the relationship and need of special activities to increase strength and the relationship to a better feeling of physical well-being.

Teaching Hints

1. Use progressive exercises to meet the needs in various age and grade levels.

2. Start with short periods of time and gradually increase time in order to build endurance.

3. Identify all activities carefully to the students and teach the benefit of them in relationship to general health and physical well-being.

4. Accept individual differences as to body build and endurance. Challenge each to better himself and not necessarily compete with his classmates.

5. Encourage a wholesome attitude toward desirable health attitudes and the promotion of physical strength and endurance.

Games of Low Organization

Definition and Objectives

The definition and objectives for these games are the same in middle childhood grades as in the early childhood grades. Skills and techniques required are naturally more difficult and challenging.

These games are valuable and very enjoyable to use when there is a short time for activity; when a teacher is not working on a special team game; for activities with carry-over value for children to use when they are not at school; for social relationship of the group; and for uniting a class.

Examples of games of low organization include Three Deep, Beater Goes 'Round, Freedom, and Jump the Shot.

Teaching Hints

1. Help your children understand the game by knowing how it was named. For example, Three Deep received its name because three people are not permitted to stand in a triple circle.

2. Before attempting to teach the game, analyze it to ascertain its exact objectives and determine whether it will meet the needs and interests of your children.

3. Check very carefully the skills and techniques involved to ascertain whether they meet the abilities of your children. They may be either too easy and give no challenge or too difficult for them to enjoy.

4. Teach the game to your entire class Then, if more active participation is desired, play two or more games at the same time by combining two squads for a game or permitting each individual squad to play a game.

5. Assist the children with the skills and techniques both as a group and as individuals.

6. Give recognition for good group relationships shown through respect of each other, such as taking turns so a few are not

being given all the opportunity to be "it" at the expense of the other children.

7. Analyze the activity while your children are participating in it to ascertain if it is meeting your objectives. If not, change certain rules to meet them or change to another activity.

8. Remember, games of low organization may be for either small or large group play. This means that a small number of children may play them with enjoyment or the entire class may participate in the game together and receive the needed physical activity, social development, fun, and challenge.

Individual and Dual Activities

Definition

Individual and dual activities are defined as activities which require from one to four players for participation. They are of value not only for immediate use but for recreational pursuits in later life as well. Shuffleboard, archery, deck tennis, advanced forms of hopscotch and rope jumping, croquet, quoits, marbles, and table tennis are examples.

Objectives

The objectives of individual and dual activities are as follows:

1. To teach activities which may be engaged in during leisure time—now and later in life.

2. To give a child an opportunity to choose and become proficient in an activity he desires.

3. To develop an interest in and love of physical activity.

4. To give an opportunity for each child to sense his own individual growth and development and to feel a sense of accomplishment.

5. To provide activities for times when only a few children are present.

6. To provide co-recreational activities for boys and girls above the fifth-grade level.

7. To provide social experiences which develop desirable social behavior patterns.

Teaching Hints

1. These activities may be taught to the group as a whole so that all children understand rules, play area, and the necessary skills.

2. After the group is oriented, individuals should be encouraged to work in small groups for practice and play.

3. Visual aids are available and helpful.

4. Blackboard diagrams which show playing areas are essential.

5. Equipment must be shared so that each person has an opportunity to use it.

6. The children should agree on a schedule for the use of available equipment and facilities.

7. Individuals should be encouraged to work at their own rate of speed and to choose partners. Many times they know with whom they can best work and play to gain the most from the experiences.

8. Aid each child individually with constructive teaching suggestions and hints.

9. Help those who wish, after they have the necessary skills and techniques, to plan tournaments. This desire should come from the class and not be forced on them at the wish of the teacher.

Preliminary and Lead-Up Activities for Team Games

Definition and Types

Certain skills and techniques are necessary for successful participation and enjoyment of team games. Teachers should analyze the team game or games they desire to teach their children and note the specific skills and techniques required. Many times these may be presented to the class in the form of a preliminary or lead-up game, thus providing an opportunity for practice.

The types of lead-up activities include relays, certain modified games which include one or more skills and/or techniques, and specific drill and practice. Students in the fifth and sixth grades are often sufficiently interested in improving their skills in team games to practice in actual formal drill.

Others will dislike drill practice and will need to develop the necessary skills and techniques in a game situation.

Examples

Three preliminary and lead-up games will be discussed showing the skills and techniques they involve which are needed in the team game of Bat Ball. They are Catching and Throwing Relay, Hot Potato, and Dodge Ball.

TABLE 10–2. *Lead-Up Games*

Lead-Up Games	Skills and Techniques of Each Game	Requirements for the Team Game of Bat Ball
1. Catching and Throwing Relay	Catching Throwing Running	All the skills used in the lead-up games are needed.
2. Hot Potato (circle passing game)	Speed in throwing Speed in accurate throwing Skill in catching	In addition, one needs to be able to bat the ball from his hand and there is much teamwork required.
3. Simple Dodge Ball	Catching Throwing at a moving target Dodging a ball Running Jumping	

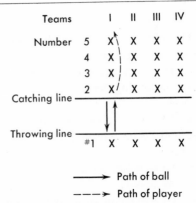

Figure 10–2. Catching and Throwing Relay.

CATCHING AND THROWING RELAY

Use an even number of squads for this game. Arrange squads in four equal lines as shown in Figure 10–2.

Number *one* on each team is given a volleyball or an inflated ball of similar size and weight. At the signal, "Go," he throws the ball to number *two* in his line. Number *two* catches it and quickly passes it back to number *one* and then runs to the end of his line behind the last player.

This brings number *three* to the front of the line. Number *one* passes the ball to him and number *three* returns it to number *one* and runs to the end of the line. Number *one* remains at his starting position until he has passed the ball to everyone in his line. When number *two* returns to the front of the line, he runs up and takes the place of number *one*. Number one then runs to the end of the line and participates in play the same as all others. Number *two* now passes the ball to each one in the line until number *three* is in front of the line. Number *three* replaces number *two*, and so the game continues until each person has had a turn to be up front and pass the ball to everyone in his line. The team finished first wins. The distance the thrower stands from his teammates is determined by the ability of the students. The first time the distance should be short but it may be lengthened as the game proceeds and the throwing skills increase.

It takes a short time to play this game and each person receives much practice in catching and throwing the ball. As the players increase their skills, the speed will also increase. Skills of catching, throwing, and running are practiced and should show improvement.

from the leader. Winners are those who were never holding the ball at the stop signal. Skills of speed and accuracy in catching and throwing are increased. After the game has been

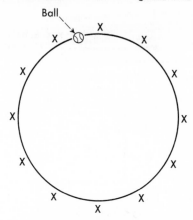

Figure 10–3. Hot Potato.

taught to the entire group, several games may be played with each group, using one or more balls as their skill permits. The same signal to stop could apply to all groups, so one leader will suffice.

HOT POTATO—CIRCLE GAME

Hot Potato is played in a circle formation. It is wise to start with one ball. The object is to pass the ball from one person to another as fast as possible. At intervals the leader claps his hands or blows a whistle. At this signal, the ball passing stops and the person holding the ball is caught with the "hot potato." The object, of course, is not to have the ball when the whistle blows.

If the class remains together in one circle for this game, several balls should be used to add interest and challenge. When more than one is used they must be passed around the circle in the same direction, skipping no one. Balls should be given to each third or fourth student in the circle to start the game. A change of direction may be made at a given signal

DODGE BALL

The rules of this game, discussed in Chapter 14, are familiar to most people. Children gain practice in the skills of catching, throwing at a moving target, dodging, and running. Each of these skills is needed in the team game of Bat Ball which is used here for illustration purposes to show how lead-up games are used in preparation for a team game.

BAT BALL—TEAM GAME

Two teams of from eight to twelve players each are recommended, with a rectangular playing area marked off as illustrated in Figure 10–4. A volleyball or inflated ball of similar size and weight is used. One team is at bat and the other in the field as diagramed. There are no specific places for fielders to stand, except that no one may be closer than 6 feet to the base.

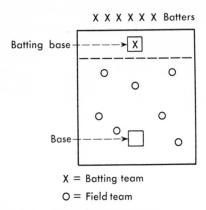

X X X X X X Batters

Batting base ┄┄┄┄→ X

Base ┄┄┄┄→

X = Batting team

O = Field team

Figure 10–4. Bat Ball.

The game is played by innings. Three outs constitute one-half an inning and the fielding team then has its turn at bat. When each team has batted and made three outs, one full inning is completed. Seven or nine innings may be set for a game. The score of the last complete inning may be used to designate the winning team.

The first person at bat holds the ball in one hand and endeavors to bat it over the dotted line so the fielders may not catch it. A fly ball caught by a fielder is an out. If the ball fails to cross the dotted line, the batter is out. The distance of this line from the batter's base varies from 3 feet to 6 feet, depending on the ability of the children and the size of the playing area. The court may vary in size according to the amount of space available. The size will again vary with abilities of children.

Once a batter bats the ball over the line, he becomes a runner and endeavors to run to the one base and return home without being hit with the ball. He may either circle the base or touch it. He is never safe on the base.

The fielders endeavor to hit the runner below the waist before he returns home and

crosses the dotted line. Fielders must pass the ball from one to another. They may not walk or run with it nor hold it longer than three seconds. The batter, then, either makes a run or an out before another player is up to bat. Note the speed element needed which was practiced in the Catching and Passing Relay and in Hot Potato.

By the use of the Catching and Passing Relay, Hot Potato, and Dodge Ball, one may readily understand the value of preliminary and lead-up games as aids for teaching skills and techniques needed in the team game of Bat Ball. This plan of progression, using lead-up games and activities to assist with skills needed in team games, is recommended very strongly.

Teaching Hints

1. Analyze the team game you and your children have agreed to play. Then plan lead-up and preliminary games to include the skills and techniques necessary for it.

2. Interest your children in the games by giving them the reason for practicing the skill or technique.

3. Demonstrate with another child or have children with whom you worked prior to class time demonstrate the game.

4. Provide an opportunity for questions.

5. Use as little playing time as possible before starting the activity.

6. Encourage all children to participate.

7. Expect and encourage good sportsmanship and social relationships.

8. Discourage comparison of one student with another. All will not excel equally well in physical education activities any more than all will be at the same level in other parts of the curriculum.

9. If relays are used, plan the scoring so each team or squad may score each time it is played. For example, if four squads participate, the winner may score ten points; second place, eight; third place, five; and

last place, two. Play relays more than once. They do not take long and give good opportunity for needed practice.

10. Never have more than 8 players in a squad or team for a relay. Some teachers with 32 children divide them into two groups of 16 each. When this practice occurs, children lose interest because they must spend too much time waiting for a turn. Remember, four groups will give each child twice the fun and activity in the same amount of time, and in addition will prevent waning interest and problems.

Self-testing Activities and Stunts

Definition and Types

Stunts and self-testing activities are those activities which afford the participant an opportunity to test his skill with others, to manipulate his body in many unusual positions both stationary and locomotive, and which are concerned with large-muscle development, flexibility, strength, and agility.

TABLE 10–3. *Types of Self-testing Activities and Stunts*

Individual Activities	Couple Activities
Push-Ups	Indian Wrestle
Jump-the-Stick	Acrobatic Handshake
Forward Roll	Cock Fight
	Tandem

Group Activities	Pyramids
Skin the Snake	Rick Rack
Merry-Go-Round	Ten Pins
Wooden Man	Picket Fence
Thousand-Legged Animal	Heart

Objectives

The objectives of self-testing activities and stunts are as follows:

1. To develop agility, flexibility, balance, and strength.

2. To offer an opportunity for bigmuscle development.

3. To provide opportunities for a student to develop satisfaction through his own accomplishments.

4. To provide fun and social relationships.

5. To provide an activity which develops a rhythmic sense.

6. To develop initiative and courage.

Teaching Hints

1. Demonstrate each activity or teach it to student leaders in advance so they may demonstrate.

2. Make necessary arrangements so that proper clothing will be worn during the program.

3. Do not hurry children in these activities.

4. Do not expect each child to do all of them.

5. Teach safety measures necessary for each activity.

6. Progress from relatively easy to more difficult activities.

7. Provide mats, mattresses, or other safe protection.

8. Avoid strain.

9. In couple stunts, choose partners wisely and carefully.

10. Do not force any child to participate who is afraid.

Team Games

Definition

Team games are activities which require more organization and are played between two or more groups, units, or squads. They are concerned with the development of specific skills and techniques, group understanding and participation, specific attitudes in relation to sports, and the understanding of teamwork with emphasis on the "we" and cooperative spirit.

Objectives

The objectives of team games are as follows:

1. To teach social responses through cooperation and competition.

2. To teach the child to work for the good of the team, which at times requires repression of his own individual desires.

3. To teach the child, through group cooperation, self-discipline and self-control.

4. To develop good leadership and followership characteristics.

5. To develop respect for officials and to show the need for definite rules and requirements.

6. To develop specific skills and techniques as required and needed in the game situation.

7. To develop the ability to officiate through an understanding of the rules, sportsmanship, alertness, and being impartial.

Examples

Some examples of team games suitable for the middle childhood are Line Soccer, Newcomb, Bat Ball, Kick Ball, Kick Baseball, Kick Pin Baseball, Captain Ball, and Long Ball.

Teachers should choose and teach team games to their children which meet their needs, interests, and abilities. The fourth grade requires team games with fewer rules and less highly developed skills and techniques than the sixth grade.

An example of progression using three team games mentioned above will be discussed so that teachers may thoroughly understand how they may work for progression from team game to team game within a given grade or from grade to grade.

The three games to be used for illustrative purposes are Kick Ball, Kick Baseball, and Kick Pin Baseball. Each game is played on a diamond like a softball diamond. The size of the diamond will differ depending on the ability and ages of the children and the available play area.

KICK BALL

Kick Ball may begin in the fourth grade. It is played by two teams of from eight to twelve children. One team is at bat and the other is in the field as shown in Figure 10–5. X's indicate the batting team and O's indicate the fielding team. The game is played by innings like Softball and Bat Ball. Seven or nine innings may be agreed on for a complete game. These may not all be completed in one period of physical education and the game may be continued during the next period.

A soccer ball, volleyball, or inflated rubber ball of the approximate same size is used.

The fielding team has only one specific player, a catcher, who stands behind home plate. Other players cover the field as they desire so they may field the balls kicked by the team at bat.

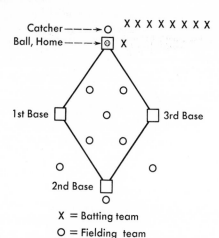

Catcher ———→ O   X X X X X X X X
Ball, Home ——→ ⊡ X

1st Base ☐   O   ☐ 3rd Base

2nd Base ☐

X = Batting team
O = Fielding team

Figure 10–5. Kick Ball.

Number one of the batting team kicks the ball which lies stationary on home plate. If he kicks a fly ball and it is caught by a fielder, he is automatically out. The next batter is then up. If he kicks a fair ball which is not caught by a fielder, he becomes a runner. He runs as many bases as he can before the fielders recover the ball and throw it home to their catcher. When the runner sees the ball nearing home, he stays on base until the ball is kicked by another player.

Fielders have but one rule to remember when they field a ball. They must always throw it home to the catcher—never to any other base. As soon as the catcher receives the ball, he immediately places it on home plate. The object is to catch the runner off any base. Only one player may be on any one base at a time. Base runners may not advance on caught fly balls. If they do run on a caught fly, they must return to base before the ball is thrown home and placed on home plate or they are out.

Notice the few rules necessary to play the game. For the runners they are as follows:

1. Keep running as long as the ball is away from home plate.

2. Do not run on a caught fly ball. If you advance, quickly return to the base you have just left, before the ball is placed on home plate.

For the fielders the rules are as follows:

1. Field the ball immediately and throw it home to the catcher.

2. Keep all areas of the field covered and endeavor to catch fly balls.

The skills and techniques needed for the game include:

1. Running.

2. Kicking a *stationary* ball.

3. Throwing a ball to one specified base.

4. Catching a ball.

Kick Baseball, another team game played on the same diamond with two teams of equal numbers of children, will be discussed next.

❧ ❧

KICK BASEBALL

The rules for Kick Baseball game are harder. More actual thinking is necessary. More skill is required because the kicker must kick a ball which is rolled or bowled in from a pitcher. The fielding positions include a catcher, bowler (pitcher), and a player on each base. The runner is played at each base as in a regular softball or baseball game. He may stop at any base and advance on the next kick. Hence the fielders have to think and know, when each new person comes up to kick, where they will throw the ball when they field it. The game is played by innings the same as Kick Ball.

Progression to this game involves more rules, more skills, and more techniques.

1. Each player must be able to kick a moving ball rolling toward him from the bowler or pitcher.

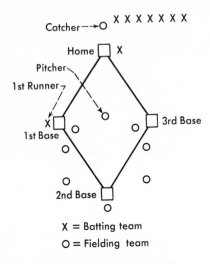

X = Batting team
O = Fielding team

Figure 10–6. Kick Baseball.

2. Skill is required to bowl the ball.

3. Fielders must catch and throw the ball as in Kick Ball, but must know which base to make their throw to for an out.

4. Many more people must be skilled in catching because each baseman, first, second, and third, as well as the catcher, will receive many thrown balls as well as kicked balls.

KICK PIN BASEBALL

Advancing to Kick Pin Baseball requires more speed and skill. This game is also played on a diamond by two teams. On each base, including the home base stands an Indian club, an old bowling pin, a milk carton, or a similar object.

The bowler (pitcher) bowls the ball to the kicker. If the bowler knocks over the pin at home plate, the kicker is out. Notice the accuracy needed by the bowler. If the kicker knocks his own pin over, he automatically puts

himself out. He should stand by the side of the pin so that he will not kick it with the backward swing of his leg, and so that the bowler has an opportunity to aim at the pin.

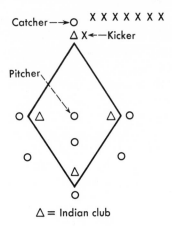

△ = Indian club

Figure 10–7. Kick Pin Baseball.

If the kicker kicks a fly ball which is caught, he is out. When he kicks a fair ball he becomes a runner and if he makes a complete circuit of bases he scores a run. He must run behind each club, so he does not knock them over, and return to home plate. He is never safe on any base. He either scores a run or makes an out before a new kicker is up.

The fielders field the ball and pass it to first base, to second base, to third base, and home, endeavoring to get it to a base ahead of the runner. The ball must make the same complete circuit of bases as the runner. If the ball reaches any base ahead of the runner, the baseman kicks the pin down. This makes the runner out. If the runner beats the ball home, he makes a run for his team.

Notice the skill and speed needed in fielding the ball and the accurate throwing to each base which is required to put a runner out. Notice also the additional speed needed in running the bases. Remember, a runner is never safe at any base. He is safe only after he crosses home base ahead of the ball.

Skills and techniques involve all of those

mentioned in the other two games plus additional ones:

1. Skill in bowling a ball to hit a pin.

2. Timing the kick correctly to obtain placement and distance.

3. Good judgment in order to protect the pin at home plate from being bowled over.

4. Accurate and fast passing of the ball to every baseman.

5. Skill in catching and getting the throw away rapidly.

From the discussion of these three team games it is hoped the teacher will understand their use for progression in different groups or grades. For example, Kick Ball might be used in the fourth grade, Kick Baseball in fifth grade, and Kick Pin Baseball in sixth grade.

When planning programs of activity teachers will be able to find games which develop in skills, rules, and techniques from relatively easy to hard. They will also find their children happy and interested in progression and continued advancement to more challenging play experiences.

Teaching Hints

1. Use the blackboard and all possible visual aids to teach children the over-all view of the field, playing area, and positions of players.

2. Prepare children for skills and techniques needed through the use of lead-up games or games of low organization before the actual team game is started. It is very difficult to teach new skills and techniques as well as new rules at one time.

3. After the team game has been started, analyze the children's needs and plan the first five or ten minutes of the period with games or situations in which they may practice the skill.

4. Prepare various children to act as umpires, judges, or referees. In this way a class of 32 children may have two team games going on at once with twice as much fun, activity, and learning experience.

5. Use every possible teaching opportunity to encourage teamwork. For example, a ball will travel faster if thrown to a teammate than it will if a player runs it to a given base; when one fielder goes after a ball, other players should wait to relay it to the needed base instead of all running after it.

6. Encourage students with good skills to help those who have lesser abilities, the same way they help each other with work in a classroom.

7. Encourage sportsmanship at all times.

8. Stress cooperation, not competition.

9. Teach children to be good winners as well as good losers and to know that the important thing is not the score but the way they play and cooperate.

10. Plan tournaments if the class is interested in them.

Track and Field Events

Definition

Track and field events are activities which are competitive and self-testing and which are excellent for the development of agility, strength, speed, and endurance. A child enjoys them because they are able to be measured and he may see his own improvement as well as compete with others.

Track events include dashes at varying distances depending on age level, shuttle relays and, if desired, novelty relays such as sack, obstacle, and three-legged races.

Field events include the high jump, running and standing broad jumps, hop step and jump, throws for distance using balls such as basketball and softball, shot put (8–10 lb.), punting footballs and kicking soccer balls for accuracy and distance.

Objectives

The objectives of track and field events are as follows:

1. To develop strength, speed, and endurance.

2. To assist in developing the locomotor skills of running, jumping, and throwing.

3. To increase interest in self-improvement through individual participation and measurement.

4. To meet the desires of children to challenge and be challenged.

Teaching Hints

1. Teach the need for safety in each activity.

2. Select activities and distances on basis of age.

3. Have a diversified program.

4. Work with each individual and do not eliminate anyone.

5. Do not have boys and girls competing with each other.

6. Use modified meets as a culminating activity with children classified according to age and weight groups.

Classroom Games

Definition and Objectives

Classroom games for children in the middle childhood grades do not differ in definition or objectives from those used in early childhood (see Chapter 9). They may place additional emphasis on social and recreational importance and worthy leisure-time pursuits. Relatively little physical activity may be developed in the classroom program.

Examples are Black Magic, Bird, Beast, and Fish, Telegrams, Coffee, Tea, and Milk, Going to Jerusalem, Upset the Fruit Basket, various relays, pencil and paper games, and blackboard games may be used in the classroom. Games such as darts, indoor quoits, and ring toss are suitable for these purposes.

Teaching Hints

1. Teach games which will be suitable for recreational pursuits.

2. Teach the need for close cooperation and respect for other people. Children can have fun without disturbing those in other rooms.

3. Permit children to choose activities by democratic procedures.

4. Change rules of games if they are not safe in your classroom situation.

5. Substitute yarn balls, bean bags, or clean erasers for balls.

Aquatics

For many schools it is not geographically possible to use aquatics as a part of the physical education program. If lakes or pools are available, however, teachers may well add swimming, boating, and canoeing. Care must be taken that activities are taught by competent persons. Only a qualified instructor should attempt to teach swimming. Assistance may be received from qualified persons in the community in order to add these activities to the program when facilities are available.

QUESTIONS AND PRACTICAL PROBLEMS

1. Some activities in the middle childhood grades are recommended to be used with boys and girls in separate groups. Discuss all of the pros and cons of the above statement from the viewpoint of the physical, social, psychological, and biological bases.

2. Select one team game you wish to teach. Analyze this game thoroughly and then choose the preliminary or lead-up activities you wish to use before starting the team game. What class organization will you use for your lead-up activities? Why?

3. The children in your fifth grade are not interested in rhythms or the dance. You have been told you must include them as a part of your physical education program. Plan ways of motivating your class and show how you will work this problem through to a successful end.

4. Plan a well-balanced, 10-week program of physical education for the grade of your choice in the middle childhood level.

5. Show the progression for this program based on suggested daily activities for a two-week period.

6. Your school has no gymnasium or play-room. All of your physical education program during inclement weather must therefore be held in your classroom. Plan pieces of equipment your children may make to use for the classroom game situation. What activities will you use other than games? Specify types and names of each activity. Plan the most satisfactory class arrangement for the average size classroom to insure maximum benefit for all children.

7. Make up two original classroom activities for the grade of your choice.

8. You are in an area where there is a nice lake near the school. How would you make use of it? Plan specifically for its use including going to and returning from the lake.

9. Your boys and girls do not wish to participate together in their physical education program. You are teaching the sixth grade. How will you meet this problem? Be specific.

SELECTED REFERENCES

COTTERAL, BONNIE, and DONNIE COTTERAL, *The Teaching of Stunts and Tumbling,* New York, A. S. Barnes and Company, 1936.

CURTISS, MARY LOUISE, and ADELAIDE CURTISS, *Physical Education for Elementary Schools,* Milwaukee, Bruce Publishing Company, 1945.

DAVIS, ELWOOD C., and JOHN LAWTHER, *Successful Teaching in Physical Education,* Englewood Cliffs, N.J., Prentice-Hall, Inc., 1948.

GERI, FRANK H., *Games, Play Runs, and Stunts for Children,* Englewood Cliffs, N.J., Prentice-Hall, Inc., 1956.

HALSEY, ELIZABETH, and LORENA PORTER, *Physical Education for Children: A Developmental Program* (Revised edition), New York, Holt, Rinehart, and Winston, 1963.

HIXSON, CHALMER G., JR., "Bowling in the Elementary School?" *Journal of Health, Physical Education and Recreation,* **33**:30 (January 1962).

IRWIN, LESLIE W., *The Curriculum in Health and Physical Education,* Dubuque, Iowa, W. C. Brown Company, Inc., 1960.

JACK, HAROLD K., *Physical Education for Small Elementary Schools,* York, A. S. Barnes and Company, 1941.

LASALLE, DOROTHY, *Rhythms and Dances for Elementary Schools* (Second edition), New York, A. S. Barnes and Company, 1951.

LEWIS, GERTRUDE M., *et al., Educating Children in Grades Four, Five and Six,* Washington, D.C., Superintendent of Documents, U.S. Government Printing Office, Bulletin No. 3, 1958.

MASON, BERNARD, and ELMER MITCHELL, *Social Games for Recreation,* New York, A. S. Barnes and Company, 1947.

"PLAYGROUNDS—DESIGN FOR CHILDREN," *Arch Forum,* **117**:84–105 (November 1962).

PRUDDEN, BONNIE, "Let Dancing Help Them," *Dance Magazine,* **34**:26+ (November 1960).

STUART, FRANCES, and JOHN LUDLAM, *Rhythmic Activities* (Series 2), Minneapolis, Burgess Publishing Company, 1955.

CHAPTER **11**

Creativity in Physical Education

Creativity is not new in body movement and/or activities for physical education. However, we have perhaps been giving too little opportunity for its use in our programs and are therefore depriving children of this means of self-expression. Basically there are no new physical actions. Cavemen walked, ran, jumped, swam, hung, and threw. All motions were necessary for their livelihood.

DEFINITION AND ROLE IN EDUCATION

Today few physical activities of any consequence, required in a strenuous combination, are necessary for us to use to maintain our homes or earn our living. Hence, since man by nature desires activity and since physical activity is necessary for physical well-being, the fundamental activities have been put in other forms for the enjoyment of children and adults. These forms consist basically of games, gymnastics, dances, team sports, and track and field events.

Each game and activity we know, participate in, and teach has been created by some imaginative person to meet the physical needs of certain age groups. Through the use of such activities, the physical activity necessary for the growth and development of the body is provided.

Instead of running from dangerous animals we run to catch a ball, to tag a player in a game, to get on base in a team game, and, perhaps, in later life, to catch a bus. We throw not to kill an animal with a stone or

a spear, but to engage in many games and sports. We jump not to move from ledge to ledge or to cross a brook, but to clear a jumprope or a crossbar, to better our previous broadjump from the toe board toward the far end of the sawdust pit.

Someone, sometime, had to use imagination and create new patterns of the needed physical activities for use by humans. Hence, imaginative uses of the basic physical activities in the forms of games and activities that give pleasurable experiences to those participating in them is old. Most of these activities, however, have been planned to be used in exact ways. They are organized with exact and specific rules that leave some room for creating new ways to do things but not as much as we perhaps desire.

To create is to produce, to bring into being, or to cause to exist. To be creative means we have the power to create or to bring something new into being. Imagination must be used and connotes creative power.

In physical education the use of imagination results in a creation of the mind that can be shown or demonstrated through the movement and expression of the body. This is what is meant by creativity in physical education.

Children learn when they create. They interpret what they see or feel when confronted with specific music or certain situations in which the teacher has directly or indirectly guided them. Creativity is a way of expression and of putting into action the imagination of a child or an adult. Each will be able to use his imagination and create something based on his *experiences*, the *motivation* used to start or help him gain a desire to create, what he *sees*, and what he *thinks*. He will then *express* through his body movements the way he *feels*. There are many op- portunities and challenges for children to be creative in physical education as well as in art, music, and other parts of the curriculum.

Creativity in physical education brings into existence a child's conception produced by body movements. The individual thinks and produces ideas, ideals, and movements. Through the challenge of the creative process he explores and investigates all known experiences, actions, and ideas and emerges with a reorganization or rearrangement of these in a unique and individual pattern. These are new patterns, previously un- known even to the producer, the child. These movements may be created in dance, in a new way to move about in a story play, or by depicting a different character in a dramati- zation.

PRINCIPLES OF CREATIVITY

How can we assist, challenge, and en- courage the creativity of children in physical education? First, we must think of certain basic principles. These may include elabora- tions of and additions to the following six over-all guides:

1. Our desire and understanding of creativity and its worth to the child.

2. The creation of an atmosphere con- ducive to challenge the imagination and hence produce a creative response. This re- quires freedom for action and not a stereo- typed program.

3. Arrangements of situations which are necessarily challenging for exploration.

4. Supplying materials which call for exploration.

5. Planning experiences which give various backgrounds in both skills and knowledges to the child so he may have background from which to create.

6. Encouraging all children to be crea- tive by accepting this as an important and vital part of their education and encouraging each one to remain an individual in his or her creativity.

EXAMPLES OF CREATIVITY

Based on the specific types of activities recommended in the well-rounded program of physical education, some examples will be considered illustrating how each activity area may be used by the alert teacher to challenge creativity.

Figure 11–1. Square dancing is fun.

Playground Equipment

Children think of playground equipment in many ways and with different uses and movements. Some look at a jungle gym as a high house with no outside walls, a big tree, a monkey cage in a zoo, a tower for looking out far over the land, or, to some, a space station near the moon. On it, they will explore and create movement. Some will climb high, others will use only the lower bars. Some will sit astride a bar and make believe they are riding a horse or pedaling a bicycle. Some will skin a cat or hang by their knees. Encouragement given by an understanding teacher gives confidence to the fearful child to also start experimenting in various forms of movement on such equipment.

Story Plays

1. Dramatize basic activities common to children's experiences in their readers, during the holiday seasons, in everyday life (deep snow walk, for example).

2. Portray community helpers at work —the fireman, the ambulance driver, the policeman.

3. Create results of nature activities— wind blowing, leaves falling, leaves swirling, snowflakes falling and being blown by the wind.

Dance

1. Integrate movements based on certain types of music showing free axial movements: up-down, sidewards, forward, backwards, and rotating.

2. Create dance patterns based on fundamental locomotor movements of walking, running, skipping, hopping, leaping, sliding, and galloping.

3. Add patterns using non-locomotor

movements of pushing, pulling, lifting, swinging, and striking.

4. Plan creative dances of countries studied in social studies, e.g., Indian dances, Mexican dances, and so on.

5. Interpret music as to big steps, high steps, heavy running, and light running.

6. Create accompaniment on percussion instruments.

7. Make percussion instruments.

8. Create additional movement patterns based on characters from outer space, songs and poems, television, and different sports.

9. Create movements in specific floor patterns and designs such as squares, circles, and figure eights and then develop the sequence of movements to be used.

Games

1. Create new games of several different types.

2. Create new challenges by changing rules or adding rules and skills to games already known.

3. Formulate games and rules to fit unique situations—small areas, little equipment, many participants, few participants.

4. Plan and make new pieces of equipment, e.g., yarn balls, different kinds and shapes of bean bags.

Examples

Two examples of children's creativity in games are given. The first game was created by a fifth-grade child to help his smaller brother to learn colors, counting, various shapes, and accurate tossing of a bean bag, rubber mason jar rings, or rubber heels from old shoes. Needless to say, the game was also used and enjoyed by the fifth-grade children.

CREATIVE TOSS–BOARD

Each section of the board is painted a different color and is numbered, as shown, from one to five. The board contains squares, triangles, one circle, and two uneven and unnamed geometrical figures.

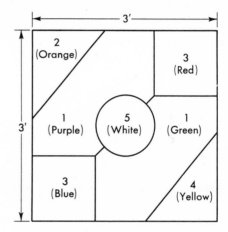

Figure 11–2. Creative Toss-Board.

The board is placed on the floor at different distances from the players according to age and ability.

Each child has a chance to toss three bean bags, jar rings, or rubber heels at the board. He then tells the colors he has hit and adds his score, which is taken from the numbers in the areas hit. Next, as he picks up the rings or bean bags, he names the geometric figure each was in.

The second game, shown in Figure 11–3, involves creating scrambled words in specific forms. This arrangement was made by a sixth-grade student. Other children were challenged and designed forms. These included a witch on a broom, used at Halloween; a turkey and a pumpkin, used at Thanksgiving; rabbits, ducks, and a plant for Easter; and a snowman, used during a snowy season.

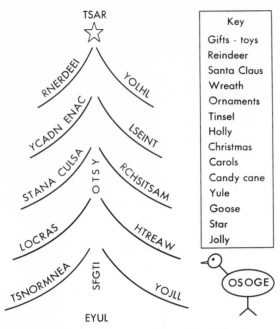

Key

Gifts - toys
Reindeer
Santa Claus
Wreath
Ornaments
Tinsel
Holly
Christmas
Carols
Candy cane
Yule
Goose
Star
Jolly

Figure 11–3. Creative Scrambled Words.

Individual and Dual Activities

Creativity is called for in the following individual and dual activities.

1. New ways to jump rope including new rhymes to use.

2. New hopscotch court diagrams and ways to play on the new areas.

3. New activities for restricted areas.

4. New activities with new equipment.

5. Activities using certain groups of muscles for those children with physical handicaps, such as arm or hand paralysis or heart conditions.

Swimming

Where swimming supervision is available, swimming activities can also be creative.

1. Create different swimming patterns, such as line, circle, and star formations.

2. Plan a theme and work out appropriate water activities.

3. Swim in time to music using different strokes.

Self-Testing Activities and Stunts

The following self-testing activities and stunts involve creative action.

1. Action showing animals walking or running, showing fear or happiness.

2. Airplanes starting, taking off, flying, and landing.

3. Various combinations of body movement in new patterns, e.g., run—jump—roll; hop—skip—jump.

4. New combinations, e.g., hanging—swinging—jumping.

Camping and Outdoor Education

Many creative outdoor education activities can be added to the following:

1. New ways to mark trails.

2. New types of shelters.

QUESTIONS AND PRACTICAL PROBLEMS

1. Select an idea or theme and set the stage for a creative program to be presented to a Parent-Teachers' Association. Choose your grade level.

2. List subject matter topics which may be used for creativity in dances; in games and in story plays. Designate some for each grade level from one to six.

3. Make two percussion instruments and write the directions used in making them. Do not *buy* any materials.

4. Use your own creativity and make

three pieces of equipment which may be used for games. Write up uses and rules.

5. Develop a dance for the grade of your choice.

SELECTED REFERENCES

ANDERSON, HAROLD (Editor), *Creativity and Its Cultivation,* New York, Harper and Brothers, 1959.

ANDREWS, GLADYS, *Creative Rhythmic Movement For Children,* Englewood Cliffs, N.J., Prentice-Hall, Inc., 1954.

BOARD OF EDUCATION OF THE CITY OF NEW YORK, *Curriculum and Materials,* New York, Board of Education of the City of New York, 1959.

BROER, MARION, *The Efficiency of Human Movement,* Philadelphia, W. B. Saunders Company, 1960.

Creativity of Gifted and Talented Children, New York, Bureau of Publications, Teachers College, Columbia University, February 1959.

LOWENFELD, VICTOR, and W. LAMBERT BRITTAIN, *Creative and Mental Growth* (Fourth edition), New York, The Macmillan Company, 1964.

MURRAY, RUTH LOVEL, *Dance in Elementary Education,* New York, Harper and Brothers, 1953.

PIPER, RALPH, and ZORA PIPER, *Developing the Creative Square Dance Caller,* Minneapolis, 1956.

ROMNEY, GOLDEN, "Creative Teaching," *Journal of Health, Physical Education and Recreation,* **32:**17 (October 1961).

SMITH, H. M., "Creative Expression and Physical Education," *Journal of Health, Physical Education and Recreation,* Vol. 33 (May 1962).

STEIN, MORRIS I., and SHIRLEY J. HEINZE, *Creativity and the Individual,* Glencoe, Ill., The Free Press, 1960.

TORRANCE, PAUL, *Guiding Creative Talent,* Englewood Cliffs, N.J., Prentice-Hall, Inc., 1962.

WESSELL, JANET A., *Movement Fundamentals,* Englewood Cliffs, N.J., Prentice-Hall, Inc., 1961.

WILT, MIRIAM E., *Creativity in the Elementary School,* New York, Appleton-Century-Crofts, Inc., 1959.

ZIRBES, LAURA, *Spurs to Creative Teachings,* New York, G. P. Putnam's Sons, 1959.

CHAPTER 12

Class Organization

The physical education program offers the teacher a challenge for good class organization which will not only be of great assistance to her but will offer worthy experiences to each child. The learning accomplished through good class organization is invaluable to all children if it is properly planned and administered. The children should always assist in the planning. It is not the prerogative of the teacher alone.

Terms frequently used in class organization for the physical education program are *squads, units,* or *teams.* Of the three, squads or units are preferable terms. The word *team* almost always connotes competition, and class organization should not be used to foster a sense of competition. It is a recommended means of teaching cooperation, group consciousness, leadership, followership, and similar desirable traits.

MEANS OF ORGANIZATION

Suggested Number of Squads

It is usually recommended to organize a class into four or more squads depending on the total number of children. A class with 32 pupils divided in four squads of eight each is a satisfactory number. Each teacher should plan the number which will best suit the group.

Organizational Methods

Squads may be organized in many ways. Two of the most widely used methods will be discussed.

Homogeneous Grouping

Children may be grouped according to their abilities. The results of skill tests, strength tests, physical fitness indices, and/or general all-round ability, as well as size and age may be used.

The teacher who has no means of measuring the specific abilities of the children, but who knows their over-all abilities, may wish to organize the children on this basis. To accomplish this he or she would select four children of similar abilities and place each one on a different squad. This method may be continued until each child has a place. Groups will then be very evenly matched. While the squad plan is not used mainly for competition, it does help to have

Figure 12–1. Squads ready for action.

children of near-equal ability on each side when they are playing relays, team games, or running and tagging games.

Random Placement

Squads may be organized by random methods in several ways. They may count off by fours if the number of desired squads is four. Then all "ones" are together, all "twos" are together, and so on.

Leaders may be selected first and they may choose the members of their squads. This is the least recommended method of all. Squad leaders know the differences of ability among their classmates. The few children who have poor muscle coordination, skills, and techniques are always last to be selected. They know that no squad wants them and they are there because they must be. It points out individual differences to the entire group and is not desirable for certain children.

The drawing method may be used. An equal number of four different colored pieces of paper are placed in a box. Each child draws a piece. All greens form a group, all reds another. Each color indicates one squad.

Months of birthdays, house numbers, and the number of letters in either the child's first or last name are other methods of random placement. Children will contribute many ideas for different means of organization, and the teacher may think of other methods. It is interesting to note that squads chosen through the random placement method are usually evenly matched in skills.

Desirable Length of Service

Squad members should be changed often. If they are permitted to work and play together for too long a period of time cliques result and the children lose the desired social experiences. One example of this was illustrated in a school where teams, the term they used, were organized in September and stayed together until June. Undesirable rivalry built up between the teams both in school and outside.

It is desirable to change squads every three or four weeks to avoid undesirable antisocial experiences. This will give more children a chance to act as squad leaders and to develop desirable qualities of leadership as well as followership. Children need to be able to work and play with each person in their class, either individually or in small or large groups.

Selection of Squad Leaders

Squad leaders may be selected in various ways. Whatever way is used should be thoroughly understood by the children and also should meet with their approval.

In some instances teachers arbitrarily select the squad leaders, either before the children are organized in squads or from the squads. This is not recommended because the children gain no learning experiences and many times resent the leader because of the honor bestowed on him by the teacher. Where this plan is practiced it appears to be an assumed arbitrary right of the teacher.

If desired, leaders may be nominated and elected by the children before squads are organized. The qualifications necessary for leadership should be discussed, posted, and well understood by all children. When children are given the opportunity to nominate and elect, they are learning the method that leaders are elected in a democracy. Voting may be by a show of hands or by written ballot.

Squads may be organized first, after which each squad may elect its own leader. This is another method worthy of a try.

The teacher who works carefully with the class and teaches the desirable qualifications for leaders need not worry that the children will merely choose the most popular student. Given an opportunity, under careful guidance, they do a fine job of selection.

UNDERSTANDING NEEDS

Children need to know desirable followership characteristics to enable them to be valuable members of a group. Teachers should encourage their children to help plan these qualifications. If the grade level permits, they may make one chart listing the qualifications for good leaders and one for good followers. In grades where children are unable to make the charts, it is a valuable teaching aid for the teacher to make them. Children may learn new words for their vocabulary and spelling from the charts, as well as learn to read them.

While leadership and followership abilities differ among children, it is hoped that through clear understanding of the qualifications each child will work toward reaching them and may sometime during the school year have an opportunity to act as a leader. If squads are reorganized each month, a classroom operating on a four-squad plan would need forty leaders for a ten-month session. This would make it possible for each child to act as a leader once, and some twice, during the year. It is strongly recommended that teachers plan the reorganization period with their classes.

Leadership Qualifications

The specific qualifications needed for leaders should be thoroughly understood by the children. They may add other qualities not listed below. In general, it is believed that a good leader must:

Figure 12–2. Children follow squad leaders. (Courtesy of Miracle Equipment Co.)

1. Be able to take care of himself before he can aid in the organization of others.

2. Be well prepared to organize his group.

3. Be honest and a good sport.

4. Be dependable.

5. Have and keep the respect of his group.

6. Be courteous and thoughtful.

7. Be able to give and receive suggestions.

8. Be enthusiastic.

9. Give encouragement to all participants by giving constructive help.

10. Have the interest of his entire group in mind.

11. Be fair in making decisions and be able to act as judge or referee in game situations.

12. Have the ability to keep everything running smoothly in his squad during each activity.

Followership Qualifications

It is as important for a child to possess the qualities of a good follower as of a leader. This should be taught and stressed. Each child may add additional qualifications for followership to those listed. Specific points believed essential for a good follower include the following:

1. Be respectful to the leader.

2. Be willing to cooperate and participate to the best of your ability.

3. Be able to accept constructive help.

4. Be a good sport at all times.

5. Listen to the leader's opinions as

well as those of your teammates and be guided by good judgment.

6. Follow directions well.

7. Be conscious of your part in the social group and abide by group standards.

8. Be unselfish.

9. Have a desire to gain a knowledge of the rules and directions of all activities.

10. Be able to follow and not try to take over the leader's responsibilities while he is in charge of the group.

11. Be able to discipline yourself and have self-control at all times.

12. Work as a part of the group for group consciousness and harmony and forget yourself as an individual.

VALUE OF SQUADS

Aids to Teachers

Squad organization is a great aid to teachers. Squad leaders may help by:

1. Assisting with the planning of the program of activities.

2. Acting as equipment managers.

3. Helping assign the positions of various players in the game situation.

4. Making decisions concerning their players.

5. Ascertaining that each child has his rightful turn in play.

6. Checking the play area and equipment for safety factors.

7. Assisting with their group in securing wraps and in going to and from the play areas, the basements, and the lunchroom.

8. Acting as leaders in the classroom as well as on the playground.

9. Acting as leaders for small-group play, individual activities, skill tests, and so on.

10. Acting as referees, umpires, and score keepers.

11. Aiding in sectioning the playground into playing areas and in marking courts or specific areas needed for play.

12. Aiding, through their understanding of problems pertaining to facilities and equipment, in the mutual understanding and cooperation of their group.

13. Acting as demonstrators of skills and activities in their group if the teacher works with them first in a leader's corps.

14. Assisting in evaluating activities and the entire program.

15. Assisting in setting good examples of sportsmanship for others.

16. Helping make the teacher less necessary, which helps meet the objective set by John Amos Comenius, "To find a method of instruction by which teachers may teach less and learners learn more."

Squads aid the teacher by:

1. Saving valuable time for each class period because children are already in groups and ready for various activities and formations.

2. Making it easy for the teacher to work on skill tests.

3. Assisting the teacher in being ready for relays and games requiring several groups.

4. Facilitating small-group work and offering good opportunities for her to notice children who need specific help. (This is easier to spot in a group of eight than one of 32.)

5. Being combined in one large group or in two groups for team activities.

6. Aiding in teaching group consciousness by departing from the "I" stage to the "We" stage.

7. Offering a fine opportunity to teach democratic relationships.

Aids to Children

Squad organization offers many varied experiences which may aid children by:

1. Developing leadership.
2. Developing followership.
3. Providing helpful socializing opportunities.
4. Providing a laboratory for aiding teamwork.

5. Eliminating individual emphasis through group consciousness.
6. Developing responsibility.
7. Teaching democratic procedures and actions.
8. Presenting social experiences of a group nature which give vent to the gang instinct.
9. Developing sportsmanship.
10. Giving individual satisfaction through belonging to a group and being needed.
11. Teaching cooperation.
12. Teaching the child to accept his place in a group.

HINTS FOR TEACHERS

1. Squads may be organized in all grades including the first.
2. Be sure children understand the values and objectives of organization.
3. Give them an opportunity to aid in the organization.
4. Help them develop by aiding them in assuming leadership and followership positions.
5. Do not use squads merely for competitive purposes. This will add to problems rather than assist them.
6. Change squads often.

7. Provide opportunities for each child to act as a leader at some time during the year, if at all possible.
8. Give the leaders responsibility both on the playground and in the building.
9. Use the squads for other purposes than in the physical education program.
10. Use each reorganization period as a valuable teaching opportunity.
11. Evaluate the group organization constantly.
12. Make it a cooperative experience at all times.

EVALUATION OF PUPIL GROWTH

Teachers may use the squad organization for evaluation purposes to assist the group in seeing its growth and accomplishments. She may help each individual squad to prepare a chart. This may be done during an art class. Children usually like to name their squads. A chart may be made for each squad containing the name, an appropriate drawing characterizing its name, and all

members' names. Adequate space should be permitted for leaders to write in the daily accomplishments of their squad. These accomplishments may include the names of the games played, rating of sportsmanship and various other characteristics, skills, and techniques learned, specific positive comments by the teacher, and the like.

Each child may also wish to keep his

own monthly record, listing the name of his squad, his specific accomplishments while working with the group, and his comments and reactions to each particular squad.

Children may write about their reactions or speak before their group. They should gain much from the organization experiences and should be given an opportunity each week to think together and evaluate their experiences.

In conclusion, it appears that organization gives an opportunity for the correct adjustment of relationships between children and/or adults in an effort to accomplish certain specific goals.

A good program of physical education, correctly organized, offers a great opportunity to teach democracy because it aids in developing social consciousness, which assists a child in taking his place in a group.

Good class organization in physical education is an invaluable aid to the teacher and to the child.

QUESTIONS AND PRACTICAL PROBLEMS

1. Plan exactly how you would go about interesting children in squad organization in your class. What points would you stress? How would you introduce the idea? What teaching situations would you set up?

2. Explain three different ways children may be divided in four squads in the grade of your choice. Justify each method.

3. How can you integrate squad organization with other parts of your curriculum? Be specific. How can you use these same organized squads to assist you in parts of the school day other than the physical education period? What are the educational experiences for the children in each plan?

4. How will you stress the cooperative spirit with your organization in place of the too-frequent competitive spirit?

5. Organize a leader corps of your squad leaders and show how you would use this group as an aid for your entire class. When will you work with these leaders? How? What specific points must you keep in mind so the leaders will be accepted by their group?

6. How may we aid in the correct connotation of *gang* through the squad idea? Must the word *gang* always mean destructive and antisocial organization? Could you call your squad a gang? If so, justify it. If not, justify your stand.

SELECTED REFERENCES

BRACE, DAVID K., "The Contributions of Physical Education to the Total Education," *Journal of the American Association for Health, Physical Education and Recreation,* **20**:635 (December 1949).

———, "Education for Democracy Through Physical Education," *Education,* **70**:112 (October 1949).

BUCHER, CHARLES A., *Methods and Materials in Physical Education and Recreation,* St. Louis, The C. V. Mosby Company, 1954.

LASALLE, DOROTHY, *Guidance of Children Through Physical Education* (Second edition), New York, The Ronald Press Company, 1957.

———, "Guidance of Democratic Living Through Physical Education," *Journal of the American Association for Health, Physical Education and Recreation,* **21**:22 (November 1950).

LEE, MURRAY J., and DORIS M. LEE, *The Child and the Curriculum* (Second edition), New York, Appleton-Century-Crofts, Inc., 1950, p. 75.

MUNK, EVA, "Physical Education in Peacetime," *Journal of Health and Physical Education,* **17**:350 (June 1946).

VANNIER, MARYHELEN and MILDRED FOSTER, *Teaching Physical Education in Elementary Schools* (Third edition), Philadelphia, W. B. Saunders Company, 1963.

CHAPTER 13

General Hints for the Classroom Teacher

It is the purpose of this chapter to give the elementary classroom teacher suggestions in planning and general hints for teaching physical education. This is important since she probably will be responsible for a large part, if not the entire program, in the elementary grades. Specific teaching hints for each of the various recommended activities for a well-rounded program of physical education will be discussed in Chapters 21–24, pages 242–360, which also include directions and diagrams.

THE NEED FOR PLANNING

No architect attempts to build a house, a school, or a hospital without blueprints. No engineer builds a bridge, a clover-leaf intersection, or a tunnel without plans. Similarly, no teacher should attempt to teach physical education to elementary school children without plans.

Mistakes made by the carpenter using the architect's plans may be rectified. True, this will cost some money, but a carpenter works with materials that are replaceable. The same applies to the construction foreman working from an engineer's plan. The teacher's mistakes, however, prove much more costly, because she is working with a human being—a child—who may never be replaced. Others will come and go but Johnnie will always be Johnnie and mistakes may scar him for his entire life. Hence, the teacher is charged with great responsibility and has the pleasure of working with the most precious and the most important thing in the world—an individual, a human being, the child.

Planning will never guarantee that errors will not be made, but the builder with good plans, the engineer with good plans, and the teacher with good plans will certainly err less than those with none. Most satisfactory accomplishments result from clear and challenging anticipation followed by careful planning.

The elementary classroom teacher today is presented with one of the greatest challenges of all educators. She teaches, guides, and directs a greater percentage of children than teachers in any other field or area of education. Laws require children to attend school. Since many leave school early, they may never have the guidance of any teacher other than the elementary teacher. She must, in many cases, assume the complete responsibility for the child's formal education and do everything within her power to aid him in developing his potentialities to the fullest possible extent. Properly planned and administered programs of physical education will assist the teacher to help the pupil reach the goals that the teacher desires.

GENERAL PLANNING

In planning, the teacher must keep in mind individual differences. She must know the needs, interests, and capabilities of the children in her group. She should plan to meet them at their own levels of ability and to assist them in reaching the educationally desirable goal or goals.

She must also consider the outdoor play area, indoor facilities, equipment, type of class organization, and time allotment in relation to the state laws and local regulations.

In general, planning gives purpose and meaning to the program. It will prove helpful in coordinating physical education with other parts of the school curriculum. It aids in efficiency and is time saving. It assists in maintaining pupil interest both by meeting needs and avoiding repetition.

Bearing these specific points in mind, the teacher may plan her program of physical education on a yearly, seasonal, monthly, or daily basis.

Yearly Planning

What does the teacher expect or want her children to gain in desired skills and techniques, social growth, leadership qualities, carry-over values for leisure-time activity, and the like? Which recommended activities for children in the age and grade level of her class will best help them reach these desired goals? How much of each shall she include in her program?[1]

The teacher must know the needs of her

[1] Patterns are fully discussed giving recommended types of activities and suggested time allotment in Chapters 9 and 10.

children and then plan to meet them. She will make her yearly plan accordingly, with her over-all objectives based also on the interests and abilities of her children. She may then break this yearly plan into seasonal plans.

Seasonal Planning

The wise teacher uses seasons to assist with the child's interest and also in the correlation of her physical education program with other parts of the curriculum.

Spring and the glory and splendor of its beauty and color are great aids to her. Spring means interest in softball and/or baseball for the middle childhood grades. For various reasons her group may be unable to participate in either. Perhaps the playing space is too small. The wise teacher will plan activities which are similar to these and may be played in the space provided. Flowers and Wind, a fleeing game, will be taught in the spring and be correlated with nature. Bird Catcher, another running and tagging game for early childhood, belongs in the spring program and again gives good opportunity for correlation with nature, art, and reading.

The fall season brings interest in soccer and touch football to children in the middle childhood group. In many instances the elementary classroom teacher may have few facilities for these activities and in most cases finds them too advanced for her group. She will, therefore, choose activities resembling these highly organized team games. To the early childhood group, fall means possible dramatizations in the form of story plays, rhythms, or dances using such symbols as falling leaves, raking leaves, and gathering nuts.

Winter is the season to teach dances, using the "Skaters' Waltz" as an example. Dramatizations of building snowmen and skating and skiing to music bring interest to rhythmic and dance activities during the cold days. Games resembling basketball and volleyball will be seasonal interests for middle childhood groups.

Indoor programs suited to the available facilities must also be considered in this seasonal plan. A good teacher plans a flexible program for each season. To meet hot days there is less-active play and for brisk days there is active movement for the health of all concerned.

The alert teacher will think of a wealth of possibilities. Seasonal planning may then be broken up into monthly planning and used to advantage.

Monthly Planning

Every school month gives the teacher many ideas for choosing interesting activities for her physical education program. All special days and events are clues. October brings Halloween, November means Thanksgiving, December denotes Christmas, March or April brings Easter. These are but a few examples of holidays falling in certain months which may be used advantageously in physical education.

Early childhood classes may use each of these holidays in story plays, rhythmic and dance dramatizations, games of low organization for outdoor play, and classroom games for indoor activity. A goblin dance, the game of Old Mother Witch, and a story play of Santa's helpers are examples of activities based on special days.

Middle childhood may use gay Christ-

mas music in December for rhythms and creative dancing. Self-testing activities and stunts may be based on toys of interest to them. Running and tagging games such as Catch the Caboose, which uses the nationwide Christmas interest in electric trains, will be thoroughly enjoyed.

In planning, the teacher usually works with two types of plans—the unit plan and the separate or individual class plan. Illustrations of each are given and points are discussed for the use of each type.

Unit Plans

Much interest is maintained through unit planning in each specific subject field and through correlation with the other subjects in the curriculum. Physical education is no exception to the value which may come from unit planning.

For example, a teacher in the sixth grade may wish to use softball as a team game in the spring program. Such a unit plan could include:

1. Introduction to the activity.
2. General objectives to be attained: (a) worthy use of leisure time, (b) teamwork, (c) social qualities, (d) sportsmanship, (e) safety.
3. Specific skills: (a) preliminary games used to develop these skills, (b) organization of class to best advantage.
4. Teaching rules: visual aids, (a) films, (b) blackboard.
5. Motivating interest.
6. Correlation with other subjects.
7. Evaluation techniques.

From such a unit of work, planned both by the *teacher* and the *pupils,* the weekly and the daily progression necessary to reach the established goals would be determined. Thus a weekly and/or daily plan is developed.

Weekly and/or Daily Plans

Each specific plan should be the combined efforts of the teacher and the pupils. Teacher-pupil planning stimulates more interest and results in worthy experiences in group dynamics. These plans will consider space, equipment, weather, size of class, and differences in individual skills and techniques. General and specific objectives desired to be accomplished each week and day will be set up.

All planning must be directed toward the specific objectives of physical education which in turn are based on the general purposes of education. Children need to understand these goals and the teacher must help make them attainable. These goals may be accomplished much better and faster if the child has a clear concept of what he is trying to attain.

An example of a simple daily form for a plan in physical education is as follows:

1. Aim of lesson.
2. Specific objectives.

3. Activities: (a) type, (b) time of each, (c) equipment needed.
4. Method of procedure: (a) introduction, (b) class organization necessary, (c) demonstration, (d) teaching hints, (e) ending.
5. Anticipated difficulties (i.e., small playing space, roughness).
6. Outcomes desired: (a) skills, (b) knowledges, (c) attitudes.

Specific details which should receive positive answers, according to Voltmer and Esslinger, are as follows:

1. Is there healthful procedure? Is the play area clean and safe? Are the indoor facilities ventilated and lighted as well as possible? Are all safety precautions used? Is big-muscle activity present but not overdone?
2. Is the activity planned with the specific facilities in mind? Is there sufficient room and is there equipment available for it? May it be played safely in the allotted area?
3. Is the plan educationally sound? Does it meet pupils' needs, interests, and abilities? Does it provide for student leadership? Is there carry-over value for leisure time?[2]

GENERAL HINTS

Through years of successful teaching many general hints have been found to be valuable. These may assist the classroom teacher to enjoy teaching physical education and help her children gain desirable educational experiences.

Hints For Planning

1. Plan the program of work yearly, seasonally, monthly, and daily. It is better to overplan than underplan.
2. Keep in mind the objectives of phys-

ical education and the specific objectives of each particular lesson.
3. Plan activities which are appropriate for your particular group. Know your children and plan to meet their specific needs, interests, and abilities.
4. Plan to help each child learn something each day. Bear in mind individual differences, needs, and rates of learning.
5. Plan activities for the exceptional child. Know which activities are beneficial to

[2] E. P. Voltmer and A. A. Esslinger, *The Organization and Administration of Physical Education* (Second edition), New York, Appleton-Century-Crofts, Inc., 1949, pp. 287–288.

him. Use him to help officiate, score, or assist with equipment. Make him feel needed and *a part of* the class, not *apart from* it.

6. Plan to play outside every day the weather will permit.

7. Have a flexible plan to use for inclement weather.

8. Plan to teach the time allotment required by state or local regulations. Remember, in each case this is only the recommended *minimum* time.

Personal Hints

1. Dress comfortably. Many teachers keep a pair of loafers, saddle oxfords, or sneakers in their closet to wear for physical education. This saves damage to expensive footwear, makes the teacher more comfortable, and gives him or her a greater incentive to enter into the activity.

2. Keep your voice natural and conversational. This may be accomplished by having your class know the meaning of a whistle, a piano chord, or a hand clap and abiding by it. Do not talk when your class is noisy. Teach the rules of etiquette and social manners and use the physical education class to develop these social qualities acceptable to all. Use your signal sparingly but whenever necessary.

3. Accept your responsibility to teach physical education the same as you do your responsibility to teach reading. Remember that the whole child comes to school and you teach this child in his entirety. Physical education can be fun for the teacher as well as for the pupil. The wise teacher will learn much about each individual during physical education which will be beneficial in her total guidance of him.

Organizational Hints

1. Organize your class in the most ef-
ficient way possible. This will avoid much loss of time and trouble and may be used to match students evenly in competitive activities.

2. Use student leaders for squads, teams, and/or units. Develop responsibility in all students by making them responsible for equipment.

3. Use students for demonstration. Work with these children before actual class time.

4. Use color bands, pinnies, or other distinguishing emblems to mark squad players when they are mixed during activities.

5. Have your organizational plan for going to and returning from physical education well understood. Plan this with your class so they understand the standards expected of them. Student leaders should be given this responsibility.

Safety Hints

1. Keep playgrounds free of dangerous obstacles.

2. Do not use stones or sticks for bases in games or to mark running areas.

3. Have rules about the recovery of equipment going in a busy road or street thoroughly understood.

4. Do not permit children to run to walls or fences as goals. Make lines a safe distance from such barriers.

5. Inspect equipment regularly.

6. Inspect facilities regularly.

7. Provide proper safety protection for children in all game situations (e.g., mask, body protector, and glove for catcher in softball).

8. Teach children the proper way to tag so they do not injure each other or tear clothing.

9. Teach respect for each other and for all equipment and facilities.

10. Good organization will aid safety.

11. Be sure students awaiting their turn in certain games, such as softball, stay away from the batter to avoid injury.

12. Have your own playing area. Do not permit children participating in a running and tagging game to run across a soccer field, a ball diamond, or any area of play being used by other students.

13. Have children remove glasses or wear eyeglass guards.

Health Hints

1. Do not permit any child to overstrain.

2. Be sure children know they may drop out of an activity and rest if they become too tired without gaining permission from the teacher.

3. Know the health records of your children. Remember you will have physical education classes before the doctor examines your children in the fall. Use the last health records available. Discuss this with your class in your health teaching. Be cognizant of the child who has just returned from an illness. What is best for him?

4. Ventilate and light your indoor facilities the best way possible.

5. Be sure children wear proper clothing for the place and type of activity.

6. Do not permit your children to sit on the damp ground while awaiting turns in certain games.

General Teaching Hints

1. Know your work thoroughly before attempting to teach.

2. Have the necessary equipment ready.

3. Make your playroom, gymnasium, or playground as attractive as possible.

4. Use a positive approach rather than a negative one. "Let's do it this way," rather than "Don't do it that way."

5. Make explanations simple and concise, using as little of the play time as possible.

6. Demonstrate or have demonstrated each step, skill, or technique necessary. Remember, lengthy explanations cause interest to wane. Use visual aids whenever possible. Blackboard are very helpful.

7. Remember that children want action. Have 100 per cent participation.

8. Once rules are established for a given condition, teach your children to accept them.

9. When officiating, make quick and accurate decisions.

10. Teach sportsmanship and character education at all times. Teach children to accept and respect decisions given by officials.

11. Revise rules, if necessary, to increase activity and make it purposeful.

12. Do not permit certain children to monopolize the activity, equipment, or facilities at the expense of all.

13. Aim for knowledge, habits, attitudes, and appreciation which lead to social efficiency and acceptance.

14. Use incentives to reach desired outcomes and goals. Remember that praise is good. Comment whenever possible even though improvement is small.

15. Vary your procedures.

16. Watch closely for waning interest. Kill an activity rather than have it die.

17. End your lesson appropriately.

18. Analyze the lesson each day. Did it go well? If so, why? If not, why? Was it a wrong activity? Was the presentation faulty? Was it not challenging enough for your group? Was it too hard for your group?

19. Enjoy yourself and your class.

20. Be enthusiastic! It's contagious and good contagion.

21. Give opportunity for questions and suggestions by pupils.

GENERAL EVALUATION BY SUPERVISORS

If a teacher plans wisely and uses the suggested hints, she will not need to worry about supervision from her superiors. It is, however, interesting and beneficial for her to know points which they might use to rate her work in physical education. The following points are generally considered by supervisors.

General Program Evaluation

Standards set for evaluating activities taught in physical education would include the following:

1. Abilities, interests, capabilities, and characteristics of the group are considered in planning the lesson.

2. Activities are of such a nature that there may be carry-over value into play activities after school hours.

3. Growth and developmental needs of the children are being met.

4. Health and safety factors are considered in all phases of the program.

5. Special activities are provided for the physically handicapped.

6. The objectives are selected and based according to the needs of the children, the school, and the community.

7. All of the children are involved in the program.

8. There is a diversified program of activities which is graded according to difficulty.

9. There are opportunities for self-expression and creative work through the activity program.

10. The activities provide opportunities to develop good standards of conduct and to help the pupil take his place in a social group.

Lesson Evaluation

Supervisors look for answers to these questions to evaluate a specific lesson in physical education:

1. Was the teacher well prepared?

2. Did the teacher accomplish her objectives?

3. What was the teacher-pupil relationship?

4. What was the pupil-teacher relationship?

5. What was the pupil-pupil relationship?

6. What did the pupils gain from the class?

7. Did they show enjoyment?

8. Were they good sports?

9. Was there chance for leadership among students?

10. Was the time used advantageously?

11. Did problems arise? If yes, why? How were they solved?

12. Was the teacher cheerful? Did she enjoy the class? Was she enthusiastic?

13. Did the teacher recognize and commend good work?

14. Did all children participate? If not, why?

15. Were all health and safety factors considered?

16. Was the lesson properly ended?

Effective teaching is fun and challenging. Through proper planning more fun and learning result. A good teacher welcomes all teaching aids, devices, and hints and uses them to advantage. She always remembers and uses the laws of learning, readiness, exercise, and effect. She establishes definite objectives, both general and specific, which are purposeful and are clear and meaningful to the child. She awakens in him, if neces-sary, the desire for a goal and aids him in reaching this goal. Each day as she teaches physical education to her children, she is able to answer these questions: Why do I teach this lesson? What value is it to my children? Do I know exactly how I shall teach it? How will I evaluate it?

QUESTIONS AND PRACTICAL PROBLEMS

1. Plan two lessons in physical education using the suggested outline for the plan. Choose one early childhood grade and one middle childhood grade.

2. Select a unit of work you wish to teach in grade six. Work out a complete unit.

3. Select suitable activities for various seasons of the year for each of the six grades.

4. Plan a program of activities to be taught during each of the holiday seasons for one grade of early childhood level and one grade in the middle childhood level. Remember, you must use ingenuity. For example, change the names of games and characters to meet the time selected (i.g., at Halloween play Witches and Goblins instead of Brownies and Fairies).

5. Make up one new game to be used at certain times of the year for each of the first six grades.

SELECTED REFERENCES

BAKER, GERTRUDE, *A Guide for Teaching Health and Physical Education in the Elementary School,* New York, Bureau of Publications, Teachers College, Columbia University, 1946.

DAVIS, ELWOOD, and JOHN LAWTHER, *Successful Teaching in Physical Education,* Englewood Cliffs, N.J., Prentice-Hall, Inc., 1948.

EVANS, RUTH, and LEO GANS, *Supervision of Physical Education,* New York, McGraw-Hill Book Company, Inc., 1947.

IRWIN, L. W., *The Curriculum in Health and Physical Education,* Dubuque, Iowa, W. C. Brown Company, 1960.

KOZMAN, HILDA, *et al., Methods in Physical Education* (Third edition), Philadelphia, W. B. Saunders Company, 1958.

LaSALLE, DOROTHY, *Physical Education for the Classroom Teacher,* New York, A. S. Barnes and Company, 1937.

LEE, MABEL, *The Conduct of Physical Education,* New York, F. S. Crofts and Company, 1937.

O'KEEFE, PATTRIC RUTH, and ANITA ALDRICH, *Education Through Physical Activities* (Second edition), St. Louis, The C. V. Mosby Company, 1955, Part I.

PITCHFORD, K., "How You Can Become a Master Teacher," *Journal of Health, Physical Education and Recreation,* **31:**30–31 (February 1960).

SALT, E. BENTON, *et al., Teaching Physical Education in the Elementary School* (Second edition), New York, The Ronald Press Company, 1960.

VOLTMER, ELMER, and ARTHUR ESSLINGER, *The Organization and Administration of Physical Education* (Third edition), New York, Appleton-Century-Crofts, Inc., 1958.

CHAPTER **14**

Full Participation Versus Elimination-Type Activities

DEFINITION OF TERMS

Full Participation

When reference is made to games and activities used in the program of physical education that give opportunity for full participation, the intent is that 100 per cent of the group, each and every child, regardless of his or her skills and techniques, will remain in the game until the time allotment for it in a given period is completed. Full participation, 100 per cent participation, does not mean that each child must expend himself or herself to the fullest every minute of the time. This would be most dangerous for the health of the child.

Elimination-Type Activity

The elimination-type activity refers to activities containing rules which make it necessary for a child to stop playing the game when he is caught by "It," hit by the ball, or put out by such other means as the rules of the game may demand. The objection to this type of activity is that too many of the games prevent extensive participation on the part of all children.

Each period of activity should give every child the fun he desires; allow him to participate as long as the game continues and he is physically fit to play; keep him a part of the group and not send him away from it; aid him to develop desirable skills and techniques; teach him to get along with his peers, to be a good sport, to know himself as he is, and to give him a chance to improve. These objectives are possible only if the child *continues to participate* with his peers. The law of learning, "We learn by doing," is as necessary in physical education as in any part of the curriculum.

If he is eliminated from a game because he is a slow runner and is caught by "it," has not mastered good mind and muscle coordination in dodging and darting away from a ball, cannot catch a ball well, or lacks other skills and techniques—when will he learn these? Will he continue to like to play with his group or will he find rationalizations and excuses to stay away from the play period? "I have a headache; may I stay inside today?" "Mother said I should not run and play today because I was sick last night." It is well to analyze the results of elimination-type activities.

EFFECTS OF ELIMINATION

It must be remembered first of all that children are by nature active and crave activity. They should be permitted to play and not be eliminated because of certain rules of games.

How will the eliminated child react? What will he do? How will he learn? How will he be looked upon by his group? Will he be wanted or rejected? What will his attitude be regarding the activity and, perhaps, play in general? Will this create any problems for the teacher?

All people, especially children, want to be liked, accepted, and wanted by their peers. All children and individuals differ. They differ in stature, looks, color, likes and dislikes, mentality, physical coordination, and in many other characteristics. Factors of individual differences are accepted in the general over-all education of children, and provisions are made to meet them. The same practices should be part of our physical education programs.

A child cannot be taught or helped if he is eliminated from an activity. If he cannot read his part when in the reading circle, he is not sent away from the group. Why then must he stop playing because he has skills and techniques which are not as well developed as others in his group? If he is stopped, the teacher can give him no help nor can he help himself. Learning ceases and different reactions occur.

Effects on Attitudes

The reactions of children who are eliminated from games and play will differ just as surely as the children differ. It may make one seek attention in an undesirable way. He may create a behavior problem for the teacher to try to solve. He will strive to gain attention as his way to have fun and perhaps take the teacher's time and attention away from the group from which he was eliminated.

Another child may withdraw completely. She feels bad. She knew she couldn't run as fast as many. Now it has been proved to her and she knows she'll never be like her classmates.

Still a third child may be able to cover up his disappointment and remain interested in the activity and vow he'll do better once he gets back in—if he does.

Sam blames his elimination on someone else who got in his way. John says, "They do not play fair and I do not want to play with them, anyway." Nancy admits she never did like to play ball.

There may be as many different reactions as there are children. Some will dislike the activity and find excuses for not participating when it is used as a part of the program again. When the opportunity to choose an activity for the group arises, these games will not be mentioned by those who have less ability than their peers.

Effects on Learning

All persons learn by doing. Surely no one will argue that this law of learning is incorrect. All persons will not learn the same amount or at the same speed, but if activities for a given group are correctly chosen to meet its needs, interests, and abilities, there will be learning situations in each one. If the child starts to participate and is not permitted to continue, will he learn by doing?

Learning may be aided through repetition. If a child is out, and therefore not permitted to participate, will he learn? Where will the repetition come in? He is not going to stand off by himself and practice catching a ball off a fence while his playmates are playing together. He will not run up and down the sidelines to increase his speed. Mary cannot practice keeping her eye on the ball and then dodging, jumping, or running away from it when there is no game in which she may play.

Some may ask, "Why are these activities not good ways to teach the child we are not all alike? They will have to find it out when they go out into the world." The answer perhaps calls attention to the fact that there is a correct time and place for this to be learned. During childhood, when there is much to be derived and desired in the education of children through play, their differences should not by publicized by eliminating them from an activity.

Publicized Differences

The child who needs the activity and comradeship of his peers, to gain confidence in himself and to develop certain skills, may be the first eliminated from the activity. It paves the way for classmates to note extreme differences in certain children. When the time comes to choose or elect squads or teams, the child with the lesser ability may be rejected. The majority does not want him or her in their squad. Thus the child's differences are exaggerated and he is more unhappy and emotionally upset.

Some of these elimination-type activities need not be deleted from the program. Instead, rules may be changed and they may remain an accepted part of the physical education program.

EXAMPLES OF ELIMINATION-TYPE ACTIVITIES AND SUGGESTED CHANGES

For discussion and illustration purposes three types of games will be used which contain rules for eliminating players. In each activity, changes will be suggested showing how these games may continue to be used by deleting the elimination element. When the teacher understands them it will be easy to spot games of an elimination nature and to make the necessary changes before teaching them in order to insure full participation of the children. There is no objection to changing the rules in any activity excepting standard rules for highly organized team games such as Soccer, Volleyball, Basketball, Baseball, and the like. If situations arise when the rules of these must be modified in any way, children should be definitely informed of these changes and why they are necessary.

⤜⤛

DOG CATCHER—A GAME OF LOW ORGANIZATION

The rules of Dog Catcher, a running and tagging game, direct each child in the class to choose the name of a dog. One person is "It" and receives the name of dog catcher. There are two safety goals or kennels to which the dogs may run. All dogs stand at one end of the rectangular play area in one kennel. The dog catcher takes his place midway between the two kennels.

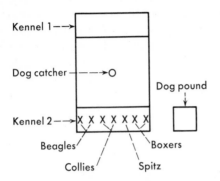

Figure 14–1. Dog Catcher.

The dog catcher calls the name of one breed of dog. Players who have selected this name run and try to reach the other kennel at the opposite end of the play area without being tagged. All dogs tagged by the dog catcher are placed in the imaginary dog pound. The pound is a small square marked outside of the regular playing area. The dog catcher then calls another breed of dog from the first kennel, tags all he can, and places them in the pound. This continues until all the dogs from the first kennel are either in the pound or have successfully reached the second kennel. Dogs are then called back to the first kennel—one breed at a time—and as each dog is tagged he goes to the pound. The last remaining dog who is not tagged is the winner. He becomes the new dog catcher if another game is to be played; the rest of the children may choose new breeds.

It is quite possible that some children will only have one chance to run the length of the play area during the game. Some will undoubtedly be tagged the first time they attempt to run to a new kennel and will be placed in the dog pound where they remain until the game is completed. Their activity and participation will have consisted of one minute or less. What do they learn? Do they have fun? How can the rules of this game be changed to permit all children to remain in it?

A SUGGESTED CHANGE TO AVOID ELIMINATION

The following is one suggested change. Others are possible. Eliminate the dog pound. Permit the children to decide how many times or chances the dog catcher may have. They may agree on three turns. He may call collies and tag two. These two do *not* go in the dog pound since there is none. They merely give the dog catcher two points and remain with the group in the game. The second time the dog catcher may call beagle hounds and catch two more. His score is now four. The two caught remain in play. For his third and last turn he may call "all the dogs in the kennel." If he does, all dogs must run. The dog catcher may feel he has a chance to tag more if he calls them all at one time. If he tags three this third time, these three are added to his original score of four and his total score would be seven. Then another dog catcher would be chosen in a way designated by the class and the game played again. By the use of this one suggested change, all the children in the group participate from the beginning to the end of the play time. A winner may be declared from among the dog catchers by the number each tagged. The one who tagged the most would be declared the winner. Other winners may consist of all those who were never tagged.

Thus, with this change, the game ceases to be of the elimination type. Children have fun, they use their imagination, gain skill in running and tagging, learn sportsmanship— how to tag and to admit when tagged, and have a lot of fun with total participation of the group.

COFFEE AND TEA—A CLASSROOM GAME

Coffee and Tea is a classroom game whose written rules make it an elimination-type game. Directions for playing it are as follows. On the floor in the classroom two or four areas, each about 3 feet wide, are marked off with chalk. An even number of areas are marked "tea" and "coffee." To start the game all children move around the room by either walking, hopping, skipping, or any way they choose or are directed. The teacher or leader claps hands at intervals and this is the signal for all children to *stop moving.* Each child who is standing in an area marked coffee or tea is eliminated and must take his seat. The game continues until there is only one child left. This last child is declared the winner.

Undoubtedly the first clap will eliminate at least one child and maybe four, depending on the number of marked areas. That constitutes their fun and activity for a period of probably 10 to 15 minutes or until the game ends. These children who are no longer playing may become restless in their seats, cause excess noise, and create a problem for the teacher.

A SUGGESTED CHANGE TO AVOID ELIMINATION

One way to change the game and use it for maximum fun and activity for the entire group is to allow all the children to remain in the game regardless of whether they are standing in a coffee or tea "pot" when the leader claps hands. They will, however, keep their score. A score of one point is made each time a child is standing in a pot when the leader claps hands. The object of the game is to get the lowest score. The persons with no score would be the winners of the game. If the game is played this way, the length of time desired to play it may be established. Even if it is to be used for only five minutes before changing to another activity, it is justifiable because all children have had participation and fun for the entire time.

DODGE BALL—A TEAM GAME

Dodge Ball is a popular game and may be played many ways. Intermediate and upper grades often like to have competition among squads. Many times it is used in this way and eliminates children as they are hit. Organization of the game places one group in a circle

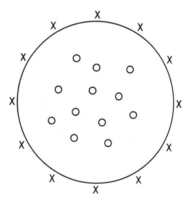

X   Denotes throwing team
O   Denotes dodging team

Figure 14–2. Dodge Ball.

surrounded by the other groups. The team which forms the circle has a volleyball or an inflated ball of similar size and weight. At the signal "Go," the captain throws the ball at a person in the center. The object is to hit the players in the circle with the ball. When a player is hit by the ball he is eliminated from the circle and from the game until all of his teammates have been hit. When only one player remains in the circle, he makes his team's score. A point is counted for each throw it takes to hit him. If 12 throws are made before he is hit, the score of the team which started in the center is 12. The throwing team then goes in the circle made by those who were eliminated. They make their score in the same manner. If it takes 15 throws to hit their last player, their score is 15 and they win the game.

Probably the first throw will eliminate some child. What fun will he have? What will he learn? Will he learn to keep his eye on a moving ball and to jump or dodge it any better? It is true he will have an opportunity to throw the ball at the other team, but there are ways the game may be changed to provide each child with an equal amount of time to practice dodging and running away from a moving ball as well as time to practice throwing it.

A SUGGESTED CHANGE TO AVOID
ELIMINATION

Start the game in the usual manner, but agree on a specific length of time for each team or group to remain in the circle. Perhaps a three-minute period will be chosen. Instead of eliminating players as they are hit, all players will remain in the circle for the entire three minutes. The captain of the thowing team or squad is responsible for keeping count of the number of hits his team makes. He calls each hit a point and keeps his score *aloud*. Every child knows at all times what the score is. All children are playing all of the time. Since time is an element, there is little ball hogging—which wastes time. There is team cooperation. If a ball leaves the circle, one child recovers it and throws it to a teammate. This saves time and gives them more chances to hit players. The score of the throwing team is the number of hits made during the three minutes of play. Teams then exchange places, and another three-minute period is used. Score is kept the same way. At the end of the last three-minute period the win-ning team is the one which earned the highest score by hitting the most players.

Notice in the suggested rule changes that all children play all of the time. No one is eliminated. Playing for time gives more incentive for good teamwork. The score is not dependent on one person who is already tired and may overdo in running, jumping, and dodging in order to make a high score for his team. Thus the activity continues to be a team game and is worthy of a place in the program. Skills and techniques involve throwing at a moving target, catching, running, jumping, and dodging. Each is repeated many times. No one player is the star. The entire team cooperates. It is fun and the total group participates all the time.

From the discussion of these three different games, with rules which make them the elimination type, and the suggested changes made to maintain participation for all children during the entire game, teachers will be able to spot games of the elimination type at once when planning their programs. It is recommended that they make the necessary changes to insure full participation of their group and avoid eliminating children from an activity. The first child eliminated may need the activity and fun the most. By avoiding the use of elimination-type games the tendency to show individual differences in children's abilities to the entire group is lessened. Such children will have less tendency to dislike the play period and physical education. Each child will have a chance to play and practice and to become better in skills and techniques. Full participation will aid in giving the social and psychological incentives and understandings needed to develop as normal individuals. A happy, healthy learning situation should exist at all times.

QUESTIONS AND PRACTICAL PROBLEMS

1. Select six games for the early childhood grades and six for middle childhood grades which are of the elimination nature. Make necessary rule changes so all children will be permitted to play during the entire game.

2. State the social, emotional, physical, and psychological characteristics of the children in each age and grade level and show how eliminating children from activities may affect them.

3. Comment on this statement: "Joy and satisfaction accompany success and are desired emotional responses." Relate this to various types of activities in the physical education program.

4. How may various types of elimination activities influence behavior patterns in children? How may these behavior patterns change when the types of activities are changed? Give examples.

5. Cite ten examples of how a child's ability may be the specific cause for him to be eliminated from certain games and activities. May this change his entire attitude toward play and recreation?

6. Do you agree that progress is apt to be more rapid and pleasurable when a child gains satisfaction and fun from it and through his experience? Defend your stand.

7. May unpleasant experiences created in elimination-type activities tend to affect the health of the child? What are some? Explain fully.

SELECTED REFERENCES

BUCHER, CHARLES A., *Methods and Materials in Physical Education and Recreation,* St. Louis, The C. V. Mosby Company, 1954.

COWELL, CHARLES C., and HELEN HAZELTON, *Curriculum Designs in Physical Education,* Englewood Cliffs, N.J., Prentice-Hall, Inc., 1955, Chapters 2 and 3.

FRANK, LAWRENCE, and MARY FRANK, *How to Help Your Child in School,* New York, Viking Press, 1950.

LAMBERT, CLARA, *Play: A Child's Way of Growing Up,* New York, Play Schools Association, 1947.

LASALLE, DOROTHY, *Guidance of Children Through Physical Education* (Second edition), New York, The Ronald Press Company, 1957.

MURSELL, JAMES L., *Psychology for Modern Education,* New York, W. W. Norton and Company, Inc., 1952, Chapters 5 and 6.

STEPHEN, ADA DAWSON, *Providing Developmental Experiences for Young Children,* New York, Bureau of Publications, Teachers College, Columbia University, 1952.

CHAPTER 15

The Early Morning, Noon-Hour, and After-School Programs

The consolidation of schools, in many cases, means that students are transported to school in the morning and back home in the late afternoon. They remain in school all day.

Many times the same buses are used two or three times to transport children to school in the morning and again to return them to their homes in the late afternoon. Because of this, children arriving on the first or second morning bus usually have from one-half to one hour free before school opens. This is a wonderful time for them to engage in physical activities that are carry-overs from the physical education program. Today, many teachers and principals are successfully and happily removing a one-time disciplinary headache with happy, worthy, leisure-time activities for their "early morning children." Free time may be filled in the same way for those children who are waiting after school to be transported home by the second or third bus; again, physical activities may occupy the time creatively.

It takes no more teachers to supervise these programs before and after school than it does to keep the children orderly when they are not occupied and to solve problems created because of this inactivity. The same planning applied to the noon-hour program will work successfully, including the sectioning of the playground.

Today, it is also true that many children remain in school during the entire day because both parents are working and no one is home during the noon hour. Other children, though not transported, may remain in school all day because of physical reasons. Some children, also, desire to remain during the noon hour for fun and comradeship and there are others whose parents find it psychologically sound for them to stay at school because they will eat a better lunch and more of the correct foods when they see their friends eating them.

Thus, the schools, because of several factors, have many children all day and, if they are doing a good educational job, they are challenged to plan, administer, and supervise programs of activities during the early morning, the noon-hour, and late afternoon that meet the needs, interests, and abilities of the children. Children like activity. Educators, doctors, and psychologists appear to agree that the child in elementary school needs from two to five hours of physical activity per day. Some of it may well be gained during morning, noon-hour, and after-school programs that meet the objective of worthy use of leisure time.

THE EARLY MORNING PROGRAM

When the first buses unload their passengers, students should be permitted to take their personal belongings to a safe place for storage. Leaders should be permitted to obtain the equipment needed for their fun and participation, and, within a period of five to ten minutes, all should be engaged in activities of their choice on the playground.

The areas of the playground may be designated for use as indicated in the discussion on the noon-hour program. Many times, however, larger areas may be used if there are not as many children as at noon.

Some teachers or administrators are present when the first buses arrive. They should arrange for equipment to be used and supervise the playground. Squad leaders, bus captains, and safety leaders should assist and readily assume responsibility when organized and correctly informed as to their duties. Through careful organization, only certain students will necessarily be charged with the responsibility of getting equipment. These leaders may remain active for several months, making the organization simple and changes relatively few.

THE NOON-HOUR PROGRAM

In relation to the total health of the child, one may reasonably ask if it is physically sound and beneficial for children to eat and then immediately start vigorous physical activity? According to good health standards, it is certainly not advisable for a child to use five or ten minutes to hurriedly gulp his lunch and immediately rush to the playground and engage in vigorous activity.

During the noon hour there should be sufficient time to eat followed by some relaxation and fun such as quiet table games, group singing, listening to music, or the like, before the children plunge wholeheartedly into a program of strenuous activities. If children know the noon-hour plan, they will find it unnecessary to eat in haste, and this period may and should be pleasant, socially acceptable, relaxing, healthful, and a worthy social and educational experience.

Planning for the noon hour must be done both for clear weather when the playground and all outdoor facilities may be used and for rainy days when only indoor facilities are available. Children, representing leaders from each class, should definitely assist in all planning and organization for the noon hour. They have good ideas, can see problems and help solve them, work well as leaders for small- and large-group activities, make fine officials for games, and help make the noon-hour assignment a happy occasion for the teacher in charge rather than a police duty without the privilege of the night stick. This group of teachers and children could well be named "The Planning Committee."

If the physical education program is adequate, there can be much carry-over from it to the noon-hour activities. A sufficiently large number of activities should be planned to interest all children.

Each teacher should assume the responsibility for assisting children in her class to plan and organize the activities they wish to engage in during the noon hour. In so doing, less teacher supervision on the playground is needed. The greatest responsibility should be given to the student leaders in each grade. They are capable and accept it well. The authors know this is possible through experience in the elementary grades from kindergarten through eighth grade.

Activities for Clear Weather

For the noon-hour program during clear weather, individual activities for children should include the use of all play apparatus such as merry-go-rounds, slides, jungle gyms, and swings. Also among the individual and dual activities should be such games as Marbles, Ring Toss, Hopscotch, and Jump Rope. If these activities are planned, they may well be self-directed by the participants. If more children desire to use the stationary apparatus than the amount of equipment allows, a time schedule may very conveniently be planned. For example, the first grade could use it from 12:30 P.M. to 12:45 P.M., the second grade from 12:45 P.M. to 1:00 P.M., and so on. A schedule may also be planned for grades to use the apparatus on alternate days. Some children will be interested in games which use equipment such as Dodge Ball, Stealing Sticks, and Stand Ball. These games may be directed by responsible student leaders.

Girls, in particular, may desire circle games, singing games, and folk dances while the older group of boys and girls may be interested in tournaments in Bat Ball, Kick Ball, and other team games which can be played within the given area. When possible, it is desirable to offer, during the noon hour, activities which may not be a regular part of the physical education program. These might include such games as Shuffleboard, Croquet, Table Tennis, Tether Ball, Deck Tennis, Parchesi, or Dominoes.

Activities for Inclement Weather

Rainy weather plans call for use of table games, classroom games, and gymnasium and playroom activities. Auditorium programs which include singing, skits, motion pictures, listening to good radio programs, or watching television are also popular. Each teacher should plan to have games such as Lotto, Checkers, Dominoes, Scrabble, and Hearts in her room ready for use during a rainy noon-hour program.

Programs in the playroom or gymnasium may include darts, novelty relays, social, folk, and/or square dancing. Classroom activities could include ring-toss games, blackboard games, rhythms, hunting games, and magic games. Many pencil and paper games are also fun and usable in the classroom.

Planning a program of activities for the noon hour must be done well in advance so that one is ready for any type of weather.

Efficient Use of the Play Area

Sectioning the playground into areas for various groups to use in their play is most important. With more children on the playground during this period than at any other time, good organization and planning and sectioning of areas is imperative if accidents are to be avoided and if chaos is not to be the order of the hour.

Space limitations automatically make certain activities impossible and impractical. Children who help with the planning can understand this very well and can help their group to accept it. This will prevent an antagonistic attitude and belligerence on the part of those who cannot play the games they wish and will keep them from doing such things as interfering with other groups. The spirit of cooperation and sharing, giving and taking, thought and respect for others may all be taught in this plan of action.

Points to bear in mind in the sectioning of play areas for various groups depend on such factors as nearness to street or road; fenced or unfenced playground; stationary apparatus such as swings, slides, jungle gyms, and sand boxes; the number of children to use the area at one time; and the actual space available.

The area near the stationary apparatus should be used only for quiet nonrunning games and activities such as marbles, hopscotch, ring toss, and rope jumping. This will, for example, keep a child who is fleeing "It" in a running-tagging game from running directly into the path of a swing. The same danger would exist with a child chasing a ball if such games were played near this area.

Games using balls should be played in fenced-in areas or in areas as far away from the road or street as possible to avoid having them fly in the street. This automatically lessens the danger of children dashing into the street to recover equipment. All safety rules must be well established and understood and *one* person in each group should be designated to recover equipment which goes in the street, road, bushes, or in dangerous places. An example of playground sectioning is shown in Figure 15–1.

The areas may be marked with red markers fastened on rubber standards so children cannot get hurt if they fall on them, or by using white slaked lime, which will not harm the eyes. If lime is used dry and put on very thick it will remain a long time. Areas 6 through 9 may be subdivided to meet the needs and interests of the group. These suggestions do not mean that boys and girls must remain separated in their activities nor does it prevent various age groups from playing together if desired by the children. Any exchange is possible to meet needs and interests but the basic plan must be understood by all children.

The Use of Equipment

The problem of equipment must be discussed and well understood by all children. What may be used? Who is responsible for taking it out and returning it? Some schools make the mistake of permitting no equipment to be used during the noon hour. These schools usually do not plan activities or designate specific areas for various groups to play in, thus causing the teacher in charge of the noon hour to detest the assignment. Children will assume responsibility if the desire to do so is created. They will use equipment carefully and will not abuse it because they realize their noon-hour play will be more fun if they have equipment to use.

Student leaders may be organized and assigned the responsibility of checking out and receiving equipment if the school stores all of it in a central storage room. If each room has some equipment, the student who takes it may merely write his name on the board, indicating what piece or pieces he has taken. When he returns it, his name is erased.

Students should be permitted to use all available equipment needed to play the activities which have been approved by the planning committee for the noon-hour program. Substitutions for some popular games may have to be made. For example, if space does not permit softball for the fifth- and sixth-grade boys, they may have as much fun using all the rules of softball but pitching a volleyball or rubber ball of the appropriate size and using the first to punch it in place of a bat. This will be a safe game for all children

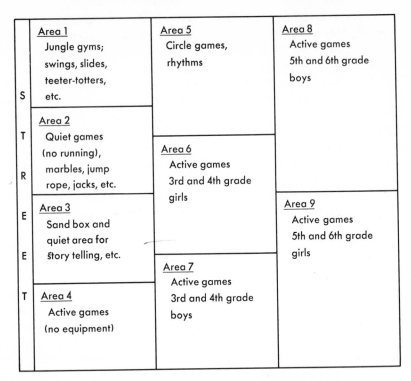

Figure 15–1. Sectional play area for six grades.

playing nearby, will require a smaller space for the diamond, but will meet the interests and needs of the boys for team play and vigorous activity.

Assistance for Teachers

The authors are fully aware of the tremendous task and great responsibility of today's classroom teacher. It is hoped that a general understanding of planning the early morning program, the noon-hour program and the afternoon program will ease a problem for her.

The health of the teacher is important. Administrators should *insist* that each teacher have some time for herself during the day—away from her children. All teachers should not have to be in the cafeteria and/or on the playground during the noon hour. Through proper planning and

scheduling, cooperation of all teachers and supervisors, and the inclusion of students in planning and executing the programs, good programs will be provided and teachers will need to spend less time on duty during the noon hour. The time they do spend will be rewarding as they observe a group of young people truly enjoying themselves under student leadership and gaining valuable educational experiences plus worthy use of leisure time.

The safety club members, Girl Scout and Boy Scout leaders, and leaders chosen by students from each class will answer many problems and needs.

It should be arranged so the teacher assigned noon-hour supervision has an opportunity to eat her lunch and relax either before the period or after coming from noon supervision. This may be handled in many ways. One method would be for a teacher who has a free lunch hour to take the students of the teacher assigned noon-hour supervision either the period before lunch or the period after it. She might use this time with the two classes combined for an art lesson, music, singing, or story-telling program. Thus the teacher assigned to noon-hour supervision would have an opportunity to eat and relax. Perhaps the best solution is a floating teacher and assistance from the supervisors and administrators. No one answer is the solution. If the teachers are permitted to assist in planning the noon-hour program and supervision, it is believed they can reach a workable plan. No teacher should be assigned more than one noon period per week. She needs the other four noon periods to relax in order to be refreshed before meeting her afternoon responsibilities.

The noon-hour program may be beneficial to the teacher if she approaches it with the right attitude. During the noon hour she has a chance to see children in informal situations and get to know them better. She learns more about them, their habits, their sportsmanship, and how they react in various situations. She may use these observations as teaching aids within her own group. She also has an opportunity herself to be out in the fresh air and sunshine.

The noon-hour program is a good time to develop student leadership and followership. The greatest amount of teacher time should be devoted to planning and organization meetings with individual groups and with combined groups when tournaments are desired by the children. This time utilized in organization is well spent and can easily make the noon hour a pleasant experience. Teachers ought to feel the noon-hour program is an integral part of the day.

AFTER-SCHOOL PROGRAMS

Because their buses make several trips, some children must wait for their bus after school. In addition, many children whose parents work and those who walk to school can benefit greatly by a program of activities after the last class. These programs again should be planned by teachers and students.

Those children who return to empty houses, whose parents do not get home from work until 4:30 or 5:00 P.M., would surely be better off playing on the school playground than running and playing unsupervised in dangerous streets. Those who must wait for their buses should also be given the opportunity to have fun.

The Question of Supervision

An after-school program brings up the question of who shall supervise it. Classroom teachers usually have a right to leave at 3:30 P.M. or whenever their class is dismissed. However, the after-school program is important from the standpoint of the child's welfare. A staggered plan of teacher supervision for an after-school program will work and will not be an overly heavy burden on any one teacher. With proper planning and organization, the children will have a joyful and beneficial experience.

Schools which have worthy programs in operation for early morning, the noon hour, and after school have reported finer attitudes and a better spirit of cooperation among the children throughout the entire school day. These schools are helping to meet the needs of the child for physical activity under correct conditions, and the child is enjoying worthy use of leisure time. A mother worries less when her son or daughter has a place to play in the proper environment and in a safe area under the proper leadership.

Playgrounds, apparatus, and equipment should be used after 3:30 P.M. Mothers and fathers, retired teachers, as well as other interested citizens in the community, are often happy to help with the supervision if the school assumes the leadership in community and school planning. This affords the school a good chance for community cooperation. Parent-teacher association groups and mothers' clubs often reveal much interest, willingness, and cooperation in a supervisory capacity.

The programs for after school can be an outgrowth of the physical education program and need not require further teaching.

Hints for Teachers

1. Plan the noon-hour program with the help of students and fellow teachers. Organize a planning committee.

2. Time spent in organization is well worth the effort and pays high dividends in program enjoyment.

3. Be sure that the equipment and apparatus used are in safe condition.

4. Plan play areas with the understanding and cooperation of all children and fellow workers. Nothing is worse than bickering about play space.

5. Accept the noon hour as a real educational experience for the children. Make it a worth-while experience.

6. Use the extra hour programs to learn more about the individual students.

7. Be proud of your part in the program. Do not grudgingly give of your time.

8. Use activities taught in physical education for the early morning, noon-hour, and after-school programs.

9. Be sure all children understand the three W's. *What* are the objectives of the program? *Why* are certain rules and regulations necessary? *When* may they use certain apparatus and equipment?

10. Understanding usually leads to cooperation.

11. Build character and sportsmanship during the early morning, noon-hour, and after-school programs.

12. Develop leadership and followership.

13. Plan well in advance. Both short-term and long-term planning are desirable and necessary.

14. Enjoy the period and your children.

15. Be prepared for rain as well as clear weather.

EVALUATION OF PROGRAMS

To ascertain whether the early morning, noon-hour, and after-school programs are meeting sound educational objectives, these points may be used for evaluation:

1. Activities are diversified to meet the needs, interests, and abilities of all.

2. Children are entering wholeheartedly into the activities with no coercion from leaders or teachers.

3. There is a genuinely happy spirit at all times.

4. There is a good social and group relationship.

5. There is much physical activity for all who are capable and desire it.

6. Cooperation and sportsmanship prevail.

7. Problems which arise are used as means of educating the children in democratic ways of solving them.

8. Children are accepting the role of leadership.

9. As the program progresses, more children desire to participate.

10. You hear happy discussion and comments among the children.

QUESTIONS AND PRACTICAL PROBLEMS

1. You are the teacher in charge of the early morning program in a school. Develop plans and steps you would use in the organization of a planning committee composed of teachers and students.

2. Set up a noon-hour program of activities for grades one through six (one class in each grade), suitable for play on a playground of approximately 1 acre of land. Each class consists of 35 children. There is no playground apparatus available. Show by diagram where the various groups of children would play and what activities might be used in each area. Students in the class should work on different size play areas and with different numbers of children.

3. Plan specifically the responsibility you would wish each student leader to assume for the noon hour. How would you work with these leaders? How would you seek to gain the full cooperation of the other children with the leaders?

4. You are a teacher in a school where the administration arbitrarily sets up and distributes copies of the noon-hour assignment for teachers. These consist of one-week assignments with no chance for a teacher to have any personal time during that week. One teacher is in charge of the primary grades and one of the intermediate grades. Organize a democratic plan of action with constructive suggestions for improving the plight of the classroom teacher and making her more receptive to the assignment.

5. How would you organize a program of after-school activities? Would you recommend that citizens in the community assist? If so, organize a specific plan of action. If you believe the teacher should assume the entire responsibility, defend your stand.

SELECTED REFERENCES

BUCHER, CHARLES A., *Methods and Materials in Phyiscal Education and Recreation,* St. Louis, The C. V. Mosby Company, 1954.

EVANS, RUTH, "The Noon Hour in Elementary Education," *Children in Focus,* 1954 Yearbook of the American Association for Health, Physical Education and Recreation, Washington, D.C., American Association for Health, Physical Education and Recreation, 1955, p. 213.

FISCHER, CARL, "Trends in Physical Education in the Elementary School," *Elementary School Journal,* 2:88 (October 1953).

KOZMAN, HILDA, ROSALIND CASSIDY, and

CHESTER JACKSON, *Methods in Physical Education* (Third edition), Philadelphia, W. B. Saunders Company, 1958.

LAPORTE, WILLIAM R., *The Physical Education Curriculum* (A National Program), Los Angeles, Parker and Company, 1951, p. 70.

McCOOE, DAVID, and CLIFFORD HUTCHINSON, "An Experiment in Noon-Time Recreation," *Journal of Health, Physical Education and Recreation,* 22:26 (October 1951).

NIELSON, N. P., and WINIFRED VAN HAGEN, *Physical Education for Elementary Schools* (Revised edition), New York, The Ronald Press Company, 1956, p. 38.

CHAPTER **16**

Tournaments for Middle Childhood Grades

COMPETITION

The recommendations of the Joint Committee in Athletics for Children of Elementary, Junior and High School Ages[1] point out that sports days and play days serve the competitive and social needs of children. Children of elementary school age are not sufficiently developed physically or emotionally, according to many medical experts, to withstand the stresses of keen competition and rivalry. Psychology, safety, and economy are the factors that *legislate directly against* strenuous competitive activities for the elementary school child.

The child who is growing rapidly is not physically developed to stand the stress and strain of highly organized competition. In some activities, he may receive injuries of the bones, ligaments, or other parts of the body which can cause permanent harm.

Neither are children of elementary school ages ready for team games of high organization. Many rules and complicated, intricate skills are better able to be developed later on as children grow and mature. They should not be expected to master these in their early years.

These children in the elementary school do not demand highly organized competi-

tion. All they seek is participation. Many children are forced into strenuous competition of highly organized team games such as football, basketball, and baseball. Competent leadership for all physical activity is essential. Leaders should place the child's interests and his welfare above all else and not expose him to programs of competition recommended only for older youth.

The program of physical education in the elementary school should be based on sound education principles and confine its work with children to wholesome, well-planned activities and not try to gain recognition in the rough field of highly organized competition. This should be something to work toward as the child matures and becomes physically, emotionally, socially, and psychologically ready for such an experience.

It is believed, however, that intramural competition, in selected activities which have been well planned and controlled, aids in building social status in a group. The child learns to cooperate and not to depend solely on himself. He learns to accept success and defeat. He learns his abilities and limitations.

These worthy experiences may be gained through participation in games which give challenge to better skills and performance because of individual desire rather than through stress from an outsider to win. Such

[1] Joint Committee in Athletics for Children of Elementary, Junior and High School Ages, "Desirable Athletics for Children," *The Journal of Health, Physical Education and Recreation,* **23**:2 (June 1952).

178

games and programs give every child a chance to play rather than just approximately 10 per cent of the "top notchers" who benefit from highly organized competitive sports programs.

Children are being prepared for good adult living when they can accept competition and cooperation because this is the basis of our democracy. Hence, the right kind of competition, well planned and organized, carefully supervised, and open to all regardless of ability has proved helpful for elementary children. Accepted kinds of competition would include intramural activities that are outgrowths of the regular physical education program such as Kick Ball, Bat Ball, and Newcomb. They would also include various types of recreational, individual, and dual activities, such as marbles, hopscotch, shuffleboard, croquet, quoit pitching, and the like. Sports days and play days are recommended within a given school, or for an occasional invitation to a nearby school. For these purposes a knowledge and understanding of the types of tournaments and how they may be organized is essential.

TYPES OF TOURNAMENTS

The most popular and successfully used tournaments include the round-robin, the ladder, the pyramid, the elimination, and the double elimination. These will be discussed separately. Examples will be used to show how they may be utilized either alone or in combination to promote desired interest, learning, and satisfaction.

The Round-Robin Tournament

The round-robin tournament is set up so each team, squad, unit, or individual has an opportunity to play with all others in the tournament play. If there are six groups or six individuals who wish to participate, a round-robin tournament would be organized by using the steps shown in Table 16–1.

To make the organization of the tournament relatively easy, and to insure that each team or individual is scheduled to play with all five, begin by matching all participants against number *one*.

The number of steps necessary is determined by the number of groups competing—for example, ten groups would require nine steps. There is always one less step than the total number of participants.

When all participants have been matched through the step process, it is then possible to plan the tournament schedule. It must be decided whether each participant will play each day, two times a week, or once each week. Time, space, facilities, and equipment will be the determining factors.

To avoid error, as the actual schedule is being planned each combination listed in the five steps should be crossed out or checked as soon as it is scheduled.

An example of a round-robin tournament with six contestants, groups, or individuals scheduled to play each day is shown in Figure 16–1.

The same organization may be used for schedules other than daily ones. It could be used for play two or three times a week or on a weekly basis.

A round-robin tournament with six groups or individuals affords an opportunity for each to play five games. In order to declare a winner, the tournament may award each contestant three points for winning, two for tie games, and nothing for a loss.

TABLE 16–1. *The Round-Robin Tournament*

Step	Matching	Explanation
I	1 vs. 2 1 vs. 3 1 vs. 4 1 vs. 5 1 vs. 6	The completion of this step assures the organizer that number *one* is scheduled to play all others. In a tournament with six contestants or teams, it means each one will play five games.
II	2 vs. 3 2 vs. 4 2 vs. 5 2 vs. 6	Notice that this step starts with number *two* since *two* is already scheduled to play *one* in the first step. Number *two* is now assured that he is scheduled for five games.
III	3 vs. 4 3 vs. 5 3 vs. 6	Step three starts with the number *three* and, when completed, number *three* is scheduled in five games.
IV	4 vs. 5 4 vs. 6	Step four starts with number *four* and *four* is scheduled to play his five games.
V	5 vs. 6	As the illustration has shown, the step number and the number of the team corresponds each time.

The round-robin tournament is most popular. It is the fairest, as it permits all participants an equal chance to play. It maintains interest because all who start participate to the end. The only objection to it is the time element. If one has a short time for tournament play, it may not be possible to use it.

If there should be ten teams or individuals who wish to participate in a tournament, it is advantageous to divide the group. For example, teams numbering one through five could play together and numbers six through ten would play in another tournament. A winner could be declared in each group. If a single winner is desired, the winners from the two groups would be matched to play each other. A three-game match is desirous over a single game and the best out of three games would declare one winner. For example, if number five won in the first group and eight in the second, numbers five and eight would participate with each other to determine a grand winner.

A round-robin tournament with an uneven number of teams or individuals makes it impossible for each participant to play every day of tournament play. This fact will not mean that the children lose interest. Round-robin tournaments afford good opportunity for teamwork and aid in developing skills and techniques. They provide much fun and cooperative competition.

The Ladder Tournament

The ladder tournament is planned as follows. Contestants' names are placed on rungs of a ladder made of oaktag. The exchange of names is made very easy if the contestants' names are written on a piece of oaktag longer than the width of the ladder itself. At the end of each rung on the ladder

Day	Date	Place	Time	Winner	Points
Monday					
1 vs. 4		Play area #1		#4	3
2 vs. 5	May 6	Play area #2	3:00 P.M.	#2	3
3 vs. 6		Play area #3		#3	3
Tuesday					
5 vs. 6		Play area #1		#6	3
3 vs. 4	May 7	Play area #2	3:30 P.M.	#4	3
1 vs. 2		Play area #3		#2	3
Wednesday					
2 vs. 4		Play area #1		#4	3
3 vs. 5	May 8	Play area #2	3.00 P.M.	#3	3
1 vs. 6		Play area #3		#6	3
Thursday					
4 vs. 5		Play area #1		#5	3
2 vs. 6	May 9	Play area #2	3:00 P.M.	#2	3
1 vs. 3		Play area #3		#3	3
Friday					
2 vs. 3		Play area #1		#3	3
4 vs. 6	May 10	Play area #2	3:30 P.M.	#5	3
1 vs. 5		Play area #3		#1	3

Contestants scoring

Number 1 = 3 points

Number 2 = 9 points

Number 3 = <u>12 points</u> = <u>Winner</u>

Number 4 = 9 points

Number 5 = 6 points

Number 6 = 6 points

Figure 16–1. Round-robin tournament with six contestants.

a slit is made and the name tags are slipped in the slits and remain in place. They are then ready to compete with each other. If eight players wish to participate, the ladder would contain eight rungs. Eight is a recommended number for each ladder. If there are more participants, more ladders should be planned.

Contestants receive their place on the rungs of the ladder by having their names drawn from a box. The first name drawn

Rung	
1	Dunn
2	Regan
3	Gross
4	Scarpa
5	Mazzoni
6	Thomas
7	Scott
8	Saric

Figure 16–2. Ladder tournament, eight players.

should be placed on rung number one, the second on rung number two, and so on until each contestant receives a place on the ladder.

The rules of the tournament should be agreed on by the contestants and be well understood before play begins. This type of tournament is usually given a time limit. It may operate for one month—from April to May, for example. The object, of course, is to be on the top rung May 1.

Players may advance to rung one by challenging the person directly above them or two rungs above. A contestant may never skip more than one rung. A winner automatically exchanges his name with the loser.

Each person must accept challenges. No one may challenge the same player twice in succession. For example, if number *three* challenged number *two* and won, he would automatically move up to the second rung and *two* would go down to the third rung. *Three* may not immediately rechallenge *two*. He must play number *one*. If he loses to number *one,* he may then rechallenge *two*. The players themselves make this tournament work. The opportunity of being able to challenge either directly above or two rungs above avoids lack of interest for persons who do not win. It is surprising to see how many times places are exchanged in a given length of time in this type of tournament. Rules may be changed to permit contestants to challenge three rungs above them if desired by the group and more than eight may be on a ladder. The important thing is to establish rules before tournament play begins and for each contestant to understand them thoroughly. The ladder tournament may be used either for individual or dual activities or for team games. It is, however, most popular for the former, as fewer persons are involved and two or four contestants can easily agree on a time to play, while 16 or 20 team members must have their

dates and times scheduled in advance so they may plan their time accordingly. Space and facilities also make this necessary.

Regarding the use of equipment, space, and facilities for the participants of the ladder tournament, it is recommended that when the first two contestants are ready to set a time and date for a match they enter this on a tournament schedule sheet posted by the ladder. Other challengers will be guided accordingly.

If there are many contestants, several ladders may be used. The same rules apply. If there are 24 contestants, for example, there could be three ladders composed of eight contestants each. At the close of the scheduled playing time, the players on the top rung of the three ladders would each have won in their respective groups. If a grand winner is desired, the three may play in a round-robin tournament.

The Pyramid Tournament

A pyramid tournament is similar to a ladder tournament. All names of contestants, either individual or team, are drawn from a box and placed in pyramid formation. The first names drawn form the base of the pyramid. Figure 16–3 shows a pyramid

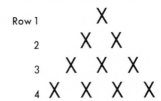

Figure 16–3. Pyramid tournament.

based on ten players, which places four at the base.

Row three is filled next with the names as they are drawn, then row two, and the last person is at the top of the pyramid.

Contestants challenge in the row directly above them and endeavor to be at the top when the time for the closing of the tournament arrives. Names may be moved back and forth as they are in the ladder tournament.

The Elimination Tournament

The elimination tournament is well named. As individuals, couples, or teams compete and lose, they are eliminated.

If there are six players or teams, an elimination tournament would be set up as follows.

The first round consists of three games, as shown in Figure 16–4. Three groups or

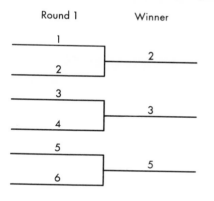

Figure 16–4. First round.

individuals are eliminated and three are left after the first round. Since three is an uneven number, one will draw a *bye*. A *bye* means that this person, couple, or team does not play in the immediate round but will automatically play the winner of that round. It is necessary to arrange for a bye whenever there is an uneven number of starters or winners in a round. It is recommended that the names of the three winners, couples, or teams be placed in a box or hat and thoroughly mixed. A person draws out one name. The name drawn receives the bye. The second

round consists, then, of one game and one bye, as shown in Figure 16–5.

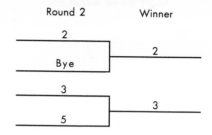

Figure 16–5. Second round.

The third round has but one game, as shown in Figure 16–6.

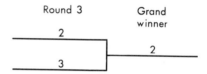

Figure 16–6. Third round.

Hence, you will note number *two* played number *one* in the first round and won. *Two* did not play in the second round because he drew a bye. He played number *three* in the third round and won the tournament.

The elimination tournament is not highly recommended to be used alone. As one can readily see, a team or person has but one chance, and half who start never get a second chance. Interest lags; it is not popular. There are misunderstandings and excuses. The outcome does not necessarily mean that the winning individual, couple, or team is the best. Too much stress is placed on winning and too little on fun and friendly, cooperative play. The one advantage is that little time is required.

This type of tournament is often used to declare a winner when there are three or more winners at the completion of a ladder tournament or a round-robin, as mentioned

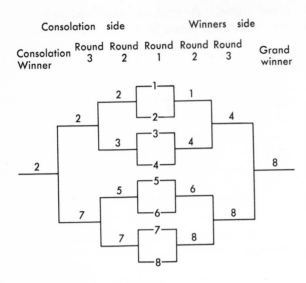

Consolation side   Winners side

| Consolation Winner | Round 3 | Round 2 | Round 1 | Round 2 | Round 3 | Grand winner |

Figure 16–7. Double elimination tournament.

in the previous discussion. For this purpose it can be justified.

The Double Elimination Tournament

A double elimination tournament is preferable to the previous type because all starters play more games. A tournament for eight is diagramed in Fig. 16–7.

Note that the first round is shown in the center and the winners' side is on the right and the losers' on the left. Eight contestants play in the first round, eight in the second, and four in the third. Ten games complete the tournament. In the straight elimination tournament for eight contestants, only seven games are played.

GROUPING INDIVIDUALS FOR TOURNAMENTS

Regardless of the activities used in the intramural program within a school, it is advisable to group individuals and teams on as even a basis as possible. Factors used in determining the groupings should include size, age, skill, sex, and, in many cases, grade level. For example, it would be rare—all things being equal—for a sixth-grade boy to be a fair match for a fourth-grade boy. An exception might be found in an activity such as a marble tournament. Even in that activity it would be advisable to schedule the tournament on a ladder basis for each grade and plan one tournament for girls and another for boys. By doing this, it is easy to declare a winner of each sex by grade. Interest would determine whether a grand winner should be chosen for each grade or for two or more grades.

In the case of team games, tournaments should be planned for those children of the same grade level and not for children from different grade levels. For example, if there are three sixth grades in a school, these three might plan a tournament among their grades. One could not expect the sixth-grade boys to be in fair competition against the eighth-grade boys in a game of Bat Ball or softball.

If there is only one section of each grade in a school and a tournament is desired, a good way to organize the groups would be to have fifth-grade boys who desire to participate sign one sheet. Sixth-grade boys would sign another sheet. The same should be done for the girls. The total number of players would indicate the number of teams possible and should be decided by both the students and the teacher. If the sport or game calls for nine players, the group may decide to place two extra players on a team to play in case illness, absence, or some other reason eliminates a player or two. The total number who have signed for the tournament should then be divided by the number agreed on for each team. For example, if sixty-six had signed and the teacher-pupil group decided that eleven are needed on each team, there would be six teams. All players' names would then be numbered consecutively from one to six and repeated until each player received a number. This would be done for both grades. If the fifth-grade boys' list stopped with number *three,* the first name on the sixth-grade list would start with number *four.* Teams would then be organized by placing all number *ones* on a team, number *twos* on another, number *threes* on a third, and so on to make six teams of eleven players each. The girls may be organized in teams by the same method and would play in a separate tournament.

It is always interesting to note how evenly matched teams become when they are organized in this manner. It is impossible for children to know where to sign in order to stay in a clique and be on the same team, because the number of players agreed necessary for each team decides the final number of teams. It is also good to mix players in this or a similar way so the students from one classroom are not playing against another room. It is a well-known fact that some classroom teachers are more interested in physical education activities than others. Many times children create a dislike for a teacher who in their opinion does not assist them enough or who does not give them as much time as they desire in their physical education program. Competition between two rooms should never be developed. Children should play *with* members of other groups rather than *against* them. The proposed plan is also usable to mix two or more groups of the same grade level for tournaments.

TOURNAMENT HINTS FOR TEACHERS

1. Be sure the children help with all plans.

2. Permit them to choose the activities they desire to use for tournament play.

3. Be sure the grouping is as impartial as possible.

4. Organize all rules and have them well understood before a tournament starts —for example, rescheduling of outdoor activities in case of rain; the least number of players a team may have in order to play; and what happens if a team forfeits.

5. Do not overstress winning. Participation and activity under proper conditions should be the aim. Children should learn to accept defeat graciously.

6. Do not permit winners to become braggarts. Teach them to win graciously.

7. Be sure officials know the rules and are fair, and that players respect the officials and their decisions.

8. Stress playing *with* rather than *against.*

9. Stress teamwork and cooperation.

10. Do not give prizes to winners.

11. Use activities for a tournament which have been taught as a regular part of the physical education program.

12. Plan a variety of individual, dual, or couple activities as well as team participation. Too much emphasis should not be placed on team activities. Marbles, Hopscotch, Shuffleboard, Archery, and the like are very necessary and popular.

13. Plan all ground rules, places for play, and time for schedules before starting any tournament. Be sure all members know these rules and agree to abide by them.

14. Arrange for members of groups to choose their own captains or co-captains. If it is impossible to work with all children in planning tournaments, these captains should represent their group.

15. Make sure the necessary equipment is available and used.

16. Set up all necessary safety precautions regarding the use of equipment, place to play, need for wearing protective equipment such as body protector, mask, and glove when catching in softball, and glass guards for protection of those wearing glasses while playing with balls.

17. Stimulate the group to have good clean fun and to be good sports at all times.

18. Never accept poor sportsmanship.

This should be well understood before a tournament begins and captains should be responsible for their players' conduct. This will aid in developing leadership and followership.

19. Use tournaments only as fun to climax or close an activity at a given time in the program.

20. Make it possible to complete tournaments in a short time. Too long a period finds interest waning and cannot be justified.

21. Remember that tournaments are only interesting, learning experiences—not matters of life or death. Teach and use them accordingly. They will prove happy, valuable educational experiences if properly planned, administered, and executed by educators.

EVALUATION OF TOURNAMENTS

Some means of evaluation is necessary for determining the value of tournaments. The following points would be helpful in making such an evaluation.

1. Are the children thoroughly enjoying the activities?

2. Is there too much competition?

3. Is there too little cooperation?

4. Are children good winners? Good losers?

5. Do the activities meet the needs of the children? Should others be planned?

6. Is there good cooperation and spirit among team members?

7. Are children emotionally stable or is this tournament play overstimulating to them?

8. Is each game a learning experience?

9. Is interest maintained throughout the tournament or does it wane?

10. Are schedules completed or are there many forfeited games and matches?

11. Do children *discuss* their tournament play among themselves or do they *argue* it?

12. What is the reaction of the parents toward the program? Favorable? Unfavorable? Why?

13. Do the children ask for other tournaments?

14. Are all children who wish to play, regardless of their ability, included in the program?

15. Do the children appear to be growing and developing good social qualities and group consciousness through the program?

QUESTIONS AND PRACTICAL PROBLEMS

1. Plan a round-robin tournament for various numbers of teams. Use both even and odd numbers.

2. Set up all necessary rules for successful tournament play in each of the types of tournaments.

3. You are asked to speak at the Parent-Teachers Association meeting on Little League Play. Prepare your talk and substantiate your stand.

4. The boys in the fifth and sixth grades are steaming with enthusiasm to organize an interschool schedule with other schools in the town and nearby areas. How would you go about working out this problem? Be thorough and exact in your planning and be sure you can substantiate your stand.

5. One of the local civic service clubs wishes to donate awards for winners in each tournament you play. What will your stand be? How can you put it in effect without ill feelings?

6. What will be guiding criteria for tournaments in various grade levels? Explain them fully.

7. What are some of recommendations of the joint committee in athletics for children of elementary school age?

8. What types of tournaments are best when maximum participation is desired?

9. List ten hints which teachers should know in regard to tournaments.

10. How can you evaluate the effectiveness of tournament competition?

SELECTED REFERENCES

AMERICAN ASSOCIATION FOR HEALTH, PHYSICAL EDUCATION AND RECREATION, "Report of the President's American Association for Health, Physical Education and Recreation Committee," *Journal of Health, Physical Education and Recreation,* **21**:297 (May 1950).

BROWNELL, CLIFFORD (Editor), *Administrative Problems in Health, Physical Education and Recreation,* Washington, D.C., American Association for Health, Physical Education and Recreation, 1953, pp. 120–121.

BUCHER, CHARLES A., *Methods and Materials in Physical Education and Recreation,* St. Louis, The C. V. Mosby Company, 1954.

"COMPETITIVE SPORTS IN GRADE SCHOOL," *The Foil,* New Jersey Association for Health and Physical Education," 1954, p. 9.

"DESIRABLE ATHLETICS FOR CHILDREN," *Journal of Health, Physical Education and Recreation,* **23**:2 (June 1952).

FISCHER, CARL, "Trends in Physical Education in the Elementary School," *The Elementary School Journal,* **2**:88 (October 1953).

HEIN, FRED, "What Stand Competition," *Children in Focus,* 1954 Yearbook of the American Association for Health, Physical Education and Recreation, Washington, D.C., American Association for Health, Physical Education and Recreation, 1955, p. 159.

HUGHES, WILLIAM L., "The Place of Athletics in the School Physical Education Program," *Journal of Health, Physical Education and Recreation,* **21**:23 (December 1950).

JOINT COMMITTEE ON ATHLETIC COMPETITION FOR CHILDREN OF ELEMENTARY AND JUNIOR HIGH SCHOOL AGES, *Desirable Athletic Competition for Children,* Washington, D.C., American Association for Health, Physical Education and Recreation, 1952.

KOZMAN, HILDA, ROSALIND CASSIDY, and CHESTER JACKSON, *Methods in Physical Education* (Third edition), Philadelphia, W. B. Saunders Company, 1958, pp. 499–500.

LAPORTE, WILLIAM R., *The Physical Education Curriculum* (A National Program), Los Angeles, Parker and Company, 1951, p. 70.

MIEL, ALICE, "Elementary Physical Education," *Proceedings,* 1954, Washington, D.C., National Convention, American Association for Health, Physical Education and Recreation, p. 85.

MILLER, KENNETH, "Let's Quit Exploiting Children's Sports," *Today's Health,* **35**:18 (May 1957).

NIELSON, N. P., and WINIFRED VAN HAGEN, *Physical Education for Elementary Schools* (Revised edition), New York, The Ronald Press Company, 1956, p. 39.

OGAN, ALICE P., "Play Day for the Elementary School," *Journal of Health, Physical Education and Recreation,* **24**:18 (May 1953).

SALT, E. BENTON, B. K. STEVENS, and DORA HICKS, "Planning the Physical Education Program for the Elementary School," *Education,* **75**:82 (October 1954).

SOLOMON, BEN, "Little League—Menace or

Blessing," *Youth Leaders' Digest,* **14:**164 (February 1953).

VANNIER, MARYHELEN and MILDRED FOSTER, *Teaching Physical Education in Elementary Schools* (Third edition), Philadelphia, W. B. Saunders Company, 1963.

CHAPTER 17

Correlation of Physical Education with Other Parts of the Curriculum

The subject-centered curriculum is passé. In recent years curriculum interpretations have been centered on the development of the individual child. Also, the boundaries between subjects are decreasing. It therefore is advisable to consider the correlation of physical education with the entire curriculum rather than merely to teach it as a subject *apart from* over-all educational goals for thirty minutes a day or whatever time is required by state or local regulations. Correlation is an attempt to bring out relationships among the subjects of the curriculum.

THE ROLE OF THE CLASSROOM TEACHER

The classroom teacher is, many times, the person responsible for physical education in her grade. In grades one through six, those considered in this discussion, the self-contained classroom is popular. Since this type of teaching situation is particularly applicable to varying situations and operates on no strict time schedule for subjects, it affords the classroom teacher an excellent opportunity to correlate physical education with the other parts of the educational program.

In schools where teachers have correlated it with their programs much interest is found among the children. It also makes possible a greater understanding of the total physical education program for parents and educators.

Recent Studies on Correlation

Baker, Annis, and Bontz,[1] in their study of physical education in elementary schools, found correlation desirable and stated that the greatest correlation of physical education was with music. Social studies ranked second.

In a survey of 457 classroom teachers in 52 schools in New Jersey, conducted by one of the authors, physical education correlated with other parts of the curriculum as shown in Table 17-1 at the top of the next page.

[1] Gertrude Baker, Elsie Annis, and Jean Bontz, "Supervision of Physical Education in the Elementary Schools," *The Research Quarterly,* **25**:379 (December 1954).

TABLE 17–1. *Correlation of Physical Education with Other Parts of the Curriculum*

Percentage of Teachers Who Correlated Physical Education*	Correlation Subject
36.9	Music
30.4	Health education
14.2	Social studies
11.1	Art

* 7.4 per cent did no correlation.

Teachers in the primary grades showed a greater use of correlation than those in the intermediate grades.

Over 30 per cent of the teachers surveyed asked for help in understanding correlation. Thirty-two per cent said they had received adequate help while in training for teacher education to assist them in understanding how the correlation of physical education with other subjects might be accomplished. Thirty per cent stated correlation was only mentioned in their preparation and 38 per cent said it was not included in any part of their educational programs. These figures may tend to show this as a specific need for persons who are being prepared to teach in the self-contained classroom.

Because of the desirability of correlation this chapter will illustrate ways in which physical education may be correlated with other parts of the curriculum. It will not be exhaustive in the use of examples but should be sufficient for the teacher to understand some ways and means of correlation in the hope that she will use them and be inspired and challenged to plan other ways in her own classroom with her own individual group of children. Some additional sources of ideas may be found in the Selected References.

MEANS OF CORRELATION

Unit Correlation

If the unit of work in the early childhood grades being studied is "The Farm," physical education may become alive and be made a part of it in many ways. By teaching various self-testing activities relating to farm animals, such as the duck walk, the bunny hop, and the dog run, children will have fun, enjoy much physical activity, and the program will be closely correlated to the unit. Interpretative dancing might include high-stepping horses, horses pulling heavy loads, and frolicking calves and colts. Other activities could include dances and singing games such as "Oats, Peas, Beans, and Barley Grow," "Jolly Is the Miller," and "The Farmer in the Dell." Games may include Lame Fox and Chickens, Flowers and the Wind, Dog Catcher, and Squirrels in Trees. Story plays could include "Helping Farmer Brown Gather Eggs," "Going to the Pasture to Bring in the Cows," and "Feeding the Chickens." Cat and Mice and Squirrel and the Nut are examples of classroom games for this particular unit.

A unit of work in social studies being planned or studied in the sixth grade might be the United Nations. Physical education could easily become a real part of this unit through studying about and participating in games and dances of the various member countries of the United Nations. Many schools today are fortunate to have children from various countries. A wise teacher will use these children to assist in the presentation of games, dances, and other physical activities of their native countries.

The two examples of units of work show in a small way how physical education may be correlated with them. The examples are by no means complete. However, through them, the teacher may understand some ways she may make her physical education a part of the total unit. If she does, it will provide more unity and will challenge more meaningful physical education activities. The names of games and activities may be changed to meet the situation.

Specific Subject Correlation

Physical education may be correlated to the various subject fields in the following ways:

Language Arts

Some projects in this area related to physical education are (1) learning names of games and equipment; (2) learning new words—vocabulary and spelling; (3) reading the directions of new games; (4) recording physical education activities on daily individual records; (5) giving oral directions of games and the discussion of the day's activities; and (6) performing pageants, plays, and dramatizations.

Social Studies

Some projects in this area relating to

Figure 17–1. Dances of other countries correlate with social studies.

physical education are (1) studying various manners of play and recreation in different countries; (2) noting environmental conditions in relation to their activities—for example, certain activities are possible and desirable because of weather and the general climate; (3) learning democracy through group work and team cooperation; and (4) noting historical changes in activities.

Safety

Some projects in this area relating to

Figure 17–2. Arithmetic correlation—How do I rate with the norms?

physical education are (1) learning and observing all safety rules and regulations pertaining to sports and play; (2) knowing safe use of equipment and apparatus; (3) checking playgrounds and apparatus; and (4) learning the need for using safety equipment in games and activities.

Health

Some projects in this area relating to physical education are (1) knowing all health rules pertaining to play and sports; (2) learning training rules for athletes; (3) safeguarding health based on proper clothing for play, showers after activity, drinking while warm, and so on; (4) knowing the effect of exercise on the body; and (5) knowing the need for food as fuel.

Mathematics

Some mathematics projects relating to physical education are (1) determining areas and perimeters of play spaces; (2) figuring averages in tournaments and various games, such as the batting average in softball; (3) marking courts, angle computation, and measurements; and (4) determining diameter, circumference, and radius of balls and circles used for games.

Science

Possible projects in science are (1) camping and outing activities; (2) hiking; (3) planning playgrounds; and (4) planting types of hedges and shrubbery in place of fences.

Music

Projects directly related to physical education are (1) learning the words for rhythms and singing games; (2) making tom-toms, gourds, rhythm sticks, and sandblocks; (3) improving rhythmic response through movement to various forms of accompaniment; and (4) understanding and appreciation of phrasing, accent, and quality of music through uses of wide varieties of accompaniment.

Art

Projects related to physical education are (1) drawing children participating in various kinds of activities; (2) diagraming the formations of a dance created by the children; (3) comparing roundness in line of a drawing to the roundness in movement to a ¾ or ⁶⁄₈ rhythm; and (4) dancing to the quality of a finger painting—curving or straight lines.

DIRECT PHYSICAL EDUCATION EXPERIENCES OFFER CORRELATION

Specific experiences in physical education and some ways in which these experiences, which start on the playground or in the gymnasium, may be made meaningful in the over-all curriculum are given in Tables 17–2 through 17–6.

TABLE 17–2. Correlation of the Dance (All Rhythmic Work)

The Fine Arts	The Sciences	Social Studies	Language Arts
1. Costumes of peoples where dance originates: (a) make sketches of costumes, (b) collect pictures of costumes and make bulletin board display, (c) bring in dolls in native costume, (d) make simple costumes.	1. Transportation in the country where the dance originates: (a) types of transportation in that country, (b) scientific principles involved.	1. Geography and history of the country where dance originates.	1. Read folk tales and stories of peoples where dance originated.
2. Make scenery for dance presentation.	2. Agriculture in that country: (a) types of soil, (b) types of food, (c) animals raised there, (d) types of farm machinery used, (e) financial value of crops.	2. Customs of the people there: (a) weddings, (b) holidays.	2. Tell stories to classmates or another grade.
3. Make program covers for presentations.	3. Health: (a) basic health needs of people in the specific country, (b) contributions to science and medicine.	3. Products of that country used by us (food, clothing, etc.).	3. Write an original play about peoples of the country for assembly program.
4. Make simple instruments (drums, gourds, musical glasses).		4. Government of that country: (a) type, (b) ambassadors to U.S.? (c) member of United Nations?	4. Write invitations to parents to attend play.

The Fine Arts	The Sciences	Social Studies	Language Arts
5. Draw the flag of the country.			5. Write letters to travel bureaus or foreign information centers to collect pamphlets, posters, and pictures.
			6. Make a vocabulary list of new words learned while studying this country.
			7. Make use of these words for spelling.

TABLE 17–3. Correlation of Class Organization (Squads, Leaders)

The Fine Arts	The Sciences	Social Studies	Language Arts
1. Make attractive charts for each squad: (a) list name of squad, (b) list names of players.	1. Divide class into equal groups.	1. Democratic organization: (a) selection of leaders, (b) division into squads.	1. Read true stories about some of our great sports leaders. List characteristics of great leaders.
2. Make attractive charts listing: (a) characteristics of good leaders, (b) characteristics of good followers.	2. Set time limit for incumbency of squads and leaders.	2. Teach cooperation, responsibility, and respect.	2. Have oral discussions: (a) characteristics of good leaders, (b) characteristics of good followers.
	3. Keep scores accurately.	3. Teach safety rules for all games: (a) use protective equipment, (b) set up safe play areas, (c) have an active safety patrol.	
	4. Make graphs of progress of squad.	4. Teach need for cooperation in a democracy. Substitute "we" for "I" in group responsibilities.	
	5. Learn how to use a stopwatch.		

TABLE 17–4. Correlation of Games and Sports

The Fine Arts	The Sciences	Social Studies	Language Arts
1. Make charts showing positions of players for game.	1. Make scale drawings, showing perimeter and area of playing courts.	1. History of the game or sport (Basketball-Naismith, Soccer-Rugby, etc.).	1. Make vocabulary list: (a) names of equipment—balls, jacks, ropes, (b) names of apparatus—jungle gym, slides, swings, (c) learn to spell the words.

The Fine Arts	The Sciences	Social Studies	Language Arts
2. Draw pictures of characters in games (squirrels in trees or fox and chickens, etc.).	2. Find diameters and radii of circles used for games.	2. The Olympics: (a) history of countries participating, (b) types of sports involved, (c) outstanding Americans participating.	2. Read stories of outstanding athletes.
3. Draw sketches of equipment and apparatus.	3. Find angles of rectangular playing fields.	3. Teamwork needed in democracy; teamwork needed in sports.	3. Make up original game; write rules; explain to class.
4. Collect pictures of athletes in action; make bulletin board display.	4. Find percentage of games won or lost.	4. Respect for authorities in life—sports present this respect for officials.	4. Make a collection of rope jumping rhymes.
5. Show films of Olympic games.	5. Learn training rules for athletes.		5. Read sports articles in newspaper.
	6. Learn personal health habits: (a) outdoor play, (b) fresh air—day and night, (c) showers, (d) individual towels, (e) sufficient rest.		6. Write sports articles for school paper.
	7. Effect of alcohol and tobacco on athletes.		7. Make oral report as sports announcer of a class game.
	8. Types of activities suitable for the exceptional child (rheumatic fever or polio victim).		
	9. Safety rules and regulations.		

TABLE 17–5. Correlation of Self-testing Activities and Stunts

The Fine Arts	The Sciences	Social Studies	Language Arts
1. Draw sketches of animals or things children mimic: (a) Duck Walk, (b) Wheelbarrow.	1. Learn life story and uses of animals mimicked (seal, duck).	1. Take field trip to farm or zoo to see animals mimicked.	1. Write letters to plan field trips.
2. Do stunts in time to music.	2. Learn how these animals protect themselves—their safety versus ours.	2. Talk about countries where stunts originated.	2. Have oral discussion of field trips.
3. Sketch people participating in stunts (circus personnel).	3. Physiology of exercise and value to man.	3. Watch TV stunts and activity programs.	3. Early childhood group can make experience chart and learn to read it.
		4. Visit circus.	4. Make vocabulary list of activities and stunts.

TABLE 17–6. *Correlation of Story Plays*

The Fine Arts	The Sciences	Social Studies	Language Arts
1. Make simple costumes.	1. Learn safety rules (fire drill, traffic, playing rules).	1. Develop respect for, and appreciation of, characters in story plays (policeman, fireman, milkman, and so on).	1. Read stories that could be used as basis for story plays.
2. Draw pictures of characters, equipment and apparatus.	2. Learn about fire prevention.	2. Lead up to study of community occupations.	2. Tell about favorite stories and characters.
3. Sing songs related to story plays.	3. Learn about seasons and weather changes.	3. Learn of holidays used to develop story play text.	3. Keep a list of story plays enjoyed.

PLAY IDEAS MOTIVATE LEARNING

The discussion thus far has been centered on ways in which physical education activities may be made meaningful in units of work and in specific parts of the curriculum and how specific physical education experiences may be made meaningful in the classroom in other parts of the broad curriculum areas. Attention is now focused on the idea of fun and play as a means of motivating children to learn and to create fun in learning.

Each idea discussed here has been contributed by an elementary classroom teacher and has been used in typical classroom situations.

Social Studies Example

In social studies, one teacher hung the map of the area or country being studied on the wall. Several suction darts were provided. The class was arranged in committees. One member from a committee threw a dart at the map. That committee then told facts about the country or area which was hit by their dart. Each committee had its turn.

Mathematics Example

Multiplication Bingo was successful in gaining interest in skill and speed. Cards were made with various number combinations appearing on them. These were flashed by one person. The first child, or group, to get five correct called "Multiplication Bingo" and flashed the cards for the next game. The same idea may be used for addition, subtraction, and division. This may be worked with groups, as well as with individuals.

Committees, squads, or groups also engaged in arithmetic fact games organized on a wheel-and-spoke idea. This may be changed to meet the needs of the class and may be used for multiplication, addition, or subtraction. Groups are given turns in answering.

Spelling Example

Spelling Bingo added to the enjoyment of learning new words and reviewing words. Each student folded his paper so it made

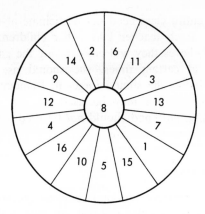

Figure 17–3. Wheel and Spoke—Arithmetic can be fun.

25 squares. As the spelling words were dictated, the children wrote them in any square they chose. The word was then dropped in a box. When all words had been dictated, each was drawn from the box, one at a time, pronounced, and spelled. The first child to have five in a row spelled correctly called "Bingo." Teachers who used this game reported children learned words which before had seemed impossible for them.

Science Example

Children gained much interest in their study of rocks when they played a game based on Upset the Fruit Basket. Each player was given the name of a rock in one of the rock classifications. When sedimentary was called, for example, each child in that group rose and gave the name of his rock and told where it was found. Then they all exchanged seats while the "Pebble" (caller) tried to get a seat. When metamorphic was called, all children had to change seats. This same idea could be used in health, for example, with the basic food groups.

General Examples

Variations on the game of Bird, Beast, and Fish are fun in all subject fields. A review of the names of countries, cities, rivers, history dates, and health rules may also be great fun with this game idea. Number facts may be used, too. Individual differences may be taken into account by counting at different rates of speed and giving the child a longer time to think before he must answer. He may also be given easier facts to answer.

A Softball game idea works well with various questions in any subject. The class may be divided into two groups. The teacher may take individual differences into account by preparing very hard questions, moderately hard ones, fairly easy ones, and easy ones. Correct answers to these questions represent a home run, a three-base hit, a two-base hit, and a single, respectively. One team, committee, or group is at bat. The first child selects the hit he desires to try for. If he answers correctly, he is on base or makes a run, accordingly. If he misses, he is out. When he misses, another child, either from his group or another, immediately answers the question, so the learning process is continual. To change the questioning often from one group to another, the teacher may wish only one out before switching questions to the next team. Runs made count for the group. One child may place the runners on the correct base on the blackboard ball diamond and keep advancing them correctly or they may move around the room on an imaginary diamond.

Respect for Individual Differences

There are many ways in which teachers may use the play incentive to challenge children to think and learn. Each teacher will be able to plan and use many more than have been discussed. It is true those discussed here, as well as any other one particular plan, may be abused and overdone.

Good judgment must be exercised, and when any are used it is imperative that individual differences be taken in account so that no child is embarrassed and made to feel inferior to his classmates. These activities may be used in different groups within a given grade in much the same way that one works with different reading groups.

The entire class need not participate at one time. Each teacher knows her children. If she believes they will enjoy trying the game idea at certain times, she should use it. Otherwise, she should forget it. Remember, the game idea may be used for fun and learning *only* and should *not* be used solely on a *competitive* basis.

QUESTIONS AND PRACTICAL PROBLEMS

1. Plan a unit of work for physical education in the grade of your choice. Show exactly how you will correlate it with all other parts of the curriculum.

2. Use a unit of work you have prepared for a given grade and subject field, and plan the correlation of physical education with it.

3. Are there any reasons against correlation? What are they? Can they be eliminated?

4. Observe a lesson in physical education. Plan ways in which you may continue interest in the activities in the classroom by including other parts of the curriculum.

5. Observe a lesson in any grade. At the conclusion show ways you might use some parts of it, or ideas from it, for activities in the succeeding physical education period. Explain fully.

SELECTED REFERENCES

ASSOCIATION FOR SUPERVISION AND CURRICULUM DEVELOPMENT, *Organizing the Elementary School for Living and Learning,* 1947 Yearbook, Washington, D.C., Association for Supervision and Curriculum Development, 1948.

COWELL, CHARLES C., and HELEN HAZELTON, *Curriculum Designs in Physical Education,* Englewood Cliffs, N.J., Prentice-Hall, Inc., 1955.

EVANS, RUTH, and LEO GANS, *Supervision of Physical Education,* New York, McGraw-Hill Book Company, Inc., 1950, pp. 153–154.

GWYNN, J. MINOR, *Curriculum Principles and Social Trends* (Third edition), New York, The Macmillan Company, 1960.

HUNT, SARAH, and ETHEL CAIN, *Games the World Around* (Revised edition), New York, A. S. Barnes and Company, 1950.

KEENE, FRANCES, *Fun Around the World,* Pelham, New York, The Seahorse Press, 1955.

KICKSICK, BERNICE, "Relationship of Physical Education to General Education," *The Foil,* New Jersey Association for Health and Physical Education, 1954.

KUPFERER, HARRIET, "An Evaluation of the Integration Potential of a Physical Education Program," *Journal of Education Sociology,* **28:**494 (October 1954).

LASALLE, DOROTHY, *Rhythms and Dances for Elementary Schools* (Revised edition), New York, A. S. Barnes and Company, 1951.

MILLER, ARTHUR G. ,"Physical Education in the Integrated Curriculum," *Journal of Health, Physical Education and Recreation,* **31:**3 (March 1960).

O'KEEFE, PATTRIC RUTH, and ANITA ALDRICH, *Education Through Physical Activities* (Second edition), St. Louis. The C. V. Mosby Company, 1955.

SEHON, ELIZABETH L., *et al., Physical Education Methods for Elementary Schools* (Second edition), Philadelphia, W. B. Saunders Company, 1955, Chapter 11.

CHAPTER 18

Evaluation of Physical Education Programs in Elementary Schools

Unless programs of physical education are evaluated, it is difficult to ascertain accomplishments. It may be the consensus that certain objectives, needs, desirable traits, habits, and attitudes are being met; but to ascertain these claims, various means of evaluation should be used.

Programs should be evaluated in many ways to justify physical education in the curriculum. Merely to plan a program of activities, make provisions for time and facilities, and provide an opportunity so children can participate and receive big-muscle activity is not enough. In all physical education there is but one end or goal. It must do something that is good for the individual. Unless it is possible to evaluate, how does one know whether this goal is being accomplished? Physical education is a part of the curriculum usually established by law, which makes it mandatory that a certain number of minutes per day be devoted to it. In addition to this basic requirement, there should be means of evaluation to ascertain if the time spent is meaningful and valuable to the participants.

A means of evaluation may accomplish many desirable goals. It refers back to the actual organization and planning of the program, which should be based on the needs, interests, and abilities of the children. Evaluation should ascertain whether the objectives of organic power, neuromuscular development, desirable social and personal adjustment, democratic attitudes, interpretation and intellectual growth, and emotional response and growth are being met. Unless objectives have influenced what the teacher does in the program and the behavior and developmental growth of the child, they cannot be justified. Evaluation will determine whether the program is meeting the needs of the whole child and that, of course, means each and every child in the given group. Evaluation is an integral part of both teaching and learning.

EVALUATION AND/OR MEASUREMENT

The progress of using various evaluation techniques in programs of physical education has been slow. Some people think tests and measurements are the answers and spend time—in certain instances more than may be justified—on them. If too great a portion of the allotted time for physical education is used for a testing program, it may result in testing and ascertaining the innate ability of the child and provide too little time for the program itself. When this happens it is impossible to evaluate what effect the activities in the program have had on the individual. This, of course, should be avoided. One should think of evaluation as a very broad process using many techniques and devices. Some of these will be discussed. Measurement gives us information about only one factor under consideration. Evalua-tion carries the process further and makes a comparison of the status of the object and all of its parts with some outcomes, values, or standards. Measurement determines the value of parts of the whole. Evaluation aids in determining the effect of the part or parts in reference to the whole. Measurement will yield quantitative data, while evaluation will yield qualitative data. Measurement may be used as an aid to better teaching, but not as an end in itself.

PURPOSES OF EVALUATION

Evaluation should assist in showing the teacher where he or she is going, how and by what means he or she is going to reach the goals or objectives, how he or she is progressing, and what effects the program is having on each individual pupil. A broad plan of evaluation should assist in improv-ing specific parts of education so it will make a great contribution to each child's growth and development.

Specific reasons for establishing a proper evaluation procedure include the fol-lowing:

1. It gives evidence as to whether physical education objectives are being met.

2. It helps parents, teachers, and pu-pils understand the worth of experiences pro-vided in physical education programs.

3. It provides a governor or check to direct and modify the experiences given in the programs to meet the needs of the pupils. This might be useful in both organ-ization and instruction.

4. It helps in the formulation of edu-cational principles and policies for the school to apply to the programs.

5. It provides basic information re-garding individual pupils for guidance pur-poses.

6. It may act as a means of motiva-tion for students to reach desired goals. Each one should be encouraged to evaluate his individual progress rather than compare himself with others.

7. It should act as a means of moti-vation for teachers to find ways to assist children to meet desirable goals and needs.

8. It may justify needs for equipment, facilities, materials, and expenditure of monies for personnel and leadership in pro-grams.

9. It may suggest preventive meas-ures that should be taken in the interest of the pupils.

10. It should be a means of improving the total physical educational program so that it contributes to greater child growth and development.

11. Evaluation can also be used as an aid in grouping pupils, predicting future per-formance, and determining where emphasis should be placed.

Teachers have been neither dishonest nor lazy when they have said, "There are no specific requirements in physical educa-tion for a child to meet before he is pro-moted; thus in our busy days something has to slip and that something may be the phys-ical education program." This is not always the fault of the classroom teacher. It may be the fault of the institutions of teacher preparation which did not help him or her to understand the needs and values of a well-planned program of physical education or teach means of evaluation to ascertain the influence of the program on the individual child.

Evaluation will keep a teacher alert and it will help make teaching physical education valuable and meaningful. It is a means of making it possible for all educators to understand its worth in the total educational program. It will satisfy both the teacher and the pupil that the objectives of the program have been met, or need revision. It is very natural and easy when both teachers and pupils know what they are trying to accomplish. It is a constant and progressive process and may be subjective, objective, or both.

TECHNIQUES USED IN EVALUATION

Evaluation is broad and comprehensive. It contains many techniques and may be accomplished jointly by the individual, the teacher, and the group as a whole. It may be both subjective and objective.

Objective Evaluation

One means of objective evaluation is skill tests. These may be either standard skill tests or those devised by the teacher and her group. Skill tests would show, for example, how many times John caught a ball out of a given number of times it was thrown to him at a given distance in September. The same test applied again in a few months, after he had received many opportunities in the program of physical education to practice catching, would show John's improvement or lack of improvement. Throwing for accuracy at targets from a designated distance is another example.

Measurement and evaluation materials in health, physical education, and recreation listed in the selected references at the end of this chapter will aid the teacher who wishes to use standard skill tests. Tests of motor skills have been constructed by such outstanding physical educators as Brace, Neilson and Cozens, and Anderson. These standard tests will also assist teachers to construct tests for their individual groups.

In addition to skill tests, objective evaluation may include tests on rules of games, strength, speed, and endurance. Certain specific tests for physical fitness have been established. Probably the most widely discussed is the Kraus-Weber test for minimum physical fitness. This battery is organized to test muscle strength of the abdomen, psoas, upper back, lower back, and hamstring. Others were discussed in Chapter 4.

Subjective Evaluation

Subjective evaluation includes individual anecdotal records, interviews, observation, socio-grams, question and answer type of records relating to social and psychological development, interests and attitudes, and specific individual goals desired by each child.

LaSalle[1] discusses methods used to evaluate desirable character traits and social development which should be developed through a good program of physical education.

[1] Dorothy LaSalle, *Guidance of Children Through Physical Education*, New York, The Ronald Press Company, 1946, p. 140.

Evaluation Results Aid Teachers and Students

Records of objective and subjective evaluation should be kept by the teacher and filed with the records of the individual children. They should accompany the child as he advances in school so he may see his growth and the teachers who receive him as a new student will know something of his ability and needs, how he has developed, and what he has accomplished.

Regardless of the type of evaluation, the child must know the result if he is to be able to help himself and adjust his work and endeavors in the correct direction. Self-appraisal is recommended. A child may do this by means of a diary or appraisal forms. These are usually compiled by the teacher and the student together. The student must first be aided in establishing his goals or objectives so that he has an idea of what he wishes to accomplish. In this way, evaluation is possible. Self-evaluation and appraisal are excellent learning aids.

The carry-over of activities taught in the physical education program to the noon hour, after-school hours, and leisure-time pursuits must not be overlooked in evaluation. If a child desires to participate in these programs, they have had some effect in making a favorable impression on him and have given him satisfying and pleasurable experiences.

SPECIFIC POINTS TO BE EVALUATED

Evaluation might first start with the general objectives of the program and then extend to specific objectives. It should include the evaluation of the teacher, the facilities, the equipment and apparatus, the actual program—both the planning and administration—and last but not least, the effects the planned program has had on each individual and the group as a whole. Some specific questions relating to each phase are listed for the help of the teacher.

Evaluation of Program Planning

Regarding program planning, the teacher must answer the following questions:

1. Am I planning activities to meet the needs, interests, and abilities of my group as a whole?

2. Are they diversified sufficiently to meet the needs, abilities, and interest of each individual child?

3. Are the activities planned according to the available facilities, equipment, apparatus, and space?

4. Do I have attainable objectives?

5. Are the objectives too general, or are they specific?

6. Is the program integrated with other parts of the school program?

7. Have I considered the indoor program for inclement weather?

8. Have I planned with the help of my students?

9. Does the program include all types of recommended activities for my general type of group?

Evaluation of Teaching

In respect to teaching, the teacher should answer these questions:

1. Am I well prepared to present and teach this program?

2. Am I teaching and reaching each individual child? Do I recognize individual differences?

3. Is there a correct teacher-pupil relationship? Pupil-pupil relationship? Pupil-teacher relationship?

4. Are the children learning and having fun?

5. Are they interested?

6. Are they meeting the objectives?

7. Do I set a good example?

8. Am I efficient in my use of time, equipment, and facilities?

9. Am I aiding good group relationship?

10. Am I democratic enough in my teaching?

11. If the activity does not appear to be successful, do I blame the children or do I stop the activity and later make a self-analysis to find reasons?

12. Do I permit pupil choice?

Evaluation of Facilities and Equipment

In evaluating facilities, space, equipment, and apparatus, these questions should be considered:

1. Am I using all of the play area to full advantage?

2. Is this area safe—free from debris? Are there well-established safety rules for the use of equipment, apparatus, and so on?

3. Am I getting the most from the available equipment?

4. Are children having opportunities to use all apparatus?

5. Are all pieces of equipment and apparatus inspected regularly and in safe condition?

Evaluation of Program Results

In evaluating the program results on the children, these questions should be considered:

1. Is each child better in some way because he has participated in this program?

2. Is he in better physical condition?

3. Is he better in neuromuscular skills?

4. Is he better in his democratic attitude toward his fellow playmates?

5. Is he a better sport?

6. Does he use good judgment?

7. Is he a good leader?

8. Is he a good follower?

9. Is he happy and enjoying the activities?

10. Is he always finding excuses to stay away from the physical education program?

11. Does he use any of the activities in his leisure time? Does he assume self-direction?

12. Is he replacing an egotistical or "I" attitude with a cooperative or "we" one?

13. Does he have a sense of responsibility?

14. Has his over-all physical skill development improved?

15. Has his over-all social development improved?

16. Is he more emotionally stable?

General Evaluation

At the close of each lesson, the teacher should discuss the activities with the class. What did they like best? Why? Would they like to play the activities again? If so, why? If not, why? The teacher will learn much from the students which will be of value to him or her and to them.

The teacher should evaluate each lesson. Why did it proceed exceptionally well, or why did it not? In so doing, he or she will not make the same error twice and will use good techniques again.

Above all the teacher should remember that physical education is an integral part of education. It does not differ in its aims or objectives—merely in its means toward these ends. Unless it aids each individual and he is better for having participated in it, something is wrong. It is the teacher's challenge to ascertain this, and it may only be accomplished through honest, broad evaluation of the teacher and the program by the teacher and the group.

In summarizing, it appears that evaluation may aid in keeping the program of physical education alive and challenging. This must be done if it is to meet the needs of children in a changing world and society. Only if this is accomplished will it assist the child in meeting various phases of life.

Evaluation will tell whether the planned and established goals have been reached, whether the manner or objectives used to reach them were the most desirable, and whether the actual goals were the most valuable and practical for a given situation, program, or individual class.

FORMS FOR EVALUATION

TABLE 18–1. *Evaluation Chart for Story Plays Kindergarten Through Grade Three*

Name _____

Grade _____

Year _____

Age _____

Teacher _____

Scoring key:

Satisfactory—S

Improved—I

Needs help—NH

	Scoring Period			
Category	Nov.	Feb.	April	June
Coordination of large muscles				
Throwing				
Bending				
Twisting				
Running				
Jumping				
Stretching				
Sportsmanship				
Friendliness				
Self-control				
Respect for others				
Enjoyment				
Imagination				
Participation				

| | Scoring Period | | | |
Category	Nov.	Feb.	April	June
Improvement				
Excellent				
Average				
Little				
None				
Average mark				
Special remarks				

TABLE 18–2. *Evaluation Chart for Self-testing Activities and Stunts, Kindergarten Through Grade Three*

Name _____
Grade _____
Year _____
Age _____
Teacher _____

Scoring key:
Satisfactory—S
Improved—I
Needs help—NH

| | Scoring Period | | |
Category	Nov.	Feb.	May
Subjective evaluation			
Does he move quickly and safely?			
Does he have good balance?			
Is he getting strong?			
Is he having fun?			
Is he making friends?			
Does he like to try?			
Objective evaluation			
Balancing: Walk across walking board, placing heel of one foot, at each step, against toes of other foot. Extend arms sideward, for balance. Look straight ahead. Turn around. Walk back. Walk backwards.			
Bouncing balls: Bounce and catch ball. Bounce to partner. Tap while standing. Tap while walking. Combine bouncing, catching, and tapping in a pattern.			
Catching: Catch, with two hands, a ball or bean bag thrown into the air. Catch ball after bounce. Catch ball or bean bag thrown by another child.			
Jumping: Jump in place, landing lightly on two feet. Jump to music. Jump individual rope 10–15 times. Jump rope in various ways—			

Category	Scoring Period		
	Nov.	Feb.	May
backward, legs crossed, or feet apart. Jump long rope to rhymes or verses. Jump long rope that is turning toward jumper or away from jumper. Jump long rope in various tempos. From standing position jump over a rope placed at various heights. Take off from two feet and land lightly on two feet. This is a modified standing jump.			
Kicking: Manipulate ball with feet. Manipulate ball using either foot. Kick soccer ball, meeting ball with top of instep to direct ball along floor.			
Leaping: Leap over a 12-inch hurdle while running, taking off from one foot at a time and landing on one foot at a time. While running, leap over rope placed at various heights from floor. Take off from one foot and land lightly on one foot at a time. This is a modified running high jump.			
Throwing: Throw a bean bag into the air and catch it. Throw underhand to partner with vigorous arm swing. Increase distance. Place correct (opposite) foot forward when throwing. Throw bean bag through largest opening in easel target, using underhand throw. Throw bean bag over net using overhand. Throw volley ball, using shoulder throw. Throw ball at wall target.			
Balancing an object: Place block on the head. Walk while balancing it. The child should walk a distance sufficient to test his skill.			
Bouncing a ball: Jump up and down lightly on toes, gradually lowering height of jump until a stooping position is reached. Stunt may be performed to rhythmic accompaniment.			
Puppy run: Walk or run on all fours using short steps.			

TABLE 18–3. *Evaluation Chart for Games, Kindergarten Through Grade Three*

Name _____

Grade _____

Year _____

Age _____

Teacher _____

Scoring key:
Satisfactory—S
Improved—I
Needs help—NH

Category	Scoring Period			
	Sept.	Dec.	Feb.	May
Subjective evaluation				
Does he show good sportsmanship?				
Is he a cheerful loser?				

Category	Scoring Period			
	Sept.	Dec.	Feb.	May
Does he control his temper?				
Does he accept decisions?				
Does he play fair?				
Does he follow directions?				
Does he participate actively?				
Is he a good leader?				
Is he a good follower?				
Can he skip?				
Does he tag properly?				
Can he dodge a thrown ball?				
Can he tiptoe?				
Can he dart?				
Objective evaluation				
How many times can he catch a ball, out of 10 tries?				
How many times can he throw a ball to a partner in 10 times? (Specific distances.)				
How many times can he jump a rope without missing?				
How long does it take him to run 60 feet without falling?				

TABLE 18–4. *Evaluation Chart for Individual-Dual Activities, Grades One Through Three*

Name _____

Grade _____

Year _____

Age _____

Teacher _____

Scoring key:
Excellent—E
Good—G
Fair—F
No improvement—NI

Category	E	G	F	NI
Activities, with skills involved				
Hopscotch: hopping, bending, keeping balance				
Marbles: shooting marbles				
Rope jumping: jumping on toes; using knees and ankles				
Ball: accurate underhand toss				
Rubber quoits: accurate toss				
Subjective evaluation				
He shows gradual development in skills.				
He uses games to gain relief from tension or physical fatigue.				

Category	E	G	F	NI
He participates daily in exercise which suits his personal needs.				
He enjoys playing a variety of activities he understands.				
He develops the power to adjust socially to the needs and wishes of his playmates.				
He finds satisfaction in a game well played whether he wins or loses.				
He has a sense of belonging to the group.				
He feels important to the group.				
He overcomes shyness or fear of being hurt.				
He gains security as skills increase.				
He develops a sense of coordination.				
His physical endurance can meet the daily demands put upon his body.				
He is willing to share equipment and take turns.				
He contributes his share as a group leader.				
He contributes his share as a group follower.				
He cheerfully plays the activity selected.				
He plays fairly.				
He wins gracefully.				
He loses gracefully.				
He puts his whole effort into the activity.				
He appreciates the skill and sportsmanship of others.				

TABLE 18–5. *Evaluation Chart for Rhythms and Dances, Intermediate Grades*

Name _____

Grade _____

Year _____

Age _____

Teacher _____

Scoring key:

Excellent—E

Very good—VG

Good—G

Fair—F

Poor—P

Movements to Music	Scoring Period		
	Sept.	Jan.	May
Walk			
Run			
Jump			
Hop			
Slide			

Movements to Music	Scoring Period		
	Sept.	Jan.	May
Gallop			
Skip			
Clap			
March			
Polka			
Waltz			
Two step			

TABLE 18–6. *Evaluation Chart for Objective Skills, Intermediate Grades*

Name _____   Scoring key:
Grade _____   Excellent—E
Year _____   Improved—I
Age _____   Needs help—NH
Teacher _____

(Addition and substitution of other activities are encouraged.)

Category	Scoring Period		
	Sept.	Feb.	May
Dribbling—in each scoring period put in the time spent by each pupil dribbling by hand and/or foot a distance of 20 yards (by foot, not kicking forward more than 5 yards).			
Throwing—football, basketball, and softball, depending upon the season—how many times they make the target with each (football —a barrel, 15 yards; basketball—a basket, from the foul line; softball—a barrel from 60 feet) in 10 tries. Then try each for distance —longest in three tries.			
Batting—with a softball (in season); how many hits with 10 swings on pitches from a pitcher.			
Catching—with football, basketball, and softball, depending on season, how many times they catch the object thrown in each (football—15 yards; basketball—width of basketball court; softball—60 feet) in 10 tries.			
Running—time taken to run the 30-, 40- or 50-yard dash, full speed.			
Push-ups—number of push-ups possible.			
Jumping—(1) distance covered in broad jump (best of three attempts); (2) distance covered in hop, skip, and jump (best in three attempts).			

TABLE 18–7. *Evaluation Chart for Team Sports, Intermediate Grades*

Name _____	Scoring key:
Grade _____	Satisfactory—S
Year _____	Improved—I
Age _____	Needs help—NH
Teacher _____	

	Scoring Period				
Objectives	Sept.	Nov.	Jan.	Mar.	May
Sportsmanship					
Gets along well with others					
Plays fairly					
Accepts officials' decisions					
Uses good judgment					
Team play					
Plays for team, not self					
Good loser					
Understands rules					
Good winner					
Democratic attitude					
Helps others learn skills					
Encourages others					
Accepts own limitations					
Cooperates					
Leadership					
Knows the job to do					
Does a good job					
Plans well					
Followership					
Helps settle disputes					
Takes suggestions					
Takes proper turn					
Participation					
Enjoys playing					
Uses time to good advantage					
Interested in learning new activities					
Interested in improving skills					
Self-direction					
Uses activities in leisure time					
Shows learnings in other situation					
Responsibility					
Shares responsibility					
Plays to the end of a game no matter how it is going					

Objectives	Scoring Period				
	Sept.	Nov.	Jan.	Mar.	May
Shows respect for equipment					
Emotional growth					
Accepts defeat					
Respects rights of others					
Right to belong					
Feeling of success					
Self-control					

TABLE 18–8. *Evaluation Chart for Individual and Dual Activities, Intermediate Grades*

Name _____

Grade _____

Year _____

Age _____

Teacher _____

Scoring key:
Satisfactory—S
Improved—I
Needs help—NH

Category	Scoring Period			
	Nov.	Jan.	Mar.	June
Skills and fundamentals				
Croquet				
1. Hitting ball accurately				
2. Knowledge of rules				
3. Knowledge of terms				
Deck tennis				
1. Catching				
2. Throwing				
3. Movement on court				
4. Rules of game				
Horseshoe and Quoits				
1. Pitching				
2. Knowledge of rules				
3. Knowledge of terms				
Badminton				
1. Volleying shuttlecock				
2. Serving				
3. Knowledge of rules				
Tennis				
1. Serving ball				

Category	Nov.	Jan.	Mar.	June

Scoring Period

Category	Nov.	Jan.	Mar.	June
2. Volleying ball				
3. Knowledge of rules				
Volley Tennis				
1. Hitting				
2. Knowledge of rules				
Shuffleboard				
1. Pushing disc				
2. Knowledge of rules				
3. Knowledge of terms				
Sportsmanship				
Fair play				
Respect for others				
Can play alone and as "we"				
Enthusiasm				
Uses equipment properly while playing				
Assumes responsibility for returning equipment				
Self-direction				

TABLE 18–9. *Self-evaluation Chart for Physical Education Students, Intermediate Grades*

Name _____

Grade _____

Year _____

Age _____

Teacher _____

Scoring key:

Always—A

Usually—U

Sometimes—S

Never—N

Report Card Periods

Category	1	2	3	4	5
Desirable social learnings					
Leadership					
1. Am I interested in the welfare of others?					
2. Do I encourage good practices of safety?					
3. Am I just?					
4. Am I fair?					
5. Am I developing self-discipline?					

Category	Report Card Periods				
	1	2	3	4	5
6. Do I respect the rights of others?					
7. Am I developing a sense of responsibility?					
Followership					
1. Am I loyal to my team?					
2. Do I play for the good of all?					
3. Do I accept and respect the judgment of others?					
Sportsmanship					
1. Do I avoid arguments over decisions?					
2. Do I play for the good of all?					
3. Do I put forth my best effort?					
4. Do I play fair and honest?					
5. Do I have a sense of responsibility?					
6. Can I lose gracefully?					
7. Can I win gracefully?					
Organization					
1. Am I prepared to play the game?					
2. Do I foresee needed equipment?					
Consideration					
1. Do I win or lose with grace?					
2. Am I fair to others?					
3. Am I kind to others?					
4. Do I know the rules which govern the game?					
5. Do I remember to play quietly in the classroom?					
Cooperation					
1. Can I adjust to the interest of the group?					
2. Am I willing to serve as an official instead of playing?					
3. Do I play my best at all times?					
Specific learnings (YES or NO)					
1. Do I know the history of some of the games?					
2. Do I know the rules of the games?					
3. Can I score the games?					
4. Have I improved in my accuracy in:*					
a. Throwing balls?					
b. Batting?					
c. Catching?					
d. Running?					
e. Jumping?					
5. Have I improved in my accuracy in pitching quoits?					
6. Have I improved in my accuracy in throwing darts?					
7. Do I play the games during my leisure?					

* *Note:* Many other skills should be added, depending on repertoire of activities the children have learned in the program.

Category	Report Card Periods				
	1	*2*	*3*	*4*	*5*
8. Have I taught games to others?					
9. Have I constructed games?					
10. Do I have good rhythm in dances?					

Games I have learned and can teach others:
1.
2.
3.
4.
5.

QUESTIONS AND PRACTICAL PROBLEMS

1. Set up specific criteria for the evaluation of (a) the total program of physical education in elementary schools; (b) each specific part of the program as recommended for early childhood and middle childhood grades.

2. Plan a lesson for one specific grade. Set up specific evaluation points for this lesson, using a chart.

3. Observe one or more classes in physical education. Evaluate them on the basis of objectives, child learning situation, child growth, and participation. Substantiate them as a valuable part of the total educational program. Think of other specific points which may be used to judge, such as skills and techniques, and evaluate them.

4. Study the evaluation check list of the LaPorte committee. Make suggestions to improve it.

5. Plan skill tests for each specific phase of the physical education program in the grade of your choice.

6. Outline a week's activities for the physical education program for a particular grade including the time given to tests and evaluation, and on the basis of this schedule examine (a) the relevance of the physical education program to the needs and special problems of various types of children; (b) whether the program offers a sufficient variety of activities to be interesting to all of the children; (c) if sufficient time is included in the week's program for tests and evaluation, and if the program could benefit from a greater amount of time given to planning and evaluation; (d) whether the program is sufficiently integrated with the other parts of the school's educational program.

7. What are some of the objectives in having the teacher and her class discuss their activities at the end of each lesson?

8. On the basis of an enlightened planning of the physical education program, what specific requirements would you ask for a child to meet before being promoted?

SELECTED REFERENCES

"A Platform for Physical Education," *Journal of Health, Physical Education and Recreation,* **21**:136 (March 1950).

American Association for Health, Physical Education and Recreation, *Evaluation Standards and Guide in Health Education,* *Physical Education, Recreation Education,* Washington, D.C., American Association for Health, Physical Education and Recreation, 1959.

Bachman, H. M., "Let Your Students Set Their Own Goals," *Journal of Health, Physical*

Education and Recreation, **26:**19–20 (March 1955).

BROER, MARION R., "Evaluating Skill," *Journal of Health, Physical Education and Recreation,* **33:**23 (November 1962).

CALIFORNIA STATE DEPARTMENT OF EDUCATION, *Criteria for Evaluating the Physical Education Program: Kindergarten, Grades One Through Six,* Sacramento, California State Department of Education, 1960.

————, *Evaluating Pupil Progress,* Sacramento, California State Department of Education, 1960.

CLARK, H. H., *Application of Measurement to Health and Physical Education* (Second edition), Englewood Cliffs, N.J., Prentice-Hall, Inc., 1950.

DAVIS, ELWOOD C., and EARL L. WALLIS, *Toward Better Teaching in Physical Education,* Englewood Cliffs, N.J., Prentice-Hall, Inc., 1961.

JACKSON, C. O., "Evaluate Your Physical Education Program," *School Coach,* **23:**36 (November 1953).

————, "How Does Your Physical Education Program Rate?" *Journal of Health, Physical Education and Recreation,* **25:**21–22 (June 1954).

JOHNSON, SARA, "The Physical Education Program in Elementary School," *Journal of Health, Physical Education and Recreation,* **30:**380 (June 1959).

LaPORTE, WILLIAM, *Health and Physical Education Score Card for Elementary Schools* (No. 1), Los Angeles, Parker and Company, 1951.

LaSALLE, DOROTHY, "Evaluation," *Children in Focus,* 1954 Year Book of the American Association for Health, Physical Education and Recreation, Washington, D.C., American Association for Health, Physical Education and Recreation, 1955, p. 267.

LATCHAW, MARJORIE, "Measuring Selected Motor Skills in Fourth, Fifth, and Sixth Grades," *Research Quarterly,* **25:**439–449 (December 1954).

MEANS, RICHARD K., "A Teacher Appraisal Scale," *Journal of Health, Physical Education and Recreation,* **31:**36–37 (May–June 1960).

NATIONAL RESEARCH COUNCIL OF THE AMERICAN ASSOCIATION FOR HEALTH, PHYSICAL EDUCATION AND RECREATION, *Measurement and Evaluation Materials in Health, Physical Education and Recreation,* Washington, D.C., American Association for Health, Physical Education and Recreation, 1950.

NIELSON, N. P., and F. COZENS, *Achievement Scales in Physical Education Activities for Boys and Girls in Elementary School and Junior High School,* New York, A. S. Barnes and Company, 1934.

RUSSELL, DAVID H., "What Does Research Say About Self-evaluation?" *Journal of Educational Research,* **46:**561–573 (April 1953).

SAUBORN, J., "Measuring Achievement in Elementary School Physical Education Programs," *Education,* **85:**78–80 (October 1954).

WAGLOW, I. F., "Marking in Physical Education," *Journal of Health, Physical Education and Recreation,* **25:**48 (May 1954).

CHAPTER **19**

Safety and Legal Liability

It is tragic that so many of the accidents which occur in the United States today involve young boys and girls with lives of hopes and desires still to fulfill. Accidents are the leading cause of death and an important cause of disability for boys and girls of school age.

Although the school has proved to be a safer place than the home, there is still much room for improvement. Accidents occur going to and from school and in classrooms, auditoriums, gymnasiums, playgrounds, laboratories, shops, corridors, and stairways. About one out of three accidents occurs in gymnasiums. Classrooms run second with one injury in five. These accidents take place during organized activities such as sports as well as during unorganized ones involved with running and falls. The accidents which occurred to pupils in kindergarten through the sixth grade during a recent year were classified into four main categories depending on the location and the activities engaged in at the time of the accident. These categories were (1) *in the school plant*—auditoriums, classrooms, playground apparatus, and unorganized activities were the most frequent locations or activities; (2) *going to and from school*—accidents occurred most frequently in the form of falls on the street and the sidewalk; (3) *the home*—injuries resulted from falls, cuts, and scratches; (4) *miscellaneous category* —play activities, falls, and accidents involv-ing bicycles and motor vehicles were the most common.

Many accidents occur in playgrounds, during recess periods, and at sports events and activities involving the physical education class. The unorganized games during recess and noon intermissions, according to the statistics gathered by the National Commission on Safety Education, are more likely to result in pupil injuries than the regularly scheduled activities which are a part of the physical education class.

Accidents that occur on playgrounds and in gymnasiums and other locations for children's play sometimes result in lawsuits. A few examples of cases that have gone into litigation follow: A pupil ran against a flagpole while playing (*Hough* v. *Orleans Elementary School, District of Humboldt County, California,* 1943). A student was injured when he was hit by a ball (*Graff* v. *Board of Education of New York City, New York,* 1940). An injury resulted when a stone was batted by a pupil (*Wilbur* v. *City of Binghamton, New York,* 1946). As a result of a defect in a slide on a playground a child was hurt. Another occurred when a pupil fell off a jungle gym (*Miller* v. *Board of Education of Union Free School, District No. 1, Town of Oyster Bay, New York,* 1936). In another case a pupil was injured in a tumbling race as a result of a loose mat. The mat was not firmly fixed and the student slipped and was injured (*Cambareri*

v. *Board of Education of Albany, New York,* 1940).

Because accidents do occur in activities involved with the physical education program in the elementary schools, it is very important for the teacher to be informed and aware of her responsibility. The growth of these specialized programs in this country has brought the problem of legal liability to the forefront. There is always danger of accidents during various activities that comprise programs of physical education. The nature of this field of work involves such things as the use of special apparatus, excursions and trips, living in camps, utilizing first-aid practices, and a considerable number of other activities which have implications for liability.

THE CLASSROOM TEACHER'S RESPONSIBILITY

Each teacher has a moral and a legal responsibility to provide for the welfare of her pupils. Morally she is responsible for the child's safety and welfare while he is in her charge. The whole concept of education in this country revolves around the premise that education is designed to provide those experiences for children which will help them develop to their maximum capacities, further their pursuit of happiness, and guide them in such a way that will prepare them to be mature, healthy adults.

Legally, too, the teacher is responsible for the safety and well-being of her pupils.

Figure 19–1. Mask, body protector, and glove help prevent injury to a catcher.

Figure 19–2. Good safety hints.

Each teacher is liable for her own negligence. If litigation occurs and negligence is established, the teacher can be forced to pay from her own funds the costs of such damages, except in a very few states where financial restitution can be made from school funds. An example of a state that has a "save harmless" law which requires that school districts assume the liability of the teacher, negligence proved or not, is New Jersey. The law in this state reads:

Chapter 311, P.L. 1938. Boards assume liability of teachers. It shall be the duty of each board of education in any school district to save harmless and protect all teachers and members of supervisory and administrative staff from financial loss arising out of any claim, demand, suit or judgement by reason of alleged negligence or other act resulting in accidental bodily injury to any person within or without the school building; provided, such teacher or member of the supervisory or administrative staff at the time of the accident or injury was acting in the discharge of his duties within the

scope of his employment and/or under the direction of said board of education; and said board of education may arrange for and maintain appropriate insurance with any company created by or under the laws of this state, or in any insurance company authorized by law to transact business in this state, or such board may elect to act as self-insurers to maintain the aforesaid protection.

Even in such states as New Jersey, however, the worry, nuisance, loss of time, together with the possible reprisal in other ways by boards of education and parents, can cause a hardship to a teacher involved in a legal dispute.

According to Bouvier's *Law Dictionary,* liability is "the responsibility, the state of one who is bound in law and justice to do something which may be enforced by action." Another definition by the National Commission on Safety Education is that "liability is the condition of affairs which gives rise to an obligation to do a particular thing to be enforced by court action." This authoritative source goes on to say, "All school employees run the risk of suit by injured pupils on the basis of alleged negligence which causes bodily injury to pupils. Such injuries occur on playgrounds, in athletics, in science laboratories, or in shop classes. . . ."

The teacher is responsible for what he or she does. The Supreme Court of the United States has reaffirmed this principle and all should recognize the important implications it has. Immunity of the governmental agency such as a state, school district, or board does not relieve the teacher of liability for his or her own negligent acts.

Teachers are expected to conduct their various activities in a careful and prudent manner. If they do not do so, they are exposing themselves to lawsuits for their own negligence. In respect to administrators, the National Commission on Safety Education states:

The fact that administrators (speaking mainly of principals and superintendents) are rarely made defendants in pupil injury cases seems unjust to the teachers who are found negligent because of inadequate supervision, and unjust also to the school boards who are required to defend themselves in such suits. When the injury is caused by defective equipment, it is the building principal who should have actual or constructive notice of the defect; when the injury is caused by inadequate playground supervision, the inadequacy of the supervision frequently exists because of arrangements made by the building principal. For example, a teacher in charge of one playground was required to stay in the building to teach a make-up class; another teacher was required to supervise large grounds on which 150 pupils were playing; another teacher neglected the playground to answer the telephone. All of these inadequacies in playground supervision were morally chargeable to administrators; in none of these instances did the court action direct a charge of responsibility to the administrator. Whether the administrator in such cases would have been held liable, if charged with negligence, is problematical. The issue has not been decided, since the administrator's legal responsibility for pupil injuries has never been discussed by the courts to an extent that would make possible the elucidation of general principles; the administrator's moral responsibilities must be conceded.[1]

The elementary school teacher should know how far she can go with various aspects of her program and what precautions are necessary in order not to be held legally liable in the event of accident. The fact that approximately 50 per cent of the accidents involving school pupils occur in buildings, that more than 40 per cent occur in playgrounds, and 10 per cent occur in going to and from school has important implications for physical education and the classroom teacher. The legal rights involved in such cases are worthy of study. Although the law varies from state to state, it is possible to discuss liability in a general way that has implications for all sections of the country.

LEGAL ASPECTS[2]

For many years the courts have recognized the hazards involved in the play activities that are a necessary part of the educational program. The courts have recognized the possibility and risk of some injury in physical education programs and generally have not awarded damages where negligence could not be proved. However, they have pointed out that care must be taken by both the participant and the authorities in charge. They have implied further that the benefits derived from participating in physical education activities offset the occasional injury that might occur.

Many of these decisions were handed down at a time when the attitude of the law was that a government agency, which categorically included the school, could not be held liable for the acts of its employees unless they so consented. Since that time the attitude of the courts has been gradually changing. As more accidents occurred, the courts frequently decided in favor of the injured party when negligence could be shown. The immunity derived from the old common law rule that a government agency cannot be sued without its consent is slowly changing in the eyes of the courts so that both the Federal Government and the state may be sued. The

[1] National Commission on Safety Education, *Who Is Liable for Pupil Injuries?* Washington, D.C., National Education Association (October 1950), p. 14.

[2] Parts of this section on legal aspects are adapted from Charles A. Bucher, *Administration of School Health and Physical Education Programs,* St. Louis, The C. V. Mosby Company, 1963, Chapter 7.

compulsory elements of a school curriculum, such as physical education, prompt judicial decisions on the basis of what is in the best interests of the public. Those who uphold the doctrine that a government agency should be immune from liability maintain that payments for injury to constituents is a misapplication of public funds. On the other hand, liberal thinkers feel that it is wrong for the cost of injuries to fall on one or a few persons; it should, instead, be shared by all. To further their case these liberals cite the constitutional provision that compensation must be given for the taking or damaging of private property. They argue that it is inconsistent that the government cannot take or damage private property without just compensation on the one hand, yet on the other can injure or destroy the life of a person without liability or compensation. The liberal view is being adopted more and more by the courts.

Tort

A *tort* is a legal wrong which results in direct or indirect injury to an individual or to property. A tortious act is a wrongful act and damages can be collected through court action. Tort can be committed through an act of omission or commission. An act of omission results when the accident occurs during failure to perform a legal duty, such as when a teacher fails to obey a fire alarm after she has been informed of the procedure to be followed. An act of commission results when the accident occurs while an unlawful act is being performed, such as assault on a student.

The National Commission on Safety Education points out that:

A tort may arise out of the following acts (a) an act which without lawful justification or excuse is intended by a person to cause harm and does cause the harm complained of; (b) an act in

itself contrary to law or an omission of specific legal duty, which causes harm not intended by the person so acting or omitting did not intend to cause, but which might and should, with due diligence, have been foreseen and prevented.[3]

The teacher has not only a legal responsibility as described by law, but is also responsible for preventing injury. This means that in addition to complying with certain legal regulations such as proper facilities, she must comply with the principle that children should be taught without injury to them and that prudent care, such as that a parent would give, must be exercised.

Negligence

The question of whether or not negligence was involved often arises with the actions of teachers in physical education programs. Negligence implies that someone has not fulfilled his legal duty or has failed to do something which, according to commonsense reasoning, should have been done. Negligence can be avoided if there is common knowledge of basic legal principles and proper vigilance. One of the first things that must be determined in the event of an accident is whether there has been negligence.

Rosenfield in his book *Liability for School Accidents* defines negligence as follows: "Negligence consists in the failure to act as a reasonably prudent and careful person would under the circumstances involved." The National Commission on Safety Education elaborates further that:

Negligence is any conduct which falls below the standard established by law for the protection of others against unreasonable risk of harm. In general, such conduct may be of two types: (a) an act which a reasonable man would have realized involved an unreasonable risk of injury to others, and (b) failure to do

[3] National Commission on Safety Education, *op. cit.*, p. 5.

an act which is necessary for the protection of assistance of another and which one is under a duty to do.[4]

Negligence may be claimed when the plaintiff has suffered injury either to himself or to his property, when the defendant has not performed his legal duty, and when the plaintiff has constitutional rights and is not guilty of contributory negligence. The teacher in such cases is regarded as *in loco parentis,* i.e., acting in the place of the parent in relation to the child.

Since negligence implies failure to act as a reasonably prudent and careful person, necessary precautions should be taken, danger should be anticipated, and common sense should be used. For example, if a teacher permits a group of very young children to go up a high slide alone and without supervision, that teacher is not acting as a prudent person. In the case of *Lee* v. *Board of Education of the City of New York,* 1941, the defendant was found liable for negligence. A boy was hit by a car while playing in the street as a part of the physical education program. The street had not been completely closed off to traffic.

In respect to negligence, considerable weight is given in the law to the *foreseeability* of danger. One authority points out that "if a danger is obvious and a reasonably prudent person could have foreseen it and could have avoided the resulting harm by care and caution, the person who did not foresee or failed to prevent a foreseeable injury is liable for a tort on account of negligence." If a teacher fails to take the needed precautions and care, he is negligent. Negligence, however, must be established upon the basis of facts in each case. It cannot be based upon mere conjecture.

Teachers must also realize that children will behave in certain ways, that certain juvenile acts will cause injuries unless properly

[4] *Ibid.,* p. 6.

supervised, that hazards must be anticipated, reported, and eliminated. The question that will be asked by most courts of law is "Should the teacher have had prudence enough to foresee the possible dangers or occurrence of an act?"

Although there are no absolute, factual standards for determining negligence, certain guides have been established which should be familiar to teachers. Attorney Cymrot in discussing negligence before a conference of physical education teachers in New York City suggested the following which have implications for elementary school teachers:

1. The teacher must be acting within the scope of his employment and in the discharge of his duties in order to obtain the benefits of the statute.

2. There must be a breach of a recognized duty owed to the child.

3. There must be a negligent breach of such duty.

4. The accident and resulting injuries must be the natural and foreseeable consequence of the teacher's negligence arising from a negligent breach of duty.

5. The child must be a participant in an activity under the control of the teacher, or put in another way, the accident must have occurred under circumstances where the teacher owes a duty of care to the pupil.

6. A child's contributory negligence, however modified, will bar his recovery for damages.

7. The plaintiff must establish the negligence of the teacher and his own freedom from contributory negligence by a fair preponderance of evidence. The burden of proof on both issues is on the plaintiff.

8. Generally speaking, the Board of Education alone is responsible for accidents caused by the faulty maintenance of plants (schools) and equipment.[5]

[5] City-Wide Conference with Principals' Representatives and Men and Women Chairmen of Health Education, *Proceedings,* New York, City of New York, Board of Education, Bureau of Health Education, 1953.

Defenses Against Negligence

Despite the fact that an individual is negligent, damages cannot be collected unless it can also be shown that the negligence resulted in or was closely connected with the injury. The legal term used in such a situation is whether or not the negligence was the "proximate cause" (legal cause) of the injury. Furthermore, even though it is determined that negligence is the proximate cause of the injury, there are still certain defenses the defendant may use. These are as follows:

Act of God

An act of God is a situation that exists because of certain conditions which are beyond the control of human beings. For example, a flash of lightning, a gust of wind, or a cloudburst may result in injury. However, prudent action must have been taken to establish a case on this premise.

Assumption of Risk

Assumption of risk is a legal defense especially pertinent to games, sports, and other phases of the physical education program. It is assumed that a child takes a certain risk when engaging in various games and sports where bodies are coming in contact with each other and where balls and apparatus are used. Participants in such activity assume a normal risk.

Contributory Negligence

Another legal defense is contributory negligence. A child who does not act like a normal individual of similar age and nature may thereby contribute to the injury. In such cases negligence on the part of the defendant might be dismissed. Individuals are subject to contributory negligence if they expose themselves unnecessarily to dangers. The

Figure 19–3. Nonswimmers wear life jackets for safety. (Courtesy of Atlantic-Pacific Manufacturing Corp.)

main consideration in such cases is usually the age of the child and the nature of the activity in which he engaged.

The National Commission on Safety Education makes this statement in regard to contributory negligence:

Contributory negligence is defined in law as conduct on the part of the injured person which falls below the standard to which he should conform for his own protection and which is legally contributing cause, cooperating with the negligence of the defendant in bringing about the plaintiff's harm. Reasonable self-protection is to be expected of all sane adults. With some few exceptions, contributory negligence bars recovery against the defendant whose negligent conduct would otherwise make him liable to the plaintiff for the harm sustained by him. Both parties being in fault, neither can recover from the other for resulting harm. When there is mutual wrong and negligence on both sides, the law will not attempt to apportion the wrong between them.

Contributory negligence is usually a matter of defense, and the burden of proof is put upon the defendant to convince the jury of the plaintiff's fault and of its casual connection with the harm sustained. Minors are not held to the same degree of care as is demanded of adults.[6]

Contributory negligence has implications for differences in responsibility of elementary teachers as contrasted, for example, with high school teachers. The elementary school teacher, because the children are immature, has to assume greater responsibility for the safety of the child. In other words, accidents to elementary school children are not held in the same light from the standpoint of negligence as those to high school students who are more mature. The courts might decide that a high school student was mature enough to avoid doing the thing which caused him injury; whereas if the same thing occurred to an elementary school child, they would feel the child was too immature and the teacher should have prevented or protected the child from doing the act which caused injury.

Supervision

Children are entrusted by parents to physical education programs and it is expected that adequate supervision will be provided so as to reduce to a minimum the possibility of accidents.

Questions of liability in regard to supervision pertain to two points: (1) the extent of the supervision and (2) the quality of the supervision.

Regarding the first point, the question would be raised as to whether adequate supervision was provided. This is a difficult question to answer because it would vary

[6] National Commission on Safety Education, *op. cit.*, p. 9.

from situation to situation. However, one would ask if additional supervision would have eliminated the accident and if it is reasonable to expect that additional supervision should have been provided? It was ruled in a court case that one teacher cannot supervise a large playground where more than a hundred pupils are playing (*Charonnat* v. *San Francisco Unified School District, California,* 1943). In another case (*Forgnone* v. *Salvadore Union Elementary School District, California,* 1940), the courts ruled that when supervision is either lacking or inadequate, school districts not immune are liable for negligence if they do not provide adequate supervision.

In regard to the quality of the supervision, it is expected that competent personnel will handle specialized programs of physical education. If the supervisors of such activities do not possess proper training in such work, the question of negligence can be raised. In one case (*Garber* v. *Central School District No. 1 of Town of Sharon, New York,* 1937), the court ruled that unorganized play at recess or noon intermissions should be supervised by competent personnel. A school janitor was ruled not qualified to supervise play.

Waivers and Consent Slips

Waivers and consent slips are not synonymous. A waiver is an agreement whereby one party waives a particular right. A consent slip is an authorization, usually signed by a parent, permitting a child to take part in some activity.

In respect to a waiver, a parent cannot waive the rights of a child who is under 21 years of age. When a parent signs such a slip, he is merely waiving his or her right to sue for damages. A parent can sue in two ways, from the standpoint of his rights as the parent and from the standpoint of the child's own rights which he has as an individual irrespective of the parent. A parent cannot waive the right of the child to sue as an individual.

Consent slips offer protection in that the child has the parent's permission to engage in an activity as specified by the consent slip.

WHAT THE TEACHER CAN DO TO PROVIDE A
SAFE PROGRAM

It is important to take every possible precaution to prevent accidents by providing for the safety of pupils who participate in programs of physical education. If such precautions are taken, the likelihood of a lawsuit will diminish and the question of negligence will be eliminated. Some precautions that the elementary school teacher should take follow.

The Place

Play should be fun, but it will not be fun if it isn't safe. The first consideration in avoiding accidents is to make sure that the field, swimming pool, sandlot, gymnasium, or playground is not a condemned area. A street is definitely off limits. The danger of automobiles, trucks, bicycles, and other vehicles, in addition to pedestrians, is too prevalent. Also, places where construction is going on and excavations are being made, the railroad tracks, bridges, and other nuisance spots should never be considered suitable play areas. The place that is chosen should allow ample room for movement and be free of any hazards which might involve injury.

Protective equipment such as mats should be utilized wherever possible. Any hazards such as projections or obstacles should be eliminated. Radiators should be properly screened and recessed into walls. Floors should not be slippery. Shower rooms should not have slippery surfaces.

The buildings and other facilities used should be inspected regularly for safety hazards such as loose tiles, broken fences, cracked glass, and uneven pavement. Defects should be reported immediately to the person responsible and necessary precautions taken.

In planning play and other instructional areas, the following precautions should be observed:

1. There should be sufficient space for all games.

2. Games which utilize balls and other equipment which can cause damage should be conducted in areas where there is minimum danger of injuring someone.

3. Quiet games and activities should be in places which are well protected.

4. Games where there is fast motion, such as basketball and soccer, should be played where they will not interfere with other activities and can be isolated from other play and games.

5. Boundary lines should be clearly marked.

In *Safety Education Magazine,* Paul Curtis, health and physical education teacher of the Logan Elementary School in Detroit, Michigan, has written an article on playground safety that contains many worthwhile recommendations. Mr. Curtis offers some suggestions to elementary teachers for playground safety.

You (or someone on the school staff) should look out for:

Broken glass, protruding nails, wires, tin cans, and the like.

Congestion of activities.

Children attempting activities not adaptable to the grounds.

Pools of water which cause slipping.

Neglect of the first-aid kit.

Paved play surfaces.

You should teach children not to:

Ride bikes across grounds.

Leave dangerous objects on the grounds, whether junk, bottles, boxes, fruit skins, or the like.

Indulge in unnecessarily rough play, in tripping, or in pushing.

Climb fences, tres, shelter houses.

Bring dogs on the grounds.

Use apparatus slippery from rain.

Run off the grounds and across the street.

Throw stones or other objects.

SWINGS

You (or someone on your staff) should watch to see that:

There is efficient and frequent examination of swings; and that oiling and bearings are not neglected.

SWINGS ARE NOT THROWN OVER THE FRAME TO SHORTEN THEM.

You should teach children not to:

Push swings, whether occupied or unoccupied.

Jump from a moving swing.

Run, chase, or play between, around, or under swings.

Swing two at a time.

Climb on the swing frames.

Twist or sway sideways on the swing.

Swing too high, causing the chains to slacken or yank.

Stand on swings.

Face in opposite directions while swinging.

Swing with face, instead of back, to sun.

Play other games too close to swings.

SLIDES

You (or someone on the staff) should be sure that slides are:

Frequently inspected.

You should teach children not to:

Stand up on slides.

Put babies on the slides.

Force someone to slide, or push anyone.

Slide down backwards.

Run or climb up the slide.

Play tag on slides.

Grab a sliding person, while themselves off the slide.

SAND BOXES

You should teach children not to:

Throw sand.

Throw blocks used in sand boxes.

Drop glass . . . broken or unbroken bottles, for example, in the sand.

Conceal any hard or sharp substances in the sand.

SEESAWS

You (or someone on the staff) should watch for:

Badly cracked or splintered boards indicating worn-out equipment.

You should teach children not to:

Play on such equipment in need of repair.

Jump off without regard for partners.

Bump the board on the ground.

Stand or walk on the seesaw.

SOFTBALL GAMES

You (or someone on the school staff) should be responsible for:

A fence that is high enough to keep batted balls from crashing through nearby home windows.

Providing backstops, screens, or grids to prevent balls from rolling in the street.

You should teach children not to:

Run into the street after a ball.

Wear unprotected eyeglasses on the playground. (A suitable eyeshield protects against accidental breakage of glasses which might otherwise cause serious injury to eyes.)

Throw a ball too hard.

Sling the bat.

Stand on left side of right-handed batter . . . very dangerous.

Get too close to batter (children not at bat should stay in the dugout).[7]

[7] Paul Curtis, "Safety and Fun Synonymous," *Safety Education Magazine* (March 1955).

The Equipment

The equipment is an important consideration in providing for a safe physical education program. Many accidents which occur in the school gymnasium and playground involve apparatus such as parallel bars, jungle gyms, slides, rings, and other equipment. All equipment should be in A-1 condition. A defective bar or a faulty rope can cause serious injury. When apparatus is being used, proper supervision should be present. In addition, spotters should be provided for equipment like the trampoline. Mats should be used whenever there is danger of a child's body striking the floor or wall hard enough to cause injury. Personal equipment should be such as to guarantee safety. Sneakers should be worn in the gymnasium. Eyeglasses should be taken off or protecting guards provided. Special equipment should be used in sports that involve blows to the head or other parts of the body. Safe, healthy, and proper methods of moving, storing, and cleaning equipment should be followed.

Regular inspections should be made of such items of equipment as apparatus, ropes, and chains by placing extra pressure upon them and taking other precautions to make sure they are safe. Equipment should also be checked for such things as deterioration, looseness, fraying, and splinters.

The Child

If he is to avoid accidents and injury a child should be in good physical condition. A strong and healthy body which possesses the necessary stamina to engage in games and sports without becoming excessively fatigued and which has agility and flexibility to insure proper balance and mobility, together with other components of physical fitness, helps to lessen the possibility of injury. Many injuries occur when a boy or girl becomes tired and exhausted from his or her own physical inadequacies. There should be a periodic check-up by the family or school physician to make sure there is not a cardiac condition or other defect which could be aggravated through play.

It is always advisable for children to engage in competitive sports with other boys and girls of comparable size and ability. This not only results in a better but also a safer game.

The player will also find that he gains by mastering the basic fundamentals of play. Many injuries have occurred because participants did not know what to do. Regardless of the activity, a good knowledge of the fundamentals helps avoid or eliminate injuries.

Classes and Activities

Classes should be properly organized according to size, activity, physical condition, and other factors which have a bearing on the safety and health of the pupil.

Activities should be adapted to the age and maturity of the participants, proper and competent supervision should be provided, and spotters should be utilized in apparatus and other similar activities. The teacher should be familiar with the activities she conducts and supervises. She should be present at all organized activities in the program and should make sure that all the necessary precautions have been taken to provide for the child's welfare. Overcrowding should be avoided, building codes and fire regulations should be adhered to, and proper lighting should be provided. Children should not be requested to move heavy appartus or otherwise engage in activities which may be detrimental to their health and safety.

A planned, written program for proper disposition of students who are injured or become sick should be followed. The teacher should understand the basic fundamentals of administering first aid.

The Rules

Game rules and regulations are made to protect the player and to insure a good contest. Therefore, they should be observed. A good sportsman, playing within the spirit as well as the letter of the rules, will not only receive greater respect from his opponents but will also help make the sport safer. It is the responsibility of the teacher to make the rules known to the players and to place good sportsmanship first during supervision of sports and play activities. Such actions as piling on, pushing, tripping, taking advantage of the small or weak players, cheating or using unethical tactics to win a game, not allowing certain unskilled or unpopular children to play, and other unsportsmanlike conduct should not be permitted.

Procedure in Case of Accident

In the event of accident the following or some similar procedure should be followed:

1. The teacher should go to the scene of the accident immediately, at the same time notifying the principal and nurse, if available, by messenger.

2. An immediate general examination of the injured child will give some idea as to the nature and extent of the injury and the emergency of the situation. If the injury is serious, the parents, a physician, and an ambulance should be called at once.

3. If the teacher is well versed in first aid, assistance should be given. Every teacher who supervises physical education is expected to know first-aid procedures. Everything should be done to make the injured person comfortable. He should be reassured until the services of a physician can be secured.

4. After the injured child has received all the necessary attention the teacher should fill out an accident form, take the statements of witnesses, and file this information for future reference. Reports of accidents should be prepared promptly and sent to proper persons. They should be accurate in detail and complete in information. Every accident report should contain at least the following essentials: (a) name and address of injured child; (b) activity engaged in; (c) date, hour, and place; (d) person in charge; (e) witnesses; (f) cause and extent of injury; (g) medical attention given; (h) circumstances surrounding incident. The National Safety Council publishes a standard student accident report form. This form is recommended for use in school systems.

5. There should be a complete followup of the accident with an analysis of the situation and eradication of any hazards that exist.

Mr. Herman Rosenthal, as Assistant to the Law Secretary, City of New York, in addressing a health education conference in New York City, made the following remarks about reporting accidents:

Reports should be complete, full and in detail. He advised that where a case does go into litigation, there is a delay in the court calendar of 2–3 years before the case is tried. A complete and detailed report is always better than a teacher's or a child's memory. He pointed out that the completion of accident reports was the function and duty of the teacher and in no case should a child be expected to prepare the report. Reports in the handwriting of children, he said, should be limited only to the statements and signatures of the injured and of the witnesses to the accident. He emphasized that should an injured child at the time of the accident be unable to prepare a written statement or affix his signature to a report, the teacher should prepare the necessary statement and signature and indicate the reasons for so doing. He further focused attention on the fact that teachers should not attempt to color or distort the facts in order to protect the school, or the child, because such a practice does more harm than good. An extremely important point, he said, was the need to report where the teacher was at the time of the accident, the extent of the supervision and the teacher control of the activity at the time of the accident. Also, he said that with few exceptions reports should be submitted within 24 hours of the time of the accident. He explained that in some cases this might not be possible, but in such cases no report need be delayed more than 48 hours.[8]

First Aid

First aid is the emergency care that is given to an injured or sick person until the services of a doctor can be procured. Each teacher should understand simple first-aid procedures. A teacher should avail himself of the opportunity to study first-aid procedures through the Red Cross training program or other authorized agency if he or she has not previously received this training or if a long period of time has elapsed since such training. Each teacher should own a first-aid manual or book for reference and study. Space permits a listing here of only a few general rules to follow in case of an emergency:

1. Have the victim remain in a lying position. Do not allow him to move around.

2. Examine patient for severe bleeding or asphyxia. Also be alert for injuries to various parts of the body. If multiple injuries exist, treat serious bleeding first. If patient is not breathing, start artificial respiration at once.

3. Make the patient as comfortable as

[8] City-Wide Conference with Principals' Representatives and Men and Women Chairmen of Health Education, *op. cit.*

possible and keep him warm. Do not allow bystanders to disturb by crowding or making unnecessary remarks. Do not let them attempt to give treatment.

4. Provide the person who is sent to call a doctor with general information as to nature of injury.

5. Do not give the patient anything to drink if he is unconscious. Do not move him unless it is safe and absolutely necessary.

6. Only a doctor can treat—the teacher administers first aid. This fact should always be kept in mind. The teacher should remain calm and do the preliminary job as well as possible.

Insurance

The teacher should be interested in at least two types of insurance. He or she should have a policy to protect himself against liability suits and should also be interested in seeing that the children and parents are adequately protected.

Until sane, harmless laws become a part of the legal structure of every state and thus make school districts financially responsible for all law suits, each teacher should be interested in having his or her own liability policy to protect against claims. Such insurance is available at a very nominal fee. For $10 a year some policies give protection up to $25,000 against one's own negligence. This insurance is very important since damages awarded often run into thousands of dollars. In purchasing liability insurance, however, it is important to examine the various provisions very carefully. An attorney's advice would be helpful in obtaining the insurance that best protects the teacher.

The teacher should also be interested in seeing that the school has a written policy in regard to financial and other responsibilities associated with injuries. The administrator, parents, and students should be thoroughly familiar with the responsibilities of each in regard to injuries.

Every school should be adequately protected by insurance. In general there are five types of accident insurance in use. Two types are commercial insurance policies—those written on an individual basis and others written on a group basis in the form of student medical benefit plans. The other three types are medical benefit plans operated by specific school systems, high school athletic association plans, and self-insurance.

Before a school selects an insurance policy, a careful study should be made of the various types of policies available. After the type of policy which fits the needs of a particular school is selected, several insurance companies should be contacted to determine their coverage and costs. In light of this information, the one that best meets the needs of the school should be determined. After purchasing insurance there should be periodic re-evaluation of the protection that is being given. To help in this appraisal careful records should be kept in regard to all costs, claims, payments, and other pertinent data.

The American Association for Health, Physical Education and Recreation recommends that:

School administrators should insist upon the following conditions and requirements when purchasing accident insurance, (1) the coverage should include all school activities and provide up to $500 for each injury to each pupil, (2) the medical services should include (a) cost of professional services of physician or surgeon, (b) cost of hospital care and service, (c) cost of a trained nurse, (d) cost of ambulance, surgical appliances, dressings, x rays, etc., and (e) cost of repair and care of natural teeth, (3) the policy should be tailor-made to fit the needs of the school, (4) the coverage should be maximum for minimum cost, (5) all pupils, as well as all teachers, should be included, (6) a deductible clause should be avoided unless it reduces the premium substantially and the policy still fulfills its purpose, (7) blanket rather than schedule type coverage should be selected, and (8) claims payment must be simple, certain, and fast.[9]

QUESTIONS AND PRACTICAL PROBLEMS

1. Investigate the laws of your state and write a report on the legal responsibility of the elementary school teacher to the child.

2. Interview or read the opinions of five legal experts and report their comments on the teacher's legal responsibilities in her job as an instructor of children.

3. List the circumstances under which an elementary school teacher would be negligent in her conduct of a physical education class. Suggest a corrective procedure in each case.

4. Define each of the following: tort, negligence, *in loco parentis,* foreseeability, plaintiff, defendant, act of omission, and act of commission.

5. Consult the legal files in your local government unit to determine any court cases on record which have implications for the field of physical education. Describe the circumstances surrounding each.

6. Arrange a mock trial in your class. Have a jury, prosecutor, defendant, witnesses, and other characteristics of a regular court trial. Your instructor will state the case before the court.

7. Illustrate, by specific example, each of the defenses against negligence.

8. Make a list of safety procedures that should be followed by the elementary school teacher in the gymnasium, playground, swimming pool, and classroom.

[9] American Association for Health, Physical Education and Recreation, *Administrative Problems in Health Education, Physical Education and Recreation,* Washington, D.C., American Association for Health, Physical Education and Recreation, 1953, p. 106.

9. Prepare a simple form to be used for the reporting of accidents.

10. Demonstrate first-aid procedure to be followed when a student receives a severe cut in the leg while playing in physical education class.

SELECTED REFERENCES

AMERICAN ASSOCIATION FOR HEALTH, PHYSICAL EDUCATION AND RECREATION, NATIONAL ASSOCIATION OF SECONDARY SCHOOL PRINCIPALS, and NATIONAL COMMISSION ON SAFETY EDUCATION, *The Physical Education Instructor and Safety*, Washington, D.C., National Education Association, 1948.

BUCHER, CHARLES A., *Administration of School Health and Physical Education Programs* (Fourth edition), St. Louis, The C. V. Mosby Company, 1963.

———, *Foundations of Physical Education*, St. Louis, The C. V. Mosby Company, 1964.

———, *Methods and Materials in Physical Education and Recreation*, St. Louis, The C. V. Mosby Company, 1954.

CALIFORNIA STATE DEPARTMENT OF EDUCATION, *State Legal Provisions in California Relating to Health Education, Physical Education and Recreation*, Sacramento, California State Department of Education, 1952.

CITY-WIDE CONFERENCE WITH PRINCIPALS' REPRESENTATIVES AND MEN AND WOMEN CHAIRMEN OF HEALTH EDUCATION, *Proceedings*, New York, City of New York, Board of Education, Bureau of Health Education, 1953.

DOSCHER, NATHAN, and NELSON WALKE, "The Status of Liability for School Physical Education Accidents and Its Relationship to the Health Program," *The Research Quarterly*, **23:**280 (October 1952).

DYER, D. B., and J. G. LICHTIG, *Liability in Public Recreation*, Milwaukee, C. C. Nelson Publishing Company, 1949.

GUENTHER, D., "National Survey of Physical Education and Sports Insurance Plans," *The Research Quarterly*, **21:**1–20 (March 1950).

———, "Problems Involving Legal Liability in Schools," *Journal of Health, Physical Education and Recreation*, **20:**511 (October 1949).

LEIBEE, HOWARD C., *Liability for Accidents in Physical Education, Athletics, and Recreation*, Ann Arbor, Mich., Ann Arbor Publishers, 1952.

NASH, JAY B., FRANCIS J. MOENCH, and JEANNETTE B. SAURBORN, *Physical Education: Organization and Administration*, New York, A. S. Barnes and Company, 1951, Chapter 20.

RESEARCH DIVISION FOR THE NATIONAL COMMISSION ON SAFETY EDUCATION, *Who Is Liable for Pupil Injuries?* Washington, D.C., National Education Association, 1950.

ROSENFIELD, HARRY N., *Liability for School Accidents*, New York, Harper and Brothers, 1940.

STRASSER, MARLAND K., JAMES E. AARON, RALPH BOHN, and JOHN CALES, *Fundamentals of Safety Education*, New York, The Macmillan Company, 1964.

TRUESDALE, JOHN C., "So You're a Good Samaritan!" *Journal of Health, Physical Education and Recreation*, **25:**25 (February 1954).

CHAPTER 20

Camping and Outdoor Education

Jim was a Negro boy who lived in a middle-sized Michigan city. His home was a two-room apartment in the poor section of town. As in most cities, this undesirable section had little grass, poorly constructed homes, narrow streets, and congested quarters. Jim was faced with the usual problems of one who comes from the wrong side of the tracks. In addition, he was a Negro.

He soon realized he was different from the boys who lived in the big white houses with the swings and picnic tables under the shady trees. It was especially noticeable in school. His public school was a common meeting ground for the poor and the rich— all classes and religions, since laws forbade segregation. However, though Jim was tolerated he wasn't included when the gang had a picnic, and he was never nominated when a school election came up. He was not treated as an equal. He was not given the same opportunities. During his last year in elementary school, however, a new development in the educational program of the city did a great deal to break down this prejudice against Jim.

Jim and all of his classmates were taken to camp as part of their regular school program. They lived together as a family group. They ate together, worked, played, and slept together. The youngsters realized for the first time that Jim wasn't different after all. Except for the color of his skin, he felt and acted just as their brothers at home would

act in a camp. He pitched in and did his share of the work, he was happy and fun to be with, he was the best tenor when they sang songs around the campfire, and he was named honorary second chef when he turned out to be an excellent outdoor cook. As the youngsters talked over their week at camp they realized that Jim had actually contributed a lot more to the success of their outdoor experience than some of them had. This admiration carried over even after they returned to the classroom. School camping accomplished more in wiping out prejudices than any other school or community activity had been able to do. It helped Jim and it may have helped the other youngsters even more.

Human relations are developed in camping.

Children in many other Michigan communities experience school camping and learn to respect and admire people for their abilities as individuals. California, Minnesota, New York, Florida, Illinois, and many other states are also realizing such values from their school camping programs. Children learn to live democratically in these settings. Besides living, sleeping, eating, playing, and learning with all types of youngsters, they aid in planning programs and assume responsibility for upkeep of the camp.

Camping contributes to knowledge.

The development of good human relations is only one of the many values derived

231

from school camping. The child also learns many things that could never be acquired in a formal classroom. Such things as soil, forests, water, animal, and bird life take on new meanings. The child learns the value of the nation's natural resources and how they can be conserved. He learns by doing rather than through the medium of textbooks. Instead of looking at the picture of a bird in a book, he actually sees the bird chirping on the branch of a tree. The Battle Creek, Michigan, school camp uses letter writing to the family back home to develop the language arts, the camp store to practice budgeting one's allowance, and the camp bank to make arithmetic a real learning experience. The child has experiences which are not available at home or within the four walls of a school building. A few years ago New York City conducted a camping experiment for fifth- and seventh-grade children at Life Camps, Mashipacong, New Jersey. The Board of Education's Research Division, in evaluating the experience, found that children attending camp learned more than those who stayed within the school building, especially in such things as nature study, vocabulary, arithmetic, and interest inventory. It was also shown that there was no loss in the other academic subjects.

Camping meets the health needs of the child.

The health needs of the child are better met through camping. Camps are located away from the turmoil, confusion, noise, and rush of urban life. Children have their meals at regular times, obtain sufficient sleep, and participate in wholesome activities in the out-of-doors. There is also the fun and relaxation that come from participating in recreational activities. The parents of an underweight boy in Dearborn, who had tried unsuccessfully for years to have the boy put on weight, found their son had gained five pounds in two weeks at camp.

Teachers and parents benefit.

The values of camping do not accrue only to the children. Teachers who have been part of a school camping experience have pointed out that they learn more about their pupils in two weeks of camp than they do all the rest of the year in the classroom. Parents feel better when they see their children maturing socially, assuming responsibility, and becoming emotionally independent.

Ernest O. Melby, former Dean of Education at New York University, summed up what a camp experience means when he said, "[The general education outcomes of a good camping program are] a keener sensing of the responsibilities of citizenship, concern for the welfare of others, reverence in the presence of nature and of other human beings, love for and understanding of other individual human beings, and capacity for living and working with others in an artistic and wholesome fashion."

HISTORY OF SCHOOL CAMPING

When historians look back at the twentieth century there is a good possibility they will acclaim the school camping movement as one of the greatest educational innovations of the era and nature's classroom as one important means of preparing the child more effectively for successful living in today's world.

The state of Michigan has pioneered in the school camping field for some time. In the early 1930's Tappan Junior High School in Ann Arbor utilized a camp setting for its junior high school students, and the Cadillac Board of Education developed a summer camp for its elementary school children. A little later, schools in Battle Creek, Decatur, and Otsego utilized camps in their educational programs. In 1945, the state government passed legislation making it possible for school districts to acquire and operate camps as part of their education programs. A year later the departments of Public Instruction and Conservation, together with the W. K. Kellogg Foundation, joined forces to develop the program further. The late Lee M. Thurston, State Superintendent of Public Instruction, and P. J. Hoffmaster, State Director of Conservation, set as the goal for the state of Michigan, "a week of school camping for every boy and girl in the state."

The educationally significant way in which the program is operated is largely responsible for the rapid development of camping in Michigan. The groups going to camp usually include fifth or sixth graders on the elementary level or home rooms and special subject-matter areas on the secondary level. The camps are run by the teachers and students. Preplanning takes place in the classroom where such essentials as necessary clothing, projects that are to be developed, and job assignments are provided for. The usual procedure is to have two teachers for the average classroom-size group plus extra help for food preparation and camp maintenance. The family assumes the cost of food, with special provisions for those children whose families are unable to pay the expenses. Any child who wants to go to camp is given the opportunity. Schools assume the instructional cost. The school district or government agency bears the cost of the camp and its facilities. In Dearborn, Ann Arbor, and Highland Park, for example, special budgetary provisions are made by each city to pay for camp costs.

Over 100 educational systems in Michigan include camping in their school programs at the present time. More than one-half of the school districts provide camping experiences for elementary school children. This state is pioneering in an educational movement which has many potentialities for furthering the social, mental, physical, and emotional growth of children. More than 20 other states have started school camping programs in their elementary schools. Many communities across the nation are taking Michigan's example and programs are starting to flourish in their schools. However, this movement is still embryonic. The fact that fewer than 10 per cent of the children of camp age in America ever get any type of camp experience presents a challenge for other states to follow this trend.

THE CAMP PROGRAM

The program in most camps consists of such sports activities as swimming, boating, fishing, horseback riding, tennis, badminton, hiking, horseshoes, basketball, and softball; such social activities as campfires, frankfurter and marshmallow roasts, dancing mixers, and cookouts; opportunities to develop skills and appreciation in arts and crafts, photography, Indian lore, drama, music, and nature study.

Julian W. Smith, one of the nation's leaders in the fields of camping and outdoor education, has listed a sample elementary school camp program as shown in Table 20–1. Table 20–2, pages 235–236, shows a more detailed program.

Figure 20–1. Learning valuable hints for camping.

TABLE 20–1. A Sample Elementary School Camp Program
(60 Campers—Three Program Groups)[1]

Day	Teamsters	Cruisers	Lumberjacks
Monday	Planning Hike around lake Cookout Paul Bunyan stories	Planning Hike to abandoned farm Crafts	Planning Camp cruise Tapping trees Square dance
Tuesday	Blacksmith's shop Scavenger hunt Sock hop	Logging Making ice cream Cookout	Treasure hunt Planting trees Fishing
Wednesday	Boiling sap Crafts Square dance	Hike around lake Fishing Square dance	Fire building Compass hike Crafts
Thursday	Breakfast cookout Compass hike Council fire	Compass hike Plan for council fire Council fire	Cookout Boating Council fire
Friday	Evaluation Clean-up and packing Going home	Evaluation Clean-up and packing Going home	Evaluation Clean-up and packing Going home

[1] Julian W. Smith, *Outdoor Education*, Washington, D.C., American Association for Health, Physical Education and Recreation, 1956, p. 26.

A camping and outdoor education program in California that has won much recognition throughout the country is the Camp Hi-Hill program. Table 20–2 shows how the experience in this camp helps to meet the objectives of general education.

TABLE 20–2. *School Camping as an Extension of the Classroom*[2]

Basic Scientific Understandings and Appreciations

How soil is formed.	Operation of a weather station.
How plants grow.	Use of man and compass.
The rain-water cycle.	Significance of fire damage
How forest animals live.	Study of stars.
Dependence of man upon plants and animals.	Meaning of contour, grade, and slope.
Causes of soil erosion and prevention.	

Study of Seasonal Changes

Bird, animal, and insect life.	Barometric pressure.
Uses of flood control dams.	Weather observations.
How snow is used for protection and water supply for vegetation.	How animals use the food they have stored.
	Watersheds.
Migration, fire hazards.	

Worthy Skills in Recreation

Hiking to discover, study, explore, and collect native craft materials.	Outdoor sports such as skiing, boating, canoeing, fly-casting, bait-casting, swimming, skating, and mountain climbing.
Outdoor cooking techniques.	
Outdoor survival skills.	Crafts.

Spiritual Values

Experiencing the beauty of nature.	Development of finer group unity.
Appreciation of living things developed from personal contact.	Appreciation of the beauty and worth of the out-of-doors.
Better appreciation of the personal worth of others from living together.	

Wholesome Work Experiences

Conservation projects.	Setting tables.
Planting and terracing to arrest erosion.	Washing dishes.
Repairing trails.	Cleaning cabins.
Building small check dams.	Caring for animals and pets.
Planting and maintaining a forest nursery.	Learning safe use and care of simple hand tools.

[2] Adapted from the Division of Instruction, Long Beach, California, Public Schools, *Guide for the Camp H-Hill Program,* Long Beach.

Democratic Social Living

Cooperative planning by groups.
Evaluation by students.
Discussing camp safety standards.
Living in cabin groups.
Participating in campfire activities.

Solving problems arising from living together.
Understanding duties of the forest ranger.
Acting as host, hostess, and hopper at dining table.

Worthy Skills in Recreation

Nature workshop.
Square dancing.

Building outdoor shelters.
Appreciating wholesome outdoor recreation.

Healthful Living

Maintaining personal health, cleanliness.
Maintaining regular hours of sleeping.
Keeping cabin neat and clean.
Participating in wholesome exercise.

Developing better table manners and eating habits.
Planning menus.
Practicing first aid.

Democratic Social Living

Improving relationships of pupils and teacher.   Enriching and fostering democratic living.

GETTING A CAMPING PROGRAM STARTED

The classroom teacher can be instrumental in establishing a camping program for the school. Any teacher interested in providing such an experience for the pupils might pursue the following steps:

1. Obtain as much information about school camping as possible. Explore fully what is being done by other school systems across the country in this field. The names of these schools can be obtained from such places as (1) American Association for Health, Physical Education and Recreation, 1201 Sixteenth Street, N.W., Washington, D.C.; (2) Commissioner of Education, United States Office of Education, Depart-

ment of Health, Education and Welfare, Washington, D.C.

2. Discuss the camping program with the colleges and universities in the states which are active in promoting camping programs.

3. Invite a school camping specialist to discuss this program with you in more detail. Such a person might be a representative of a school system where a successful camping program is being conducted or a professor from a nearby college or university where such projects are sponsored and studied.

4. Investigate to determine if enabling legislation exists which permits school dis-

tricts to operate camps as part of the educational program. Also, determine if there are any legal barriers to camping programs in the state.

5. Organize a plan of action which, if followed step by step, will ultimately make it possible for school children to have the benefits of a school camping experience as part of their regular educational program.

6. Develop a camping program on paper showing the organization, program, grades that will attend, teachers interested, financial outlay, relationships with regular education program. Distribute to school officials and other interested parties.

7. Meet with the principal and superintendent of schools to discuss the matter in detail.

8. Investigate possible camp sites where the school could carry on such an experience. Camps could be leased, rented, or some other provisions made.

9. Have the parent-teachers association discuss its possibilities.

OUTDOOR EDUCATION

In simple terms outdoor education means using the out-of-doors as a place to learn about things which are peculiar to nature's classroom. It can take place in a camp, but there are many other settings where such experiences take place. It isn't a separate subject in itself; instead, it cuts across departmental and subject-matter lines. It is just as applicable to science and art as it is to elementary and secondary education.

An outdoor education program, where children actually learn by direct experiences, has many proven benefits. It provides direct experiences for learning about such things as plant and animal life, conservation, rock formation, and other wonders of the universe. It enables youngsters who are removed from rural life actually to see and experience things which before were known only through books and experienced vicariously. It allows for the tapping of community resources to a great degree. It also provides additional avenues to knowledges, understandings, and skills for children, broadening their educational horizons, and furthering their total development.

Outdoor Education Experiences for the Elementary School Teacher

There are many ways the elementary teacher can use the out-of-doors for educational experiences. Some of them follow:

1. Taking a hike to a nearby woods to study the flowers, trees, and other plant life in connection with a nature lesson.

2. Planting trees or shrubs to enhance the beauty of a nearby landscape and to prevent soil erosion.

3. Walking around the school grounds to acquaint students with some of nature's works of art.

4. Going on an overnight camping trip to an historic sight.

5. Making a direct study of how animals live.

6. Taking an early-morning walk to identify the many different birds that inhabit the community environs.

7. Visiting a nearby farm to see at first hand some of the jobs performed and services rendered in agriculture.

8. Having a garden in a section of the

Figure 20–2. Correct, safe way to chop a tree.

school grounds set aside for the class where pupils can do their own planting and gardening.

9. Drawing pictures of some works of nature such as trees, leaves, landscape, lake, woods, or mountains.

10. Going on a fishing trip to study the habits of various types of fish and how to catch them.

11. Caring for animals and pets.

12. Building small dams.

13. Repairing or laying new trails through the woods.

14. Engaging in some new forms of outdoor recreation.

15. Mastering the art of outdoor cooking techniques.

16. Collecting craft materials peculiar to the section of the country in which the school is located.

17. Learning how to use a map and compass.

18. Having pupils meet at night to study the stars and the moon.

19. Learning the meaning of such terms as slope, erosion, conservation, gulley, contour, terracing, and geology.

20. Going to a zoo to see the animal and bird life.

21. Visiting a quarry as a means of introducing a new unit on earth science.

22. Developing and arranging a picture exhibit of plant and animal life of the area.

23. Visiting a museum, planetarium, botanical garden, or bird or animal sanctuary.

24. Visiting the local weather station to learn about weather forecasting.

Camping and Outdoor Education—An All-School Affair

Camping and outdoor education are not limited to one grade in a school or to one subject. They have important contributions to make to the total school offering. Paul E. Harrison has pointed out the contributions various departments in many schools are making to camping and outdoor education programs. These suggestions point out the role of the total school offering in such an educational experience.

Figure 20–3. Living and working together. (San Diego City Schools Photo.)

Speech

Activities in speech and dramatics can take many forms:

1. Short plays, comedy, drama, and so on.
2. Pageants.
3. Folk festivals.
4. Readings, recitations.
5. Marionette and puppet shows.

Music

Campers can spend many happy hours with music:

1. Informal campfire sings.
2. Pageants.
3. Camp orchestra.

Mathematics

Arithmetic is a must in many camp activities:

1. Food costs.
2. Surveying and mapping.
3. Camp stores and banks.
4. Figuring land areas, elevation, tree heights, lumber footage, tree age.

Industrial Arts

Using appropriate tools and interesting natural materials where they are found:

1. Camp maintenance and repair.
2. Building new camp equipment.
3. Reading blueprints.
4. Camp activities, dramatics, staging, and so on.
5. Craft programs.

Homemaking

Good food and appropriate clothing make for a happy camp:

1. Planning and preparing foods for cookouts, campouts, and regular menus.
2. Care of clothing and camp equipment.
3. Social graces.
4. Helping with camp food service.

English

The camp can provide an opportunity for the practice of effective communication and appreciation of literature:
1. Proper language usage.
2. Writing letters, plays, poems.
3. Storytelling.
4. Reading.

Social Science

The history of the area—its land, its people, and its customs—is always an interesting problem for study:
1. A study of the area's industries.
2. Indian lore and the lumber camps.
3. Use of public property.
4. Camp government.

Science, Physical and Biological

A study of the land, water, and living things is always interesting and useful:
1. A study of forest and forest life.
2. Experiences in botany.

3. Activities in geology.
4. Study of the skies, stars, constellations, weather stations, and so on.
5. Soil.
6. Sanitation.
7. Rivers and lakes.
8. Fish and fishing.
9. Fire protection.
10. Photography—aerial, and so on.
11. Map development.
12. Reforestation.

Physical Education

Exercise is basic to camp happiness:
1. Hiking.
2. Cookouts and campouts.
3. Swimming and boating.
4. Snowshoeing.
5. Archery.
6. Bait casting and fishing.
7. Hunting and tracking.
8. Wood crafts.
9. Games and athletic events.

Art

The camper has a chance to study nature as it develops:
1. Creative drawing and sketching.
2. Painting (dramatic-music pageants).[3]

QUESTIONS AND PRACTICAL PROBLEMS

1. Visit a school camp. Describe its physical aspects as well as the program that is followed.

2. Prepare a camp program for a period of one week as an extension of some classroom activity.

3. Prepare a list of camp projects which are normally taught in the classroom but which could be done more effectively in a camp setting.

4. Make a list of the basic needs of children that can be met in a camp setting.

5. Read extensively on school camping throughout the United States and report on some outstanding programs that are written up in the professional literature.

6. Develop an outdoor education project for a class of elementary school children of one particular grade.

7. Plan a trip to a zoo. Include the details that would need attention and list the values that could be derived from such an experience.

8. Describe in detail how various subject-matter areas can be utilized in outdoor education projects.

9. List ten outdoor education experiences that every child should have.

10. Write a short report on the contributions physical education can make to camping and outdoor education programs.

[3] Paul E. Harrison, "Education Goes Outdoors!" *Journal of the American Association for Health, Physical Education and Recreation,* **24:**10–20 (December 1953).

SELECTED REFERENCES

BRIGHTBILL, CHARLES K., *Man and Leisure: A Philosophy of Recreation,* Englewood Cliffs, N.J., Prentice-Hall, Inc., 1961.

BUCHER, CHARLES A., *Administration of School Health and Physical Education Programs,* St. Louis, C. V. Mosby Company, 1963.

————, *Foundations of Physical Education,* St. Louis, C. V. Mosby Company, 1964.

DE GRAZIA, SEBASTIAN, *Of Time, Work, and Leisure,* New York, The Twentieth Century Fund, 1962.

HUTCHINSON, JOHN L. (Editor), *Leisure and the Schools,* Washington, D.C., American Association for Health, Physical Education and Recreation, 1961.

KAPLAN, MAX., *Leisure in America: A Social Inquiry,* New York, John Wiley and Sons, Inc., 1960.

KRAUS, RICHARD G., *Recreation and the Schools,* New York, The Macmillan Company, 1964.

NASH, JAY B., *Philosophy of Recreation and Leisure,* St. Louis, C. V. Mosby Company, 1953.

PARTICIPANTS IN NATIONAL RECREATION WORKSHOP, *Recreation for Community Living: Guiding Principles,* Chicago, The Athletic Institute, 1952.

SHIVERS, JAY S., *Leadership in Recreational Service,* New York, The Macmillan Company, 1963.

SMITH, JULIAN W., *et al., Outdoor Education,* Englewood Cliffs, N.J., Prentice-Hall, Inc., 1963.

CHAPTER **21**

Activities for Early Childhood, Ages Five and Six

DANCES AND RHYTHMS

Fundamentals

Children in early childhood should be able to execute the following movements in rhythmical patterns: the walk, run, hop, jump, leap, and combination movements of skipping, galloping, and sliding. These are locomotor movements. Comparable body movements are swinging, swaying, pushing, pulling, bending, and stretching. Records such as Bassett and Chestnut's "Rhythmic Activities" and Dietrich's "Rhythmic Play" are excellent to use when children perform these activities.[1]

Dramatized Rhythms

MARJORIE DAW

VERSE

See saw, Marjorie Daw,
Jack shall have a new master.
He shall make but a penny a day
Because he can't work any faster.

DIRECTIONS

Two partners face each other and join both hands. The verse is chanted slowy and the partners mimic a see saw. One child rises up on her toes while the other one does a deep knee bend. This action is then reversed and is continued throughout the chanting of the rhyme.

THE DUCKS

VERSE

Some little ducks a walk did take
Out the yard, down toward the lake.
Under the fence they had to squeeze;
Then they waddled around two trees.

[1] These records are available from Educational Records, 157 Chambers St., New York 7, N.Y.

Finally they ran to the lake with vim.
They jumped right in for a good, long swim.

DIRECTIONS

Children squat on their haunches and place their hands either on their hips or under their armpits, making their bent arms into wings. Children chant the verse and act it out while waddling like ducks. One line three they crouch as close to the ground as possible to make believe they are going under the fence. They then waddle around two trees, going by one side of one and the opposite side of the other, making a crooked path. On line five they waddle quickly to imitate a run. When they get to the lake they take one big jump and then pretend to swim.

THE SWINGS

VERSE

Up, down, up in the swing,
Up in the air so high.
Isn't it a lot of fun
To be so near the sky?
Up, down, up, down,
Watch us run under and turn ourselves round.

DIRECTIONS

Groups of three children work together. Two face each other and join both hands, forming the seat of a swing. (Do not cross hands.) The third child stands behind the swing and acts as the person who pushes the swing to make it go higher. All swings stand in a double circle and all pushers face the same direction in the circle.

While chanting the verse, the pusher makes the swing go up and down in time with the chant. On *up* she pushes it away and lets go. On *down* the arms of the two players return to her, and so on. As she pushes she steps forward on one foot and as the swing returns to her she rocks back on the other foot. This makes her do a rocking motion. On the line, *watch us run under,* the pusher runs under the swing. On

turn ourselves round the partners wring the dish cloth by turning under each other's arms. Each pusher now has a new swing. Change swings and pushers so that all children will have a chance to act out both parts.

THE ELEPHANTS

VERSES

The elephant's walk is steady and slow.
His trunk like a pendulum swings just so.
But when there are children with peanuts around,
He swings it up and he swings it down.

This self-same elephant stands and sways
His body back and forth this way.
Sometimes he lifts his foot from the ground,
But rarely, if ever, he makes a sound.

DIRECTIONS

Children chant the verses, acting out the directions as follows:

First Verse: Both hands are clasped together in front of the child to represent the trunk of an elephant. He bends over at the waist. He walks slowly, swinging his trunk to the left and right in rhythm with his step and his chant. On line four, he stops walking and swings his trunk up as high as he can and then brings it down.

Second Verse: On lines one and two, children stand and sway in time to their chant. On line three they lift their left foot from the ground and replace it quietly. On line four they lift their right foot up and replace it quietly. Repeat as interest warrants.

HICKORY DICKORY DOCK

VERSE

Hickory Dickory Dock, tick tock,

The mouse ran up the clock, tick tock.
The clock struck one, the mouse ran down,
Hickory Dickory Dock, tick tock.

DIRECTIONS

One half of the children form a circle. The other half are arranged so that each child stands 4 to 6 feet in back of a child in the circle. The children in the circle represent the clocks. Those standing behind the clocks are mice.

The *clocks* clasp their two hands together in front of them and let them hang down to represent the pendulum of a clock. They bend slightly at the waist. As they chant the verse they swing their hands and arms back and forth. On the words *tick tock*, they also stamp each foot. Clocks continue this motion throughout the verse. When the clock strikes one, children clap their hands once.

Mice stoop in a crouched position behind the clocks. On line two, mice run in front of the clocks and make believe they are climbing up by stretching up as high as they can reach. When the clock strikes one, the frightened mice run down the clock and scamper back to their original place. Clocks and mice then exchange positions and repeat the verse.

❧❧

LITTLE MISS MUFFET

VERSE

Little Miss Muffet sat on a tuffet
Eating her curds and whey.
Along came a spider and sat down beside her
And frightened Miss Muffet away.

DIRECTIONS

The verse is chanted and acted out. One half of the players form a circle, stoop in a squat position, and pretend to be eating. The other children are chosen to be spiders. They walk on all fours (hands and feet) and creep around the circle. One line three, "sat down beside her," the spiders each stop by someone in the circle. These children then jump up and run away. Repeat, changing spiders and Miss Muffets.

❧❧

JACK BE NIMBLE

VERSE

Jack be nimble,
Jack be quick,
Jack jump over
A candlestick.

DIRECTIONS

Children chant the verse. On lines one and two they skip around in a circle. On line three they jump as high and far as they can.

❧❧

SALLY GO ROUND

VERSE

Sally go round the sun.
Sally go round the moon.
Sally go round the chimney pots
Every afternoon—BOOM.

DIRECTIONS

Children form a single circle and face so they move clockwise. As they chant the verse they may walk, run, or slide, moving around in a circle. On the word *BOOM*, they quickly squat, trying to keep their balance and not fall on the floor.

❧❧

MOTION POEM

VERSES

Did you ever, ever see

Children stand as tall as we?
We can raise our hands up high,
And wave our fingers to the sky.
Quickly spread them open wide,
Then drop them down on either side.

We can raise our heels with ease,
Lower them and bend our knees,
Once again we stand upright,
Clap our hands with all our might.
Tap our feet upon the floor,
While we count 1 . . . 2 . . . 3 . . . 4.

Forward arms we can extend,
And our elbows stiffly bend,
Place our hands upon our hips,
Meet on heads our fingertips,
Spin around, just like a top,
Then sit down it's time to stop.

DIRECTIONS

The class stands and pantomimes the actions in the three verses. They learn the words as the teacher says them and, when they can, chant with her.

JACK AND JILL

VERSES

Jack and Jill went up the hill
To get a pail of water.
Jack fell down and broke his crown
And Jill came tumbling after.

Up Jack got and said to Jill,
As soon as he was able,
"You're not hurt, brush off the dirt
And let's go get the water."

So up the hill went Jack and Jill
This time they got the water.
They took it home to mother dear
Who praised her son and daughter.

DIRECTIONS

First Verse: The action is done with partners holding inside hands in a double circle. All face clockwise. One child represents Jack and one Jill. They move in the circle on the first two lines as they chant the words. On line three Jack falls down *easily* and then Jill follows him on line four.

Second Verse: Jack gets up and brushes himself off on lines one and two. On line three he turns to Jill and shakes his finger at her. Then he extends both hands and helps her up on line four.

Third Verse: Again they join inside hands and skip around the circle very happily.

TWO LITTLE BLACKBIRDS

VERSE

Two little blackbirds sitting on a hill.
One named Jack, the other named Jill.
Fly away Jack, fly away Jill.
Come back Jack, come back Jill.

FORMATION

Single circle, partners facing each other. All Jacks face in the same direction and all Jills face in the opposite direction.

DIRECTIONS

First Line: Both Jack and Jill kneel on both knees.

Second Line: Jack stands and claps his hands once. Jill stands and claps her hands once.

Third Line: Jack raises his arms and flies to his right. Jill raises her arms and flies to her right.

Fourth Line: Jack flies back to his original place. Jill flies back to her original place.

Singing Games and Folk Dances[2]

THE SNAIL SHELL

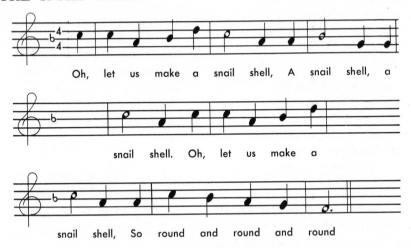

Oh, let us make a snail shell, A snail shell, a

snail shell. Oh, let us make a

snail shell, So round and round and round

Figure 21–1. The Snail Shell.

FORMATION

Divide class into groups of 10 children. Each group stands in a straight line and holds hands.

VERSES

    Oh, let us make a snail shell,
    A snail shell, a snail shell.
    Oh, let us make a snail shell,
    So round and round and round.

    Oh, let's unwind the snail shell,
    The snail shell, the snail shell.
    Oh, let's unwind the snail shell,
    So round and round and round.

DIRECTIONS

During the first verse, the first child in each line leads all children around in a large circle, which he gradually makes smaller.

During the second verse he leads them back again to a straight line. Start by walking, then change to skipping, and then to slide steps.

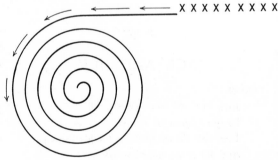

Figure 21–2. Movement during "The Snail Shell."

Sing the first verse as many times as needed to make the shell and then repeat the second verse to unwind.

VARIATION

The entire class may play this together if desired.

[2] Diagrams of various dance formations may be found in Appendix C.

IMITATIONS

Did you ev-er see a bun-ny, a bun-ny, a

bun-ny; Did you ev-er see a bun-ny, Hop

this way and that? Hop this way and

that way, Hop this way and that way; Did you

ev-er see a bun-ny, Hop this way and that?

Figure 21–3. Imitations.

FORMATION

Single circle, partners hold hands.

VERSES

Did you ever see a bunny, a bunny, a bunny;
Did you ever see a bunny,
Hop this way and that?
Hop this way and that way,
Hop this way and that way;
Did you ever see a bunny,
Hop this way and that?

Did you ever see a froggie, a froggie, a froggie,
(Repeat as above verse, substitute *jump* for
        hop.)

Did you ever see a duck, a duck, a duck,
(Repeat as first verse, substitute *waddle*.)

Did you ever see a car, a car, a car,
(Repeat as first verse, substitute *run*.)

Did you ever see a jet, a jet, a jet,
(Repeat as first verse, substitute *fly*.)

DIRECTIONS

Children hold hands and skip around the circle on the first three lines of each verse. On lines four, five, and six they pantomime the action as the word suggests (i.e., bunny—hop), going around the circle the opposite way without holding hands.

MERRY-GO-ROUND

The mer-ry-go-round goes round and round, One horse goes up and

one goes down, It's fun to reach as we go by, To catch the brass ring,

we will try; We get a free ride if we do, If not one ride and

then we're thru, The merry-go-round goes round and round, One

horse goes up and one goes down.

Figure 21–4. Merry-Go-Round.

FORMATION

Double circle. Partners holding inside hands.

VERSE

The merry-go-round goes round and round,
One horse goes up and one goes down,
It's fun to reach as we go by,
To catch the brass ring, we will try,
We get a free ride if we do,
If not—one ride and then we're through,
The merry-go-round goes round and round,
One horse goes up and one goes down.

DIRECTIONS

First Line: Eight skips clockwise around the circle. Stop; face partner and hold both hands.

Second Line: Inside partner goes way up on tiptoes. Outside partner does a deep knee bend, alternating four of each for each partner making a total of eight.

Third and Fourth Lines: Sixteen skips with partners behind each other in a single circle; each child pretends to grab the brass ring in rhythm to the skipping and the music. They stop, facing their partners, and hold hands.

Fifth and Sixth Lines: Repeat the up-and-down action of the merry-go-round horse as in line two for a total of sixteen counts.

Seventh and Eighth Lines: Drop one hand; sixteen skips with partner in double circle.

HEAD AND SHOULDERS

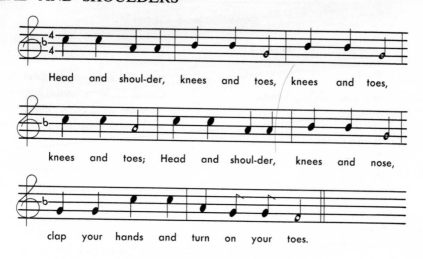

Figure 21–5. Head and Shoulders.

FORMATION

Circle or line.

VERSE

Head and shoulder, knees and toes,
Knees and toes, knees and toes;
Head and shoulder, knees and nose,
Clap your hands and turn on your toes.

DIRECTIONS

Children touch the parts of their body as they sing them.

VARIATIONS

Change words using other parts of the body and different actions at the end. Changes in tempo may also be used.

OCTOBER'S LEAVES

bright co-lored leaves?

Figure 21–6. October's Leaves.

FORMATION

Circle with children holding hands.

VERSES

Do you all love October,
October, October?
Do you all love October,
With its bright colored leaves?

First, will come the gold ones,
The gold ones, the gold ones,
First, will come the gold ones,
Fluttering to the earth.

Next, will come the red ones,
The red ones, the red ones,
Next, will come the red ones,
Fluttering to the earth.

Now, will come the brown ones,
The brown ones, the brown ones,
Now, will come the brown ones,
Fluttering to the earth.

All to earth have fallen,
Have fallen, have fallen,
All to earth have fallen,
October's bright leaves.

Now the wind comes blowing,
Comes blowing, comes blowing,
Now the wind comes blowing.
And scatters the leaves away.

DIRECTIONS

All children choose the color leaf they wish to be. Children hold hands and skip around the circle on the first verse.

Second Verse: All children who are gold leaves flutter down slowly with the music until they are as low as they can stoop.

Third Verse: Red leaves fall.

Fourth Verse: Brown leaves fall.

Fifth Verse: Sung while children are still in the crouched position.

Sixth Verse: As children sing they gradually rise moving their arms as the wind would blow them. On the last line, all the children scatter away from the circle as fast as they can.

VARIATION

Change the name and use other words, such as the springtime with its bright colored birds.

THE BIRDS

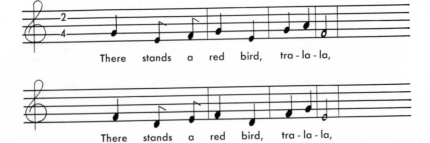

There   stands   a   red   bird,   tra - la - la,

There   stands   a   red   bird,   tra - la - la,

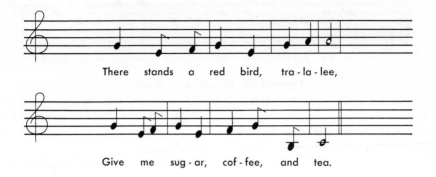

There stands a red bird, tra - la - lee,

Give me sug - ar, cof - fee, and tea.

Figure 21–7. The Birds.

FORMATION

Single circle. One pupil is chosen to stand in the center as the "bird."

VERSES

There stands a red bird, tra-la-la,
There stands a red bird, tra-la-la,
There stands a red bird, tra-la-lee,
Give me sugar, coffee, and tea.

Note: Change the color of the bird depending on the color of clothing the "bird" is wearing.)

Let me see your motion, tra-la-la,
Let me see your motion, tra-la-la,
Let me see your motion, tra-la-lee,
Give me sugar, coffee, and tea.

A very good motion, tra-la-la.
A very good motion, tra-la-la.

A very good motion, tra-la-lee,
Give me sugar, coffee, and tea.

Now fly to your lover, tra-la-la,
Now fly to your lover, tra-la-la,
Now fly to your lover, tra-la-lee,
Give me sugar, coffee, and tea.

DIRECTIONS

First Verse: Entire circle moves around clockwise either with skip, walk, or slide step.

Second Verse: Child in the center pantomimes an activity in rhythm to the music. Players in the circle clap their hands in rhythm as they sing.

Third Verse: All children do the same motion the child in the center did in the second verse.

Fourth Verse: The child in the center flies to choose a new person. All children raise their arms and pretend to fly while singing.

TO THE CANDY SHOP

Hip-pit-y hop to the can-dy shop, To buy three bars of can-dy

One for you and one for me And one for sis-ter San-dy.

Figure 21–8. To the Candy Shop.

FORMATION

Double circle, facing clockwise. Boys and girls are partners, boys in outer circle.

DIRECTIONS

Children hold hands and skip around the circle.

Second Line: Children may use free hand to hold up three fingers, to represent the "three bars of candy."

Third Line: Children stop and face each other and point their fingers as directed.

Fourth Line: "And one for sister Sandy," they turn and look all around for sister.

HOW DO YOU DO, MY PARTNER?

How do you do, my part-ner, How do you do to-day?

Will you dance in the cir-cle? I will show you the way.

Figure 21–9. How Do You Do, My Partner?

RECORDS

Folkraft Record Co., #1190; Educational Record Sales, Record 10—"Folk Dances, Song Plays, Play Parties."

FORMATION

Double circle facing partners.

DIRECTIONS

First Line: Boy bows to girl.

Second Line: Girl curtsies to boy.

Third and Fourth Lines: Partners join both hands and skip in a small circle taking 12 skips. Repeat tune singing "tra, la, la," and skip around the large circle clockwise.

RIDE A COCK-HORSE

Ride a cock-horse to Ban-bur-y Cross To

see a fine lady up-on a fine horse; Rings on her fingers and

bells on her toes, She shall have music wherever she goes.

Figure 21–10. Ride a Cock-Horse.

RECORDS

Educational Record Sales—"Nursery and Mother Goose Songs."

FORMATION

Double circle facing toward the center. Girls stand in the back with their hands on boys' shoulders.

DIRECTIONS

First Line: Four quick glide steps toward the center of the circle.

Second Line: All face right, take partners' hand and skip four steps forward.

Third Line: "Rings on her fingers," partners face each other. Raise both arms high over head and return them in a fluttering movement. "Bells on her toes," partners hold hands and jump, each extending right foot forward and replacing it. Repeat.

Fourth Line: Partners face line of direction holding inside hands and skip. Repeat the entire dance.

THE MUFFIN MAN

Oh, have you seen the muf-fin man, the

Oh, yes I've seen the muf-fin man, the

muf-fin man, the muf-fin man? Oh, have you seen the
muf-fin man, the muf-fin man? Oh, yes, I've seen the

muf-fin man who lives in Dru-ry Lane, O!
muf-fin man who lives in Dru-ry Lane, O!

Figure 21–11. The Muffin Man.

RECORDS

Folkraft Record Co., #1188; Educational Record Sales, "Kindergarten Album No. 1"; Educational Record Sales, Record 3—"Folk Dances, Song Plays, Play Parties."

FORMATION

Players hold hands in a single circle. One or more stand inside the circle.

DIRECTIONS

First Verse: The circle skips in a counterclockwise direction while singing the first two lines. First and second lines: players inside the circle walk in the opposite direction. Third line: all stop and children from inside the circle each choose a parner from the circle and take him to the center. Circle children clap. Fourth line: the children in the center of the circle join both hands and skip around. Circle children clap.

Second Verse: Before starting the second verse, the players in the center choose a partner from the outer circle to enter the circle with them; they clasp hands and dance around the circle singing the last two lines, while the outer circle does the same.

THE MULBERRY BUSH

Here we go round the mul-ber-ry bush, The
This is the way we wash our clothes, We

mul-ber-ry bush, the mul-ber-ry bush, Here we go round the
wash our clothes, we wash our clothes, This is the way we

Figure 21–12. The Mulberry Bush.

RECORDS

Folkraft Record Co., #1183; Educational Record Sales, Record 4—"Folk Dances, Song Plays, Play Parties"; Kismet Record Co., #111.

FORMATION

Single circle formation holding hands.

THIRD VERSE

This is the way we iron our clothes . . .
So early Tuesday morning.

FOURTH VERSE

This is the way we scrub the floor . . .
So early Wednesday morning.

FIFTH VERSE

This is the way we mend our clothes . . .
So early Thursday morning.

SIXTH VERSE

This is the way we sweep the house . . .
So early Friday morning.

SEVENTH VERSE

Thus we play when our work is done . . .
So early Saturday morning.

EIGHTH VERSE

This is the way we go to church . . .
So early Sunday morning.

Figure 21–13. Formation for "The Mulberry Bush."

DIRECTIONS

First Verse: Children sing first verse while skipping around circle in counterclockwise direction.

Other Verses: Children dramatize the action called for on each day, "ironing" on Tuesday, "scrubbing" on Wednesday, "mending" on Thursday, and so on.

DID YOU EVER SEE A LASSIE (LADDIE)?

Did you ev-er see a las-sie, a las-sie, a las-sie? Did you ev-er see a las-sie do this way and that? Do this way and that way, and this way and that way. Did you ev-er see a las-sie do this way and that?

Figure 21–14. Did You Ever See a Lassie?

RECORDS

Folkraft Record Co., #1183; Educational Record Sales, Record 4—"Folk Dances, Song Plays, Play Parties."

FORMATION

Single circle, facing clockwise with hands joined. One child is in the center.

DIRECTIONS

Dancers walk or skip to the left eight steps, then turn and walk eight steps to the right. As they sing line three, the child in the center does any action the children can imitate. On line four, they all imitate the action. Select a new child for the center and repeat.

LOOBY LOO

Here we dance Loo-by Loo, Here we dance Loo-by Light;

Here we dance Loo-by Loo, All on a Sat-ur-day night. 1. You

put your right hand in, You put your right hand out, You

give your hand a shake, shake, shake, And turn your-self a-bout.

Figure 21–15. Looby Loo.

RECORDS

Folkraft Record Co., #1102 and #1184; Educational Record Sales, Record 5—"Folk Dances, Song Plays, Play Parties"; Educational Record Sales, Record 10—"Honor Your Partner."

FORMATION

Single circle, all facing left with hands joined.

CHORUS

Here we dance Looby Loo,
Here we dance Looby Light;
Here we dance Looby Loo,
All on a Saturday night.

FIRST VERSE

You put your right hand in,
You put your right hand out,
You give your hand a shake, shake, shake,
And turn yourself about.

SECOND VERSE

You put your left hand in, etc.

THIRD VERSE

You put your right foot in, etc.

FOURTH VERSE

You put your left foot in, etc.

FIFTH VERSE

You put your head way in, etc.

SIXTH VERSE

You put your whole self in, etc.

DIRECTIONS

Start with the chorus. Children skip around the circle when chorus is sung. Pantomime the action as each verse is sung. Repeat the chorus after each verse, with children skipping around the circle.

HERE COMES A BLUEBIRD THROUGH MY WINDOW

Complete directions for "Here Comes a Bluebird Through My Window" are given in Chapter 9.

SHOEMAKER'S DANCE

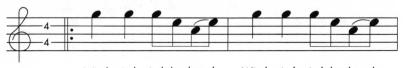

Wind, wind, wind the thread,   Wind, wind, wind the thread;

Pull, pull, and tap, tap, tap.

Cob-bler, cob-bler, mend my shoe, Have it done by half past two.
Stitch it up and stitch it down, Make the fin-est shoe in town.

Figure 21–16. Shoemaker's Dance.

RECORDS

Folkraft Record Co., #1187; Kismet Record Co., VIC 45–6171.

FORMATION

Double circle, partners facing.

VERSES

Wind, wind, wind the thread,
Wind, wind, wind the thread,
Pull, pull, and tap, tap, tap.

Wind, wind, wind the thread,
Wind, wind, wind the thread,
Pull, pull, and tap, tap, tap.

Cobbler, cobbler mend my shoe,
Have it done by half past two.

Stitch it up and stitch it down,
Make the finest shoe in town.

DIRECTIONS

First Line: "Wind the thread" by raising arms to shoulder height in front of chest, clenching fists, and winding one arm over the other three times.

Second Line: Reverse wind by rolling fists in opposite direction.

Third Line: "Pull, pull" by pulling fists apart twice. "Tap, tap, tap" by clapping own hands three times.

Fourth, Fifth, and Sixth Lines: Repeat action.

Seventh and Eighth Lines: Double circle, facing counterclockwise, inside hands joined; all skip around circle, finishing with bow.

Creative and/or Interpretive Rhythms

After the child has learned the basic single fundamental movements and their combinations in a variety of specific rhythmical patterns, he can use them to create his own patterns or interpret the standard ones in order to convey an idea suggested to him by musical accompaniment.

Such interpretations may include fall winds blowing hard and scattering leaves; airplanes taking off, flying, and landing; a day at a circus; a parade; the toy shop; joyful fairies; sad elves; Santa's helpers in a gleeful mood; or snowflakes falling and being blown by the wind.

One excellent source of music for interpretation is the ever-popular children's recording. Many records are available. Ruth Evans's "Childhood Rhythm Records," Series I, II, and IX, are excellent. Phoebe James's "Creative Rhythms," a 22-record series (AED1 through AED22) is also a rich source for creative dances. R.C.A. records offer many choices, too. Appendix A lists other sources and addresses.

Mimetics

The greater the rhythmical experiences of a child, the greater is his potential for self-expression. Activities which are specifically defined or identified by the teacher, another student, or the child himself can be imitated in mimetics. The child borrows from actual observations and mimics those defined for him. Such imitations may be of tops, wooden soldiers, animals, birds, trains, prancing horses, or skating and swinging. Records for mimetics include "Animal Rhythms," the RR2 Educational Record Album; "The Merry Toy Shop," "I Am a Circus," "Let's Be Firemen," "Let's Play Zoo," Merry Toy Shop—Album 21, Modern Activities for Primary and Elementary Schools.[3]

DEVELOPMENTAL ACTIVITIES WITH EQUIPMENT

Great fun and large-muscle activity may become an important part of the physical education program through the correct use of playground equipment. Children naturally love to climb. The jungle gym gives them the opportunity to do so. However, children must be taught correct and safe usage of equipment. See saws, swings, and slides give opportunities for the use and development of certain groups of muscles. Leg muscles are constantly used in climbing the ladder of the slides. The pulling movement of the arms on the swing and the use of leg muscles on see saws are all recommended for the growth and development of children. Other desirable pieces of equipment include horizontal ladders, climbing bars of different heights, ropes for climbing, and large tiles or barrels for crawling through.

When children are taught the safe and correct way to use these pieces of equipment and to take turns in their use so they respect

[3] Addresses of record companies are given in Appendix A.

Figure 21–17. Equipment for exercise, muscular development, safety, and fun. (Courtesy of Miracle Equipment Co.)

each other, they are learning important daily lessons in getting along together as well as gaining much fun and developing their large muscles.

GAMES OF LOW ORGANIZATION

Games with Equipment

CALL BALL

EQUIPMENT

One ball.

FORMATION

Children form a single circle. One player is in the center with a ball.

DIRECTIONS

The center player tosses the ball into the air and calls one of the children's names. The player called runs to catch the ball before it bounces more than once. If he catches the ball, he remains in the center and the one in the center takes his place in the circle. If he misses, he returns to his place in the circle and the center player calls someone else. Encourage children to toss the ball straight up and, also, as they improve, to catch it before it hits the floor.

TEACHER BALL

EQUIPMENT

One ball.

FORMATION

Several groups of eight or ten are formed. One player in each group is "teacher." The players line up facing the teacher.

DIRECTIONS

The "teacher" tosses the ball to each of the players in turn and they return it to him. When the "teacher" has tossed it to and received it from each child he goes to the foot of the line and the child from the head of the line is the new "teacher." Continue as long as interest warrants. Distances may be made greater as children become better at tossing.

VARIATIONS

Bounce the ball to each other; catch a tossed ball and bounce it once to yourself before returning it.

DODGE BALL

EQUIPMENT

One ball (any size).

FORMATION

Circle.

DIRECTIONS

Children form a single circle facing center. Place several players in the center of the circle. The players in the circle attempt to hit the players in the center below the waist by throwing the ball at them. The players in the center may run, jump, and dodge to keep out of the way of the ball. When a player in the center is hit, he exchanges places with the thrower who hit him.

HIT THE BOX

EQUIPMENT
   One ball or bean bag and one cardboard box.

FORMATION
   Circle.

DIRECTIONS
   Children stand in a circle facing the center where a box has been placed. They take turns trying to toss the ball or bean bag into the box. Each child runs in to retrieve his equipment and tosses it to the person who was on his right in the circle. One point is scored for each time the ball or bean bag stays in the box.

   Distances may be increased as children become more skillful at hitting the box. If space is restricted, a smaller box may be substituted as the children improve.

CIRCLE STRIDE BALL

EQUIPMENT
   One ball.

FORMATION
   Circle.

DIRECTIONS
   The children stand in a single circle facing the center. The players stand in a stride position so that the outsides of their feet touch those of the player next to them. One player is "It" and stands in the middle of the circle with the ball.

   "It" tries to throw or roll the ball between the legs of the players in the circle. The players must not move their feet, but they may use their hands to try and stop the ball. Knees must be kept straight. If "It" succeeds in getting the ball through a player's legs, he changes places with that player and the game continues.

Games Without Equipment

TABBY CAT

FORMATION
   Circle.

DIRECTIONS
   One half of the class acts the part of tabby cats; the other half are hungry mice. Boys may represent one and girls the other, if desired. The tabby cats sit down in a circle, if the ground is dry. Otherwise, they may stoop. The mice make a circle around the tabby cats so each mouse is at least 10 feet from the cats. A safe home for the mice is marked on the ground away from the large circle. The tabby cats pretend to be asleep. The mice chant the following

verse and do the follow pantomime actions as they creep up behind the tabby cats:

Hungry mouse is creeping and walking all
   around.
He's wearing furry slippers and doesn't make a
   sound,
Tabby cat is sleeping and dozing in the sun,
Walk softly or you'll wake her and she will
   make you run.

   On the last line—"And she will make you run," the tabby cats jump up and chase the mice. All mice run for their home. The mice caught act as cats, and cats who caught a mouse act as mice for the next game. Every child should be given an apportunity to play each part.

BIRD CATCHER

FORMATION

Rectangular area with two goals marked at either end.

DIRECTIONS

Two opposite goals are marked off at each end of the play area. One serves as a nest for the birds and the other as a cage. A mother bird is chosen and takes her place in the nest. Two other players take the part of bird catchers and stand midway between nest and cage. All other players stand in the cage. All of these players should be named for birds. Several players may take the name of the same bird. The naming of the players will be facilitated by doing it in groups.

The teacher calls the name of a bird, whereupon all of the players who bear that name run from the cage to the nest, but the bird catchers try to intercept them. Should a bird be caught it assists the bird catcher, but a bird is safe from the bird catchers if it reaches the nest and the mother bird. The players should be taught to make the chase interesting by dodging in various directions instead of running for the nest in a simple, straight line.

BEAR IN THE PIT

FORMATION

Circle.

DIRECTIONS

Children are in a circle formation. Mark two goals 10, 20, or 30 yards from each side of the circle depending on the age of the children and the amount of playing space. One player stands in the center of the circle and is the bear. The bear tries to break through the ring by parting the hands of the players. When he breaks through, all players chase and try to

tag him. If the bear is successful in reaching a goal before being tagged he may score a point and select the next bear. A player who tags the bear before he reaches the goal becomes the new bear.

CHARLEY OVER THE WATER

FORMATION

Circle.

DIRECTIONS

One player is chosen to be Charley. If there are more than 20 players, there should be two or more Charleys to make the action more rapid. Charley stands in the center; the other players join hands in a circle around him and dance around, repeating the following rhyme:

> Charley over the water,
> Charley over the sea.
> Charley catch a blackbird,
> Can't catch me!

As the last word is said, the players stoop, and Charley tries to tag them before they can get into that position. Charley has three turns. His score is the number of children tagged before they stoop. After three turns a new Charley is chosen and the game continues. All children are challenged to see if they can be fast enough to never be tagged.

FLOWERS AND THE WIND

FORMATION

Rectangular area with a home line at each end.

DIRECTIONS

The players are divided into two equal groups. Each group has a home marked off at opposite ends of the play area, with a long neutral space between. One group represents a flower. Children decide among themselves which flower they shall represent, such as daisies, lilies, lilacs, and so on. They then walk over near the home line of the opposite group. The opposite players (who represent the wind) stand in a row on their line. They are ready to run as soon as they guess the name of the flower chosen by their opponents. As soon as the right flower is named, all flowers turn and run home. The winds chase them. Each player tagged by a wind before reaching his goal scores one point for the wind. The two groups then reverse and the wind group chooses the name of a flower. After an even number of times of being both wind and flowers the group with the higher score wins.

MERRY–GO–ROUND

EQUIPMENT
    None. (A record player may be used.)

PLAYERS
    Ten to 30.

DIRECTIONS
    Form a double circle, one inside the other. Choose from one to five children to go in the middle of the inner circle. These children are the ticket takers. At the signal "Go," the players in the outside circle walk around the inner circle. The inside circle stays in place but the children move up and down representing horses on the merry-go-round. At a given signal —a whistle, a clap, or stopping the music if a record is used—the children in the outer circle try to get a horse for a ride. They succeed by placing one hand on the head of a child in the inner circle. The ticket takers try to get a horse also. Those left with no horse become the new ticket takers.

THE GARDENER AND THE SCAMP

FORMATION
    Circle.

DIRECTIONS
    All but two of the players form a circle and join hands. The circle is the garden. One of the odd players is assigned to be the scamp and stands in the circle. The other odd player, the gardener, moves around on the outside of the circle.
    The gardener calls to the scamp inside, "Who let you in my garden?" The scamp answers, "No one!" He then starts to run away and the gardener chases him. The gardener must follow the path of the scamp, in and out, under the arms of the players, who must lift their hands to let them pass. The gardener must also imitate every movement performed by the scamp, who may jump, skip, run, walk, hop, or do any other movement he wishes. When the scamp is caught, a new gardener and scamp are chosen.
    If the gardener fails to follow in the exact path of the scamp and/or perform any of the feats or antics of the scamp, the gardener must at once join the ring. The scamp then has the privilege of choosing a new gardener. If the gardener has not tagged the scamp after a few minutes have passed, two others should be chosen.

GOOD MORNING

FORMATION
    Circle.

DIRECTIONS
    Children form a circle holding hands. One child is "It" and stays outside the circle. He moves

around the circle and separates the hands of two persons. "It" stays in the vacant place left by the two, standing with his back to the center of the circle and one arm extended full length. The two children run around the circle each in the opposite direction. When they meet they extend right hands, shake hands, and repeat aloud so that all may hear, "Good morning, good morning, good morning," (3 times). They then continue around in the same direction to see who can tag the extended hand of "It" first. The winner becomes the new "It."

Variations include different ways of moving, such as hopping, skipping, or galloping. Also, seasons of the year may change the greeting to "Merry Christmas," and the like.

SQUIRREL IN THE TREE

FORMATION

Groups of three scattered over an area suitable for the number of players.

DIRECTIONS

Players stand in groups of two with hands clasped together, thus forming a tree. Trees are scattered in a large area. A squirrel is chosen to stand in each tree. One odd squirrel is without a tree. The leader of the game then claps her hands and the squirrels, including the odd player, run for a new tree. The squirrel left out becomes the odd squirrel for the next game. More than one odd squirrel may be used. Trees and squirrels change positions often.

OLD MOTHER WITCH

FORMATION

Rectangular area with a goal line at one end of the rectangle.

DIRECTIONS

One child is chosen to be Old Mother Witch. The others stand within an area marked at one end of the play space. This is the children's home. Old Mother Witch starts walking and the children follow her chanting:

> Old Mother Witch
> Fell in a ditch,
> Picked up a penny,
> And thought she was rich!

Each time the verse ends, Old Mother Witch turns and asks, "Whose children are you?" One child, who is the leader, answers anything he or she wishes, such as "The baker's," "The butcher's," and so on. After each answer, the witch continues and the children trail her again, chanting the rhyme. When the leader answers the witch's question with "Yours," the witch chases the children back to their goal. Her score is the number of children she tags. A new witch is then chosen and the game is repeated.

BROWNIES AND FAIRIES

FORMATION

Two goals are set 30 to 40 feet apart; the players are divided into two equal groups and stand in the goals. One group are the fairies and the other are the brownies.

DIRECTIONS

One group (fairies) turn their backs, while the others (brownies) creep up as quietly as possible. One fairy it watching, and when the brownies are near calls, "Look out for the brownies." The fairies then chase the brownies to their goal and tag as many as they can. Each Brownie caught scores one point for the fairies. Then the brownies turn their backs and the fairies come up quietly, and so on. The side having the greater number of points at the end of the playing time is the winner.

COME ALONG

FORMATION

The players join hands and form a single circle. One player who is "It" is on the outside.

DIRECTIONS

"It" runs around the circle, taps one of the players on the shoulder, and says "Come along." The one who is tapped starts in pursuit and tries to tag "It" before he gets into the place left vacant. If he succeeds he becomes "It" and challenges another player. If he does not tag him he takes his original place in the circle. The original "It" may have a second turn or may choose a new "It."

FOLLOW THE LEADER

FORMATION

Players form in single file behind a leader.

DIRECTIONS

The players follow the leader and do whatever he does. When one player has been leader a reasonable length of time, the teacher indicates that he is to choose a new leader. Teachers may need to help in suggesting different activities for the leader.

HILL DILL

FORMATION

Two parallel boundary lines are drawn from 30 to 50 feet apart. One player is chosen to be "It" and stands in the center. The other players stand behind one boundary line.

DIRECTIONS

The center player calls out "Hill, dill, come over the hill!" The players run to the new goal, and, as they run across the open space, "It" tags as many as he can. All who are tagged assist him thereafter in tagging the others. "It" then calls the players back to their original goal. The last player tagged becomes the new "It."

HUNTSMAN

FORMATION

Children stand in a group on a goal line. One player is chosen to be the huntsman.

DIRECTIONS

The huntsman moves around in any way he chooses. All the players follow behind him and do the actions he does. When the huntsman sees that all are away from their goal he calls "Bang." This is the signal for all to return to their goal. The huntsman tags as many as he can. Each huntsman may have three turns. His score is the number he tagged during his three turns. All children continue to play. No one assists the huntsman. After three turns a new huntsman is chosen.

RINGMASTER

FORMATION

Players form in a circle around a player chosen to be the ringmaster.

DIRECTIONS

The ringmaster makes believe he cracks a whip and calls out the name of some animal. All players in the circle mimic the actions of the animal—i.e., a tiger claws, stretches, snarls, walks rapidly back and forth. The one doing the best imitation is chosen to be the new ringmaster.

CAT AND RAT

FORMATION

Single circle facing inward. One player, the rat, is inside the circle; another, the cat, is outside.

DIRECTIONS

The cat tries to break through the circle and catch the rat. The circle does all it can to protect the rat. If the cat should break through, the circle must protect the rat by letting it out and keeping the cat in. When the rat is caught it returns to the circle. A new cat and rat are chosen. If the cat fails to catch the rat after a few minutes, reverse the names.

INDIVIDUAL AND DUAL ACTIVITIES

Children should use different activities alone or with two or three friends to develop certain skills, to share with others, and to have fun while being active.

BALL BOUNCING

Use large balls. Children may bounce the ball and catch it or they may work with partners and bounce it to a partner who catches it and bounces it back. This may also be played with four players standing in a square.

BALL TOSSING

Follow the directions for ball bouncing, but toss the balls back and forth.

CONTINUED BALL BOUNCING

When children are able, they should be encouraged to bounce a ball more than once to themselves. This develops eye and hand coordination.

BEAN BAG TOSS

Mark a circle and have children toss bean bags from different distances, trying to make them land in the circle. Circles should be of various sizes. When they become consistently able to hit a large circle, they should then be challenged to aim for a smaller one. Waste baskets and cardboard boxes are also challenging to hit.

ROPE JUMPING

Children of this age group start to learn rope jumping by having the rope turned by two persons. Some can gain the coordination necessary to turn their own rope and skip at that same time.

SIMPLE HOPSCOTCH

Very simple diagrams for hopscotch are usable with this age group. Diagrams and directions may be found in the activities for seven- and eight-year-olds.

SELF–TESTING ACTIVITIES AND STUNTS

DOG WALK

Figure 21–18. Dog Walk.

Place hands on floor. Walk on hands and feet like a dog.

DUCK WALK

Figure 21–21. Duck Walk.

Deep knee bend to squat position. Hands on hips or tucked under armpits. Walk without raising hips.

JUMPING JACK

Figure 21–19. Jumping Jack.

Take squat position, touch hands on floor between knees, then suddenly jump up and at same time extend arms horizontally to sides.

ELEPHANT WALK

Figure 21–22. Elephant Walk.

Bend forward keeping knees straight and place hands flat on the floor. Walk forward and backward keeping knees and elbows straight.

TIGHTROPE WALKING

Figure 21–23. Tightrope Walk.

Draw a 10-foot line on floor. Walk line using arms to balance.

MONKEY JUMP

Figure 21–20. Monkey Jump.

On all fours, imitate a jumping monkey.

RABBIT JUMP

1

Squat position. Place hands on floor in front of feet. Push off on the feet and lift hands from floor. Catch weight on hands and bring feet to hands to imitate a rabbit hop.

2   3

Figure 21–24. Rabbit Jump.

STORY PLAYS

Titles for story plays may be planned on a monthly basis using seasons, holidays, and special occasions. The following are suggested by month. Teachers will readily find many more of interest to their children. Refer to Chapter 9 for a story play showing complete development, progression, and correlation.

TABLE 21–1. *Possible Themes for Story Plays*

September	
Preparations for returning to school.	Taking a long hike through the woods.

October	
Getting ready for Halloween.	Gathering autumn leaves.
Going to the country to get pumpkins.	Picking apples.
Raking leaves and helping Mother and Dad.	

November	
Thanksgiving—going to Grandma's house.	Gathering nuts.
Going to a turkey farm to get a turkey.	November winds.
Fixing and delivering baskets of food to ill and needy families.	

December	
Santa's helper.	Christmas toys.
Santa's reindeer.	Trimming the Christmas tree.
Getting the Christmas tree from Farmer Brown's farm.	

January

Shoveling snow.

Making snowmen and knocking off their hats with snowballs.

Skating on a pond and up a creek.

Coasting.

February

Stories relating to Washington.

Stories relating to Lincoln.

Valentine's Day.

A snow storm.

March

The Easter Bunny's helpers.

March winds.

April

Raking and mowing lawns.

Planting a garden.

House cleaning.

Baby birds.

May

Going to the woods to pick flowers.

Preparing and delivering May baskets.

Trees in a storm.

Going swimming.

June

Getting ready and going on a picnic.

Getting ready and going to the lake or sea-shore for a swim.

Picking cherries.

Going fishing.

CLASSROOM GAMES

SEVEN UP

PLAYERS

Entire class.

DIRECTIONS

Pupils are all in their seats. A captain is in charge at the front of the room. The captain calls seven pupils to the front of the room. The captain instructs all players in their seats to put their heads on their desks and close their eyes. The seven pupils at the front of the room then tiptoe around the room. Each one touches one person gently on the head. Then they return to the front of the room. The person touched raises his hand so that he will not be touched twice. All heads remain down until the captain tells them to raise them by saying "Seven up." The captain then asks each person with a raised hand to guess who touched him. If he guesses correctly, he exchanges places and goes to the front of the room. If he fails to guess who touched him, the toucher remains as one of the seven to play the next game.

must answer, "Hi ho Silver." The Lone Ranger tries to identify the voice. He may have three tries. If he does not guess correctly, the player who fooled him is blindfolded and becomes the Lone Ranger.

TRAFFIC LIGHT

EQUIPMENT

Three circles cut from 9-inch by 12-inch pieces of construction paper. One is red, one yellow, and one green. Music—any march.

PLAYERS

Entire class.

DIRECTIONS

Choose one child to be a policeman and supply him with the red, yellow, and green circles. All children march around the room in time with the music. The policeman flashes first one color then another. Children must obey the traffic lights. Green light means "Go" and they march. Yellow light means "Caution," and they mark time in place. Red light means "Stop," and they move no part of their body. Various steps, such as skipping, tiptoes, giant strides, and so on, may be used. Change the direction and paths the children take.

THE LONE RANGER

EQUIPMENT

A bandana to cover a child's eyes.

PLAYERS

Entire class.

DIRECTIONS

The class chooses one child to be the Lone Ranger. He is blindfolded. The other children form a circle with the Lone Ranger in the middle. He whirls around three times, points to a person and calls "Hi ho Silver!" This person

YARN BALL DODGE BALL

EQUIPMENT

One yarn ball.

PLAYERS

Entire class.

DIRECTIONS

Divide the class into two groups. One group sits in their seats in the center of the classroom. The other group forms a square around them. The group which is standing up gets three minutes to hit as many sitters as they can with the yarn ball. Each hit is a point. The score is kept aloud by the leader of the throwing team. After three minutes the groups change. The higher score wins.

QUIET AS MICE

EQUIPMENT

Five chairs; five blackboard erasers, bean bags, or objects of similar size.

PLAYERS

Entire class.

DIRECTIONS

Five children are chosen to be big mice; each one sits on a chair in front of the room. One object representing a big cheese is placed under each chair. All other children act as baby mice who try to steal the cheese from the big mice. The big mice close their eyes and five baby mice are selected to steal the cheese.

They go up as *quietly as mice*. Even if the big mouse hears a baby mouse, he or she does nothing. When each baby mouse has a cheese, all children exchange seats very quietly so the big mouse cannot trace the sound and guess who stole his cheese. Each big mouse is given one guess to determine who stole his cheese. If he is successful, he remains a big mouse. If he fails, each successful baby mouse grows to a big mouse.

SELECTED REFERENCES

See the end of Chapter 22.

Activities for Early Childhood, Ages Seven and Eight

DANCES AND RHYTHMS

Dramatization and Creative Rhythms

Additional dramatizations and creative rhythms are an important phase of the rhythm program at this level. The child is encouraged to utilize the basic fundamental movements and combination movements to convey ideas suggested by the children's experiences, the teacher, or musical compositions. These age groups may be expected to develop movement compositions (floor patterns) by using combinations of the various fundamental movements to interpret ideas or suggestions conveyed by music.

New steps should include the basic schottische and modified polka, which are easily learned combinations of fundamental movements.

1. Schottische—step (L)–step (R)–step (L)–hop (R).
2. Modified polka—step (L)–together (R)–step (L).

Other activities that may be included are rope jumping and ball bouncing to music. Suggested records for these rhythms are Evans, "Skip Rope Games," Series IV, Evans Childhood Records; and Durlacher, Album 12, "Rope Skipping."[1]

[1] The addresses of some record companies are given in Appendix A.

Singing Games and Folk Dances

THE THREAD FOLLOWS THE NEEDLE

The thread fol-lows the nee-dle, The thread fol-lows the nee-dle,

In and out the nee-dle goes, As Mo-o-ther mends the child-ren's clothes.

Figure 22–1. The Thread Follows the Needle.

RECORDS

Folkraft Record Co., V22760; Victor E–87–5064.

FORMATION

Children form a single line, all hands joined in a chain.

DIRECTIONS

To sew the stitches, the leader guides the line under the raised arms of the last two chil-dren in line. When the complete line has passed under the last two children's arms, these two turn to face the opposite direction and cross their arms across their chests. The Leader con-tinues guiding the children in and out, down the line. Each one passed turns about. This con-tinues until all the children are facing in the opposite direction, with their hands crossed over their chests. To rip out the stitches, each child turns under his top arm and the line is straight again.

JUMP, JIM JOE

Jump, jump, oh jump, Jim Joe. Take a lit-tle whirl, and a-round you'll go.

Slide, slide, and stamp just so. Then take an-oth-er part-ner and you

jump, Jim Joe.

Figure 22–2. Jump, Jim Joe.

RECORDS

Folkraft Record Co., #1180; Educational Record Sales (78 r.p.m.), Record 1, "Folk Dances, Song Plays, Play Parties."

FORMATION

Dancers form a double circle with both hands joined. The girls are on the outside, boys on the inside.

DIRECTIONS

First Line: Partners take five jumps in place.

Second Line: Hook right arms and turn in a small circle with partners with ten running steps.

Third Line: Face partners, both hands at sides. Each partner takes two slide steps to the right and three stamps in place on "stamp just so." They should then be facing new partners.

Fourth Line: Hook right arms with new partner and turn in a small circle with nine running steps. On "Jump, Jim Joe," partners jump three times in place. Repeat dance.

JOLLY IS THE MILLER

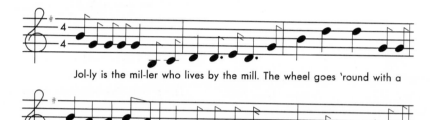

Jol-ly is the mil-ler who lives by the mill. The wheel goes 'round with a

right good will; One hand in the hop-per and the oth-er in the sack, The

right steps for-ward and the left steps back.

Figure 22–3. Jolly Is the Miller.

RECORDS

Folkraft Record Co., #1192; Educational Record Sales, Album 10, "Honor Your Partner" Albums; Educational Record Sales, (78 r.p.m.) Record 12, "Folk Dances, Song Plays, Play Parties"; Decca, Set 283.

FORMATION

Double circle, with all of the children facing the line of direction. Partners join their inside hands.

DIRECTIONS

First and Second Lines: Players march forward in time to music. On line two they also circle their free arm in a clockwise direction.

Third Line: Partners stop and pantomime action.

Fourth Line: Partner on the outside of the circle (R) steps forward and the partner on the inside circle (L) steps back. This should give them new partners.

Repeat verse and action.

A-HUNTING WE WILL GO

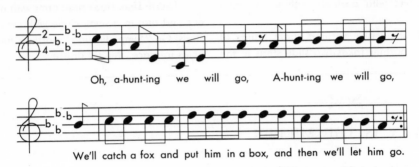

Oh, a-hunt-ing we will go, A-hunt-ing we will go,

We'll catch a fox and put him in a box, and then we'll let him go.

Figure 22–4. A-Hunting We Will Go.

RECORDS

Folkraft Record Co., #1191; Educational Record Sales, (78 r.p.m.) Record 11, "Folk Dances, Song Plays, Play Parties."

FORMATION

Two parallel lines, facing each other.

CHORUS

Tra, la, la, la, la, la, etc.

DIRECTIONS

First Line: Head couple joins both hands and slide to the foot of the line.

Second Line: Head couple slides back to the head of line.

Third Line: Repeat slide steps to foot of line.

Fourth Line: Repeat slide steps to head of line.

Chorus: Head couple drops hands and marches around behind their own line. Persons in each line follow their leaders. When leaders meet they form an arch and other couples pass through under the arch. A new head couple starts the dance again, repeating all the movements.

NUTS IN MAY

TUNE

"Mulberry Bush"; see Figure 21–12, Chapter 21.

RECORDS

Folkraft Record Co., #1183; Educational Record Sales, Record 41, "Folk Dances, Song Plays, Play Parties"; Kismet Record Co., #111.

FORMATION

Children form into two single lines facing each other about 10 feet apart.

VERSES

Here we go gathering nuts in May,
Nuts in May, nuts in May.
Here we go gathering nuts in May,
So early in the morning.

Whom will you have for nuts in May,
Nuts in May, nuts in May?
Whom will you have for nuts in May,
So early in the morning?

We will have _____ for nuts in May,
Nuts in May, nuts in May.
We will have _____ for nuts in May,
So early in the morning.

Whom will you have to take (him or her) away,

Take _____ away, take _____ away?
Whom will you have to take _____ away,
So early in the morning?

We will have _____ to take (him or her) away,
Take _____ away, take _____ away.
We will have _____ to take _____ away,
So early in the morning.

DIRECTIONS

Children in each line hold hands. One line is known as line one, the other as line two.

First Verse: Both lines skip toward each other and back in place two times in time with the music.

Second Verse: Line one repeats the action, singing the verse to line two.

Third Verse: Line two sings and repeats the action, naming the one child they wish from line one.

Fourth Verse: Line one sings and moves as before.

Fifth Verse: Line two sings and moves forward and backward and names the child in its line that will pull the other child away.

Then the children from lines one and two who were named drop hands and move to the center between the two lines. They join both hands and try to pull each other over a 1-foot line or mark placed on the ground or floor. The child pulled across the line joins the line of the puller and the rhythm is repeated from the beginning.

GO ROUND AND ROUND THE VILLAGE

Figure 22–5. Go Round and Round the Village.

RECORDS

Folkraft Record Co., #1191; Educational Record Sales, Album #1, "Singing Games and Folk Dances."

SECOND VERSE

Go in and out the windows, etc.

THIRD VERSE

Now stand and face your partners, etc.
And bow before you go.

FOURTH VERSE

Now go with me to London, etc.

DIRECTIONS

First Verse: All players move around in a circle as they sing. Three children on the outside move the opposite way around the circle.

Second Verse: Circle stops and raises arms for windows. Players on outside go in and out the windows.

Third Verse: Each of the three players who went in and out the windows faces a partner. Children inside clap as they sing, and bow as they sing the last line.

Fourth Verse: Children and partners skip around the inside of the circle holding inside hands. Repeat all verses and actions.

CHILDREN'S POLKA

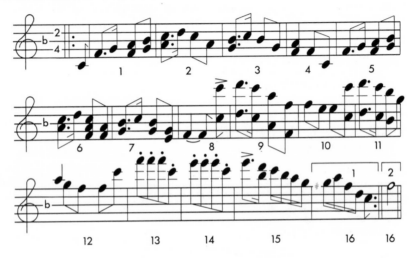

Figure 22–6. Children's Polka.

RECORDS

Folkraft Record Co., #1187; Educational Record Sales, Album 3, "Folk Dances and Singing Games."

FORMATION

Single circle, partners facing each other, hands joined and arms extended shoulder high.

DIRECTIONS

a. *Measures 1–2:* Partners take four slides to center of circle.

b. *Measures 3–4:* Four slides back to places.

c. *Measures 5–8:* Repeat a and b.

d. *Measure 9:* Clap own thighs, then clap hands in front of chest.

e. *Measure 10:* Clap partner's hand three times.

f. *Measures 11–12:* Repeat d and e.

g. *Measure 13:* Point right toe forward and resting right elbow in left hand, shake forefinger of right hand at partner three times.

h. *Measure 14:* Repeat g with left foot and hand.

i. *Measure 15:* Jump four times in place, making a quarter turn each time and turning away from partner.

j. *Measure 16:* Stamp three times, beginning with right foot.

Measures 1–16: Repeat all.

DANCE OF GREETING

Figure 22–7. Dance of Greeting.

RECORDS

Folkraft Record Co., #1187; Kismet Record Co., VIC 45–6173; Educational Record Sales, Album 2, "Singing Games and Folk Dances."

FORMATION

Single circle. Partners facing center, hands on hips. Boy on left of each couple.

DIRECTIONS

Measure 1: Clap hands twice, turn to partner and bow.

Measure 2: Clap hands twice, turn to neighbor and bow.

Measure 3: Stamp twice (right, left).

Measure 4: Turn around in place to left, with four quick running steps.

Measures 1–4: Repeat.

Measures 5–8: Join hands in circle, and, starting with the left foot, run 16 steps clockwise.

Measures 5–8: Turn and run 16 steps counterclockwise.

Repeat all actions.

CHIMES OF DUNKIRK

Figure 22–8. Chimes of Dunkirk.

RECORDS

Folkraft Record Co., #1188; Kismet Record Co., VIC 45, 6176.

FORMATION

Double circle, partners facing each other, hands on hips.

DIRECTIONS

Measures 1–2: Stamp right, left, right, hold.

Measures 3–4: Clap one, two, three, hold.

Measures 5–8: Partners take hands and turn each other around once, with running steps in place.

Measures 1–8: Repeat all. If desired, at end of turn, partners may change, going forward one place.

I SEE YOU

I see you, I see you, Tra,-la,-la,-la,-la,-la,-la. I see you, I see you, Tra, la,

la, la, la, la, la.   You see me and I see you, Then you take me and

I'll take you. You see me and I see you, Then you take me and I'll take you.

Figure 22–9. I See You.

RECORDS

Folkraft Record Co., #1197; Educational Record Sales, Record 17, "Folk Dances, Song Plays, Party Plays."

FORMATION

Two double rows facing each other and about 6 feet apart. In each of the double rows, those in front are No. 1 and those in back are No. 2. Each No. 1 places hands on hips; each No. 2 places hands on the shoulders of his partner, No. 1.

VERSES

I see you, I see you,
Tra, la, la, la, la, la, la.
I see you, I see you,
Tra, la, la, la, la, la, la.
You see me and I see you,
Then you take me and I'll take you.
You see me and I see you,
Then you take me and I'll take you.

DIRECTIONS

First Part:

1. No. 2 bends first to the left and then to the right, looking over No. 1's shoulder at No. 2 in the opposite line. Sing "I see you, I see you," measures 1–2.

2. No. 2 makes three quick movements of the head, leaning left, right, left, looking at No. 2 opposite. Sing "Tra, la, la, la, la, la, la," measures 3–4.

3. Repeat the directions accompanying measures 1–2 and 3–4, above, while singing measures 5–8.

Second Part:

1. All clap hands on the first beat of the measure, and No. 2 skips forward, meets No. 2 from the opposite line. Joining hands, both swing around once to the left. Sing "You see me and I see you, Then you take me and I'll take you," measures 5–8.

2. All clap hands on the first beat of the measure and join hands with partner and swing around to the left, finishing with No. 1 in the rear of No. 2. Sing "You see me and I see you, Then you take me and I'll take you," Measures 1–4.

Repeat all, with No. 1 in rear.

PAW PAW PATCH

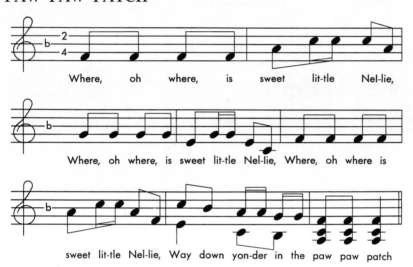

Figure 22–10. Paw Paw Patch.

RECORDS

Folkraft Record Co., #1181.

FORMATION

File formation, set of six to eight couples.

SECOND VERSE

Come on boys, let's go find her . . .
Way down yonder in the paw paw patch.

THIRD VERSE

Pickin' up paw paws, put 'em in her pocket . . .
Way down yonder in the paw paw patch.

DIRECTIONS

First Verse: The first girl in the line skips clockwise in a circle around the set. (Note: Use the name of the girl involved.)

Second Verse: The same girl skips around the set again, and is now followed by the entire line of boys until they all return to their places.

Third Verse: Head boy and head girl again lead their lines in a circle clockwise around the original set. When the head couple meet they form an arch and, as each couple meet, they go through the arch. A new lead couple comes through and restarts the dance.

VARIATION

First sing girl's name. Next time sing boy's name and change words and actions accordingly.

Figure 22–11. Climbing is good exercise for children of all ages.

DEVELOPMENTAL ACTIVITIES

Activities with Equipment

Continued use of playground equipment and indoor equipment, such as ropes, horizontal ladders, and horizontal bars, is important to the further development of children at this age level. Time should be allotted in the program for this with instruction and encouragement. Not all children are as agile or as strong as others and special body types should be considered in terms of achievement.

Activities Without Equipment

RUNNING IN PLACE

Start slowly and increase speed. Increase time as children become conditioned.

JUMPING IN PLACE

Do for one minute. As children get conditioned, increase time.

HOPPING IN PLACE

Hop on alternate feet. Stress lightness in landing.

BICYCLE

Figure 22–12. Bicycle.

Lie on floor with feet high in the air. Back is supported by hands, with weight of body placed on shoulders. With legs and feet imitate the motions of pedaling a bicycle.

JUMPING JACK

Child jumps with feet apart to a stride position and claps hands over his head by moving arms sideward. He then returns to an erect standing position. Repeat and gradually increase number of times as children become conditioned.

SIT-UP

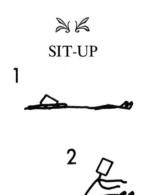

Figure 22–13. Sit-Up.

Lie flat on back, legs straight out, and feet together. Clasp hands over head or behind neck. Come to a sitting position by keeping feet on floor and legs straight. Slowly lie down again.

PROPELLER

Child stands erect, arms extended sideward at shoulder, height, palms down. Maintaining this position, he inscribes small circles with the hands. Circles can be inscribed forward and backward.

ABDOMINAL CURL

Child lies on floor on back, arms at side of body or extended sideward at shoulder level. Lift both legs from the floor and attempt to touch the floor above the head with the toes.

BOUNCING BALL

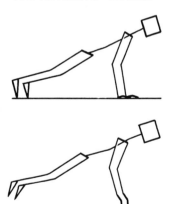

Figure 22–14. Bouncing Ball.

Assume pushup position, by bending forward extending the arms and placing the hands on the floor, shoulder width apart, fingers pointing forward, and extending trunk and legs backward in a straight line. The body is supported on the hands and toes.

Bounce up and down by a series of short, upward springs. (Try clapping hands together while body is in the air.)

FROG STAND

Figure 22–15. Frog Stand.

Assume squat position, hands on floor, fingers pointing forward. The elbows are inside of, and pressed against, the knees.

Lean forward slowly, transferring body weight to hands, raising feet clear of the floor. Maintain balance, keeping head up. Hold for several seconds, then return to starting position.

Repeat, maintaining balance for increasingly longer periods.

WHEELBARROW

Figure 22–16. Wheelbarrow.

Children pair off. One takes "hands and knees" position. The hands are directly under the shoulders, fingers pointing forward. His partner grasps the kneeling pupil's ankles, raising his legs.

The first pupil walks forward on his hands. His feet and legs are supported by partner walking between the outstretched legs.

GAMES OF LOW ORGANIZATION

Games with Equipment

FOX AND RABBIT

EQUIPMENT
Two balls or bean bags.

FORMATION
Circle.

DIRECTIONS
Two bean bags or two balls should be used. One should be white; the other, a different color. The white one represents the rabbit; the other represents the fox. One child in the circle is given the rabbit, which he sends around the circle by passing it quickly to the child next to him, and so on. A moment later

the fox is started, giving chase to the rabbit. The rabbit must reach the starting point before the fox overtakes it.

RUN AND HIT

EQUIPMENT

One rubber ball for each group.

PLAYERS

Five to ten in a group; two groups.

DIRECTIONS

One group lines up horizontally and the other vertically in a square or rectangular playing area. Half of each group is on each side of the area. A goal is marked across the two ends of the play area. The running group occupies its place behind these goal lines—half on each side. The other group is given a ball. At the signal "Go," the running group endeavors to exchange goals. The throwing group endeavors to hit as many of them as possible before they cross the goal lines. If one is hit before he

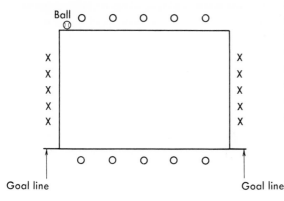

O's = Throwers' Team

X's = Runners' Team

Figure 22–17. Run and Hit.

crosses the line safely it is one out. If all cross the lines and no one is hit, the team scores a

run. Each hit constitutes an out. Three outs constitute one half an inning and the groups exchange places. The highest score of the last complete inning declares a winning group.

WESTERN ROUNDUP

EQUIPMENT

A piece of rope 4 or 5 feet long and a bean bag for every five children.

PLAYERS

Fifteen to 25.

DIRECTIONS

Five children are chosen to be steers. Each steer is given one piece of rope and a bean bag. He ties the bean bag to the end of the rope. This represents the tail of the steer, and each steer drags it. The other children are either horses or cowboys and are paired off. Each couple makes a horse and a cowboy or cowgirl. Couples hold hands. The game begins by permitting the steers to wander off. Cowboys and horses must wait behind a line until the steers call "Ready." Then the cowboys and horses gallop off and try to catch a steer by catching its tail. Only the cowboy—*not the horse*—may attempt to catch the steer. When one steer is caught, all players return to the original starting position. Children then choose a new role and start the game again.

JOHN BROWN

EQUIPMENT

One Indian club, empty salt box, or milk carton for each group.

PLAYERS

Divide all players into groups of 10 each.

DIRECTIONS

Place a club, milk carton, or salt box in a square about 30 feet from the starting line. Draw another square 5 to 10 feet away from it. Leave it empty. The ten children on each team or squad stand in a straight line facing the objects and the squares. They number themselves from one to ten. Each child must remember his number. At the signal "Go" number one on each team runs forward, picks up the object, and puts it in the other square. He then runs

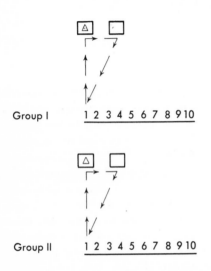

Figure 22–18. John Brown.

back to the line and calls out "One." This is the clue for number *two* to run. He puts the object back in its original square. When he returns to his starting position he calls out "Two," the signal for number *three* to run. The game continues in this manner until all ten children have had one turn. After number *ten* returns to the line and calls out "Ten," the game is only half completed. His call of "Ten" is the signal for number *nine* to run again, his call of "Nine" is the signal for number *eight,* and so on back to number *one.* When number *one* returns to the starting line he raises his hand and calls out

"John Brown." The first group to finish is the winner.

CHASE THE BONE

EQUIPMENT

One rubber dog bone for each group.

PLAYERS

Eight to 10 in a group.

DIRECTIONS

Each group forms a circle. In the center of each circle, a 3-foot circle is drawn on the ground. One child is chosen for the thrower and one for "It." The thrower takes the dog bone, stands in the 3-foot circle, and throws it as far as he can. All players, except "It," then run and hide. "It" chases the bone, retrieves it, and runs back with it to the 3-foot circle, where he drops it. He may then start calling the names of all people he can see. They are caught and return to the area. He must search for the others. As he finds them, he calls them out by touching his foot on the bone in the circle. While he is away from the bone, a player whom he has not found may sneak in, get the bone, and throw it out of the circle again. If this happens, all persons who were caught are again free to run and hide. "It" must then secure the bone, place it back in the circle, and start the hunt all over. "It" may call all players in at any time by calling "chase the bone." To do this he throws the bone from the circle and those who are still hiding may come in and are all free. A new thrower and "It" are chosen and the game begins again.

CIRCLE RUN

EQUIPMENT

Two rubber balls and four colored flags.

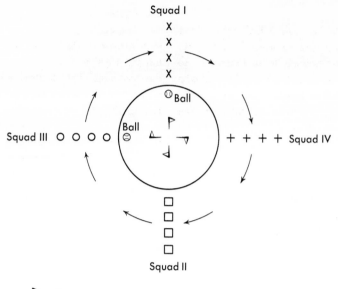

 = Flag

Figure 22–19. Circle Run.

PLAYERS

Four squads, four to eight players each.

DIRECTIONS

Squads one and two are arranged on opposite sides of the circle. They play together. Squads three and four are opposite sides and they play together. The flags are placed in the center of the circle. All players face left, the direction in which they will run. The first players on squads one and three are given balls. At the signal "Go," they pass the balls back over their heads until they reach the last child. When he receives it, he runs around to the opposite squad, stands in front of it, and passes the ball over his head back again to the last person (i.e., number *one* runs to squad two; number *three* to squad four). The game continues until squads one and two have changed places and squads three and four have done the same. When all players of a squad arrive at their new home, number *one* of that squad goes to the center of the circle, picks up the flag, and raises it in the air. The two squads that raise flags first are the winners.

BOUNCE BALL

EQUIPMENT

One 8- or 10-inch rubber ball for each group.

PLAYERS

Four to six players in each group.

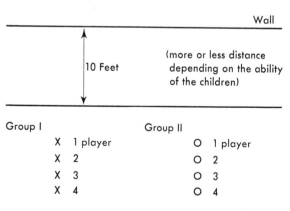

Figure 22–20. Bounce Ball.

DIRECTIONS

The first child bounces a ball against the wall. Number *two* runs forward and tries to catch it on the first bounce. If he catches it, he scores a point. Number *two* throws the ball and number *three* runs to catch it. As each child throws it, the next one tries to catch it. The team that has the most successful catches at the end of a given amount of play time wins.

CENTER BASE

EQUIPMENT

One ball.

DIRECTIONS

The players stand in a circle formation. One player is "It" and stands in the center of the circle. He tosses a ball to a player in the circle who catches it, brings it to the center, and places it in the base. The base is a small circle marked in the center of the circle of players. After he has placed the ball in the base, he chases the player who threw the ball to him. Both the runner and the chaser must leave the circle through the space left in the circle by the player catching the ball.

The runner is safe by coming back into the circle through this same space and touching the ball. If the chaser tags the runner, he becomes "It." If not, a new "It" is chosen.

CENTER CIRCLE PASS BALL

EQUIPMENT

Bean bag or ball.

FORMATION

Single circle facing the center. One person stands in the circle and has the equipment.

DIRECTIONS

The center player throws ball or bean bag to a player in the circle, who immediately returns it. He then tosses it to another player and this continues until all players in the circle have had a turn. Another player is then chosen to be center player.

As soon as the game is learned three or four circles should be playing to give more activity. Variations of passing a ball may include underhand, overhand, and bounce pass.

OVERHEAD TOSS

EQUIPMENT

Volley or other inflated ball.

FORMATION

Groups of not more than eight children. One player with a ball stands on a throwing line. He stands with his back to the group. The other players stand around in the playing space. They may be at different distances from "It."

DIRECTIONS

The player with the ball tosses it with both hands, backward, over his head. The other players attempt to catch it before it hits the ground. When a player is successful in catching the ball he changes places with the thrower and the game continues.

If the class has difficulty catching the fly ball, it may be caught on one bounce for a change of leaders.

CIRCLE TOSS

EQUIPMENT

A ball or bean bag for each of the players except one.

FORMATION

All the players form a circle facing center. They are separated from one another by a space of 3 or 4 feet.

DIRECTIONS

At a signal from a leader, each player turns toward his right-hand neighbor and tosses his ball or bean bag to him. He then turns at once to receive the bag or ball which is coming to him from the left. The game should move rapidly. If children are not quick enough, it may be advisable at first to play the game with a smaller number of balls or bean bags. Do this until the children grow accustomed to tossing and turning quickly to catch. Change directions of the tossing when you wish—and when the children least expect it—to add interest once the basic movements are learned.

DAYS OF THE WEEK

EQUIPMENT

A ball

FORMATION

The class stands side by side in seven groups. Each group is named for the days of the week. A child stands in front of the group and is the leader.

DIRECTIONS

The leader throws the ball in the air and calls out one of the days of the week. The players from this group run forward. Each one attempts to catch the ball in the air or on the first bounce. The one who catches it becomes the new leader. The others return to their places.

Games Without Equipment

COWBOY AND INDIAN

FORMATION

Double circle facing center.

DIRECTIONS

The class forms a double circle facing the center. The children in the circle represent trees. Two players are selected from the group and take their places outside the circles. One is named the Indian and the other is the cowboy. At the signal "Go," the cowboy chases the Indian around the circle and attempts to tag him. The Indian may avoid being tagged by stopping *in front* of a group of two. This makes three in the group, and the third one (the one on the outside) becomes the new Indian. The chase continues. If, at any time, the cowboy catches the Indian, the chase is reversed and the Indian attempts to catch the cowboy.

Change cowboys and Indians often. Some may never be tagged.

MIDNIGHT

FORMATION

Rectangular area.

DIRECTIONS

One player is the fox and the others are sheep. The fox may catch the sheep only at midnight. The game starts with the fox standing in a den marked in one corner of the playground, and the sheep in the sheepfold marked in the diagonally opposite corner. The fox leaves his den and wanders about the playground, whereupon the sheep also come forth and scatter around approaching as close to the fox as they dare. One player is designated as the leader of the sheep and asks, "What time is it?" The fox answers any hour he chooses. Should he say "Three o'clock" or "Eleven o'clock," the leader asks again; but when the fox says "Midnight!" all sheep run for the sheepfold as fast as possible. The fox chases them. Any sheep caught changes places with the fox, and the game is repeated.

LAME FOX AND CHICKENS

FORMATION
  Rectangular area with two goals.

DIRECTIONS
  One player is chosen for the fox and stands in a den marked off at one end of the playground. The rest are chickens and have a chicken yard at the opposite end of the ground. The chickens advance as near as they dare to the den of the fox and tease him by calling out, "Lame fox! Lame fox! Can't catch anybody!" The lame fox may take only three steps beyond his den, after which he must hop on one foot, trying to tag the chickens while hopping. All tagged chickens become foxes and go home with him, thereafter sallying forth with him to catch the chickens. They must all then observe the same rule of taking but three steps beyond the den, after which they must hop. Should any fox put both feet down at once after his three steps while outside the den, the chickens may drive him back. Care should be taken that the hopping be always done on one foot, though a fox may change his hopping from one foot to the other. The last chicken caught wins the game and becomes the first lame fox in the new game.

CHINESE WALL

FORMATION
  Rectangular area with a middle area

marked for a wall and a goal at each end of the area.

DIRECTIONS
  The Chinese wall is marked off by two parallel lines straight across the center of the playground, leaving a space between them about ten feet in width. This space represents the wall. On each side of the wall, at a distance of from 15 to 30 feet, a parallel line is drawn across the ground. This marks the safety point or home goal for the besiegers.
  One player is chosen to defend the wall and takes his place in the area. All of the other players stand in one of the home goals. The defender calls "Start!" All of the players must cross the wall and go to the opposite goal. The defender tries to tag as many as he can as they cross, but he may not overstep the boundaries of the wall himself. All players tagged join the defender in trying to tag future players exchanging goals. The game ends when all have been caught. The last player tagged becomes defender for the next game.

FROG IN THE MIDDLE

FORMATION
  Circle.

DIRECTIONS
  One player is chosen to be the frog and sits in the center of the circle with his feet crossed in tailor fashion. If there are more than 20 players, it is well to choose at least two frogs. Other players stand in a circle around the frog, repeating "Frog in the sea, can't catch me!" They dance forward toward the frog and back, tantalizing him, and taking risks in going near him. The object of the game is for the frog to tag someone. When he does he changes places with the tagged player. The frog may not at any time leave his sitting position until he has tagged another player. If the frog or frogs are unsuccessful after a few min-

utes, more frogs should be chosen or new ones should replace the first ones.

BLACK AND WHITE

FORMATION

Small area.

DIRECTIONS

One player is chosen as leader. The remainder of the players are divided into two equal groups. Each player in one group should tie a handkerchief on his left arm to indicate that he belongs to the Whites; those in the other division are called the Blacks. The players stand around the playing ground at random, the Whites and Blacks being mingled indiscriminately.

The leader is provided with a flat disk which is white on one side and black on the other, and hung on a short string to facilitate twirling the disk. He stands at one side of the playing area and twirls this disk, stopping it with one side only visible to the players. If the white side should be visible, the party known as the Whites may tag any of their opponents who are standing upright. The Blacks should drop instantly to the floor, as in Stoop Tag. Should the black side of the disk be shown, the party of Blacks may tag the Whites. Any player tagged scores one point. The side wins which has the most points. The leader should keep the action of the game rapid by twirling the disk frequently.

HOUND THE RABBIT

FORMATION

Couples holding hands.

DIRECTIONS

A considerable number of the players stand in couples holding hands. Each couple makes a small circle which represents a hollow tree. In each tree is stationed a player who takes the part of a rabbit. There should be one more rabbit than the number of trees. One other player is chosen to be the hound.

The hound chases the odd rabbit who may take refuge in any tree. But no two rabbits may lodge in the same tree. As soon as the hunted rabbit enters a tree the rabbit already there must run for another shelter. Whenever the hound catches a rabbit, new players are chosen for the hound and rabbit. Trees change places with rabbits so each child has a chance to be both a rabbit and a tree.

BLACK TOM

FORMATION

Rectangular area.

DIRECTIONS

Two parallel lines are drawn on the ground with a space of from 30 to 50 feet between them. All of the players except one stand beyond one of these lines. In the middle territory between the lines the one player who is chosen to be "It" takes his place. He calls, "Black Tom! Black Tom! Black Tom!" repeating the words three times, whereupon the other players must all run across to the opposite line. "It" chases them and tags all that he can. Anyone so caught joins him in chasing the others.

The particular characteristic of this game lies in the fact that the center player, instead of saying, "Black Tom!" may trick or tantalize the runners by crying out, "Yellow Tom," or "Blue Tom," or "Red Tom," or anything else that he may choose. Any player who starts to run upon a false alarm is considered captive and must join "It" in the center. This is also true for any player who starts before the third repetition of "Black Tom." The last one to be caught is "It" for the next game.

BLIND MAN'S BUFF (WARM WEATHER GAME)

FORMATION

Circle.

DIRECTIONS

One player is chosen to be blindfolded and stands in the center. The other players join hands and circle around him until the blind man claps his hands three times. The circle stops moving and the blind man points toward the circle. The player at whom he points must at once step into the circle. This player will naturally try, by noiseless stepping, dodging, and so on, to give the blind man some difficulty in catching him, but when once caught he must stand without struggle for identification. The blind man must then guess who the other player is. If the guess is correct, they change places. If not correct, or if the blind man has pointed at an empty space instead of at a player, the circle continues and the game is repeated.

RED LIGHT

FORMATION

Two parallel lines, 50 feet apart. One is the starting and one the finishing line. One player, the policeman, stands behind the finish line. He has his back to the group. The other players stand on the starting line.

DIRECTIONS

The policeman calls out, "Green light, one, two, three, four, five, red light." When he says "Green light," the players may start to advance toward the finish line. When he says "Red light," all must stop and stand still. The policeman turns around quickly. All players he sees moving their feet must return to the starting line and begin again. The policeman turns again and counts. The players move. The object is to move to the line the policeman is on and return

to the starting line. The first one back to the original goal is the new policeman.

RUN FOR YOUR SUPPER

FORMATION

Players hold hands in a single circle. One player is inside and is "It."

DIRECTIONS

"It" breaks the hands of two players in the circle and says, "Run for your supper." The two run around outside the circle in opposite directions. The one who first returns to his original place wins. He is "It" for the next game.

MOVING DAY

FORMATION

Circles are drawn on the ground in a relatively large area to represent houses.

DIRECTIONS

Each player except "It" must have a house and stand in it to start the game. One player is chosen to be "It." He walks up and down the streets between the circles. At intervals the teacher calls "Moving day." The residents along the street change houses and "It" tries to get a house while it is vacant.

After any one player has been "It" for a reasonable length of time and has been unable to secure a house, a new "It" should be chosen. Winners are those who were never caught without a house. More than one "It" may be used if desired.

SCAT

FORMATION

Players form a circle. One child is chosen

to be "It" and stoops in the middle of the circle. Several bases are marked away from the circle.

DIRECTIONS

All players move around in the line of direction in the circle. When "It" calls out "Scat!" players drop hands and run to the bases. If "It" catches any of the players they become his aids and help him. The last one caught is the winner.

TOUCH

FORMATION

Form parallel lines with an equal number of players in each. All face the same direction.

DIRECTIONS

The leader or teacher gives a direction such as "Touch wood," "Get a stone," or "Touch the fence." All players obey the command and return to their places quickly. The line in position first, providing all carried out directions, wins. Repeat as long as interest warrants.

TRADES

FORMATION

The players are divided into two groups. Lines are drawn about 40 feet apart. Teams stand on a line, facing each other.

DIRECTIONS

One group decides upon a certain trade. They advance to within several feet of the other group and announce, "Here we are from New York." The group staying at home says, "Have you a trade?" The first group replies, "Yes." The second group then orders, "Get to work." The first group imitates the trade to which they belong. The second group tries to guess it. When the correct trade is guessed the players representing the trade run for their home line and the guessers chase them. Each player tagged before reaching his home line gives one point to the tagging team.

The other side now has a chance to represent a trade. At the end of the game, the side with the greater number of points wins.

COOKIES IN THE JAR

FORMATION

The baker marks out several 2-foot circles in a clearly defined territory. These are his cookie jars. One parallel line is marked "Home," from which the children leave and return.

DIRECTIONS

The children leave their home as the baker moves around the area. The baker chants:

Dear children, dear children
You dare not go far,
For if I catch you,
You'll land in my jar.

When the baker catches a child, he places him in the cookie jar. Any child may be freed if tagged by another player, if he is the only one in the jar. When the baker gets two cookies in each jar, the game is over and may be restarted.

INDIVIDUAL AND DUAL ACTIVITIES

HOPSCOTCH

EQUIPMENT

A stone or a button.

FORMATION

Various diagrams may be used—see following.

DIRECTIONS

A player tosses a stone or button into the spaces in numbered order. After each toss, he hops into the space, picks up the stone, and then hops out. The stone or the foot must not touch the line. He repeats, going from number one to as high a number as possible until he

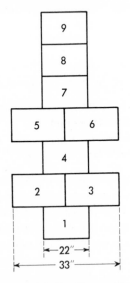

Figure 22–21. Hopscotch.

misses by tossing the stone in the wrong area, losing his balance and touching both feet to the ground, or stepping on a line. When one is

through, the next player starts. Only three or four children should use one hopscotch area at one time. In areas two-three and five-six, one foot may be placed in each.

LADDER HOPSCOTCH

| 9 |
| 8 |
| 7 |
| 6 |
| 5 |
| 4 |
| 3 |
| 2 |
| 1 |

Figure 22–22. Ladder Hopscotch.

1. In one version, the player tosses the stone into space one and hops over space one into space two. He picks up the stone and hops out, touching space one. Next, he tosses the stone into space two, hops over space two into space three. Picking up the stone, he hops into space two, space one, and out. He continues up the ladder, then down the ladder.

2. In another version, the procedure is the same except the player kicks the stone out instead of picking it up. He hops into the area

with the stone and kicks it up the ladder and back.

FINLAND HOPSCOTCH

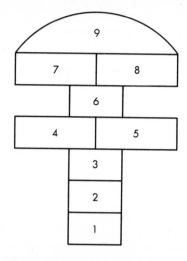

Figure 22–23. Finland Hopscotch.

Toss the stone or button into space one. Then hop into space one, pick up the stone, and hop out. Toss the stone into space two and hop into space one, then into space two, pick up the stone, and hop out. Continue up and back. In spaces four-five and seven-eight, both feet may touch, one in each square. A player misses by touching lines, using two feet in other than allowed squares, changing feet, or tossing the stone in the wrong section.

ITALIAN HOPSCOTCH

Toss the stone into space one and hop into space one. Then kick the stone into space two and hop into space two. Continue with space three, and so on, up to space eight. In space eight, both feet may be put down. The player

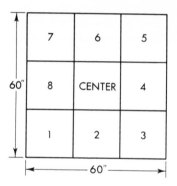

Figure 22–24. Italian Hopscotch.

picks up the stone and hops out a winner. Start again backwards, from space eight to space one in the same manner, if desired.

PICK-UP HOPSCOTCH

Figure 22–25. Pick-Up Hopscotch.

The stone is always tossed into the center block. The player tosses the stone into the center and hops into block one. He picks up the stone and hops out. He again tosses the stone into the center block, hops into block one, then into block two, picks up the stone and hops out, touching block one. He continues advancing from block to block and picks up his stone each time from the correct block. The winner is the one who is able to go from block one to block eight without missing the center square with his stone, without losing his balance when picking up the stone, or without hopping on any lines. A miss permits the next player to start.

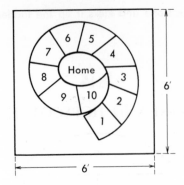

Figure 22–27. Snail Hopscotch.

TOURNAMENT HOPSCOTCH

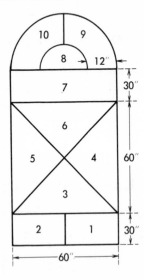

Figure 22–26. Tournament Hopscotch.

The stone is kicked as many times as necessary to move it from number one to number ten. It is a miss if it lands on a line. A double-foot landing may be used in areas one-two and four-five, and both feet may land in area seven. The stone is kicked at first with the free foot. After children become good at this, encourage them to kick it with the foot on which they hop.

SNAIL HOPSCOTCH

Snail Hopscotch is played the same way as regular Hopscotch. Endeavor to move from number one to ten without tossing the stone in wrong area, touching both feet to the ground, or stepping on a line.

JUMP ROPE GAMES

Jump Rope is a very fine activity for children of all ages and is especially enjoyed by the seven and eight year olds. Many jump ropes may be had at a minimum cost by buying a hundred feet of clothesline and cutting it into various lengths—for two to turn and for individuals to use alone. Tie knots at the ends of each length to keep the rope from raveling.

Records for Jump Rope are available.

Rhymes children chant are plentiful. Children should also be encouraged to make up rhymes and actions to combine with jumping.

TEDDY BEAR JUMP ROPE

VERSE

Teddy bear, teddy bear, turn around;
Teddy bear, teddy bear, touch the ground;
Teddy bear, teddy bear, show your shoe;
Teddy bear, teddy bear, please skidoo!

DIRECTIONS

Two players turn the rope and one child jumps at a time. Others await their turn and one moves in on the word *skidoo*. The child jumping acts out the words in the verse.

STRAWBERRY SHORTCAKE JUMP ROPE

VERSE

Strawberry shortcake, huckleberry pie,
V-I-C-T-O-R-Y,
Can you jump it?
I'll say, "Yes."
Salt and pepper, and now take a rest!

DIRECTIONS

Two players turn the rope. One jumps as the verse is chanted. On the last line, "salt and pepper . . . ," the rope is turned rapidly. On the word *rest*, the player jumps out and a new one starts at the beginning of the verse.

DUAL ROPE TURNING

When two people turn the rope, jumping variations are plentiful:

1. Jumper starts by standing in the middle.

2. Jumper runs in while rope is turning, jumps a designated number of times, and runs out.

3. Jumper runs in, drops a stone or a button, and picks it up on the jump number designated by the group.

4. Jumper runs in and bounces a ball while jumping. Number of times should be designated by the group. Start with two and work upward.

INDIVIDUAL ROPE TURNING

Variations for individuals who are capable of turning their own rope are challenging.

1. Turn the rope forward and jump.

2. Turn the rope backward and jump when it is in back of the feet.

3. Jump on one foot.

4. Jump on two feet.

5. Jump first with one foot and then with the other in a stepping fashion.

6. Hold hands with a partner. Each holds one end of the rope with the free hand and turns. Then they jump together.

7. Face your partner and jump together.

8. Jump covering the ground in various formations—squares, lines, and so on.

MARBLES

AREA

A circle 10 feet in diameter.

EQUIPMENT

Thirteen marbles arranged in a cross in the center of the circle. One shooter for each player not less than one half of an inch or more than three quarters of an inch in diameter.

PLAYERS

No less than two, no more than six.

DIRECTIONS

Players stand on a line approximately 6 to 8 feet from the circle and toss their shooters, one at a time. A line extended beyond the circle is called the lag line, this is where the players try to land their marbles. The one whose marble is nearest to the lag line is the first shooter. The first player knuckles down at any place outside the circle line he chooses and shoots at the marbles. He continues to shoot as long as he knocks a marble from the ring and his shooter remains in the ring. Each marble knocked from the ring is his for a score of one. He takes his next shot from where his shooter stayed in the circle. When he is unsuccessful in knocking a marble from the ring or when his shooter leaves the ring, he is through and picks up his shooter. The next player starts from whatever place he wishes around the ring. The player with the most points when all 13 marbles have been shot out of the circle is the winner. Players do not keep the 13 marbles.

Tournaments are very popular in this sport in the spring and summer.

BOWLING

AREA

Smooth surface.

EQUIPMENT

Six or 10 Indian clubs, plastic pins, or milk cartoons, and one 6- or 8-inch ball.

DIRECTIONS

Set pins up in a triangular formation (see Figure 22–28). Mark a starting line 20 to 30 feet from the pins. Each person bowls the ball

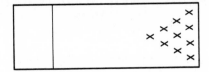

Figure 22–28. Bowling games.

in turn at the pins. The score is the number of pins that are knocked down. One child starts as the pinsetter. After the first bowler rolls, he becomes pinsetter. Two to four players may play on one court. The score may be determined by number of pins hit in 10 tries (the number of tries may be lessened or increased, depending on the interest of the players and the time available).

SELF-TESTING ACTIVITIES AND STUNTS

ROCKING CHAIR

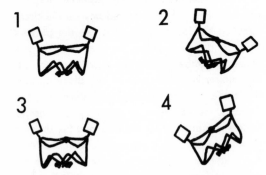

Figure 22–29. Rocking Chair.

Two children of near equal size and weight sit on the floor facing each other. They extend their legs and each then sits on the feet of his partner. They clasp their hands on the upper arms of their partners. One pulls back and lifts his partner a little distance from the floor. This is then reversed in a rocking fashion.

SIAMESE TWIN WALK

Figure 22–30. Siamese Twin Walk.

Stand back to back with partner. Lock arms together. Walk together with partner. Permit each one to walk forward and backward.

WHEELBARROW

Figure 22–31. Wheelbarrow.

One child puts his hand on the ground or floor. Child *two* stands behind him and picks his feet off the floor. The weight is on number *one's* hands. Number *one* walks on his hands while number *two* holds his legs, which represent the handles of a wheelbarrow.

SEAL CRAWL

Figure 22–32. Seal Crawl.

Prone position, hands on floor, legs together, weight on toes and hands. Walk on hands, drag feet.

COCKFIGHT

Figure 22–33. Cockfight.

Each child has a partner. Partners face each other and fold their arms across their chests. They practice hopping on one foot. When they are ready they bump each other, endeavoring to make one lose his balance and place both feet on the ground or floor.

CHURN THE BUTTER

Figure 22–34. Churn the Butter.

Stand back to back with partner of near size. Hook arms. One leans over and takes weight of partner on his back. His feet are off the ground. Place him back on his feet and he will then raise his partner the same way. Work together in slow rhythm.

HAND WRESTLE

Figure 22–35. Hand Wrestle.

Two children face each other and grasp right hands. Each raises his right foot balancing himself on the left. At a signal, each endeavors to make the other child place his right foot on the ground.

CRAB WALK

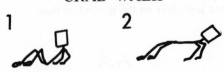

Figure 22–36. Crab Walk.

Sit on floor, face up. Raise and support weight of body by keeping hands and feet on floor, keep back straight. Walk backward, forward, and sideward using hands and feet.

FROG HOP

Figure 22–37. Frog Hop.

Take squat position. Place arms between legs and hands on the floor. Take short hops by placing hands on floor ahead of feet and bringing feet up to hands.

INCH WORM

Hands on floor, shoulder-width apart, extend legs to rear, feet together supporting body on hands and toes. Arms are straight and body straight from head to heels. Keep hands

stationary and knees straight. Using little steps, move feet to hands keeping knees straight.

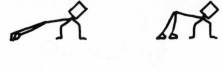

Figure 22–38. Inch Worm.

When they are as close to hands as possible, walk with hands as far as possible. Repeat bringing feet to hands, and so on.

Note: Hands and feet move alternately not at same time. Body must not sag. Progress forward by repeating activity.

INDIAN GET-UP

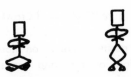

Figure 22–39. Indian Get-Up.

Sit on floor with feet crossed and arms folded shoulder high. Rise to an upright position without losing balance or unfolding arms. Return to sitting position.

JUMP AND SLAP HEELS

From standing position, jump up, extending heels up to the side, and reach backward to slap heels.

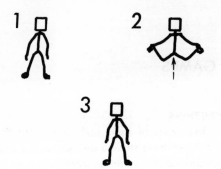

Figure 22–40. Jump and Slap Heels.

KNEE LIFT

Figure 22–42. Knee Lift.

Stand with feet apart, hands forward at hip level; jump up making knees touch hands.

KANGAROO HOP

Figure 22–41. Kangaroo Hop.

Fold arms over chest, squat; jump up keeping knees flexed, then go back to squat position.

LAME DOG WALK

Figure 22–43. Lame Dog Walk.

Same as Dog Walk only hold up one foot, first right and then left.

STORY PLAYS

Story plays may be enjoyed by seven-year-olds. However, teachers must use their judgment in determining the use of story plays for the eight-year-old since children mature at different levels. The use of this part of the program must be determined by each individual teacher. Selection for topics and materials for story plays will also depend upon the background, experience, and maturity of the children.

CLASSROOM GAMES

DRAWING OBJECT RACE

EQUIPMENT

One piece of drawing paper fastened on the wall or bulletin board for each group. One colored crayon for each group.

PLAYERS

Entire class divided in groups of six to eight players each.

DIRECTIONS

Choose an object to be drawn. It may be a school, barn, farmyard, and the like. Decide the number of lines each artist may draw, depending on the subject. For example, he may be given a chance to make two lines or four. Each group stands the same distance from their paper which is on the wall. The game starts with the first person going to the paper and drawing the given number of strokes or lines. He returns and gives the crayon to the second player, who does likewise. The winning group is the one with the best recognizable drawing, not the one finished first.

LEAF HUNT

EQUIPMENT

Many autumn leaves should be hidden in the room. They may either be real leaves or ones made from colored paper. Separate bare trees are drawn on the blackboards. Each tree is named—for example, Oak, Maple, or Ash.

PLAYERS

Entire class.

DIRECTIONS

The types of trees and leaves are those the children have studied and know. The object is for each child to find as many leaves as possible in an allotted time. When the time is up, all players sit down. Then each child has a chance to place his leaves in the chalk tray under the correct tree. The child who has the most leaves will *not* win if he places them on the wrong tree. If this game is to be played a second time, the children may hide their eyes with heads on the desk while the leaves are again hidden.

THE LOST CHILD

FORMATION

All children are seated.

DIRECTIONS

This is a quiet game designed to test the memory. The players are all seated, with the exception of one who is sent from the room. When this player is well out of sight and hearing, the leader or teacher beckons one of the players, who leaves the group and hides. In the schoolroom, this may be done under the teacher's desk or in a wardrobe. The rest of the players then change their seats and the one who is out is called back. He tries to tell which player is hidden. He may have one, two, or three guesses depending on grade level. If he guesses correctly he scores a point and may choose another player to be the guesser. If he fails to identify the hidden child, the hidden child becomes "It" and is allowed to leave the room for the new game while the teacher chooses another hider.

NUMBER TOSS

EQUIPMENT

Ten pieces of oaktag or construction paper, approximately 4 inches by 6 inches for each group. Number each piece from one to ten, or use higher numbers depending on the mathematical ability of the group. Three rolled socks for each group.

PLAYERS

The entire class is divided into groups of four, five, or six each.

DIRECTIONS

Each group lays its ten papers on the floor so the edges touch each other. They make no specific pattern regarding number placement. Mark a line 10 feet away. This may be lengthened or shortened depending on the ability of the group. Each group of children lines up behind a leader. The first child has the three rolled socks and tosses them on the paper. His score is taken from wherever the socks land. He writes his score on the board and tosses the socks to the second child. Each child recovers the socks he tossed and writes his own score on the board. The last person totals the scores. One round is played and the winner is the group with the highest score. The game may be played as many times as the group wishes to play it.

CLOTHESPIN RACE

EQUIPMENT

Two clothespins for each group and a length of clothesrope which will reach the width of a classroom.

PLAYERS

Any number.

DIRECTIONS

The children are divided into groups of from four to eight each. The first child on each squad holds two clothespins. Any distance away, and facing the squads, are two children holding the rope taut between them. At the signal "Go," the first child in each group starts the race by running up to the rope and putting the clothespins on it. He runs back and tags the next person in line who runs up and carries the pins back and hands them to the third child. Each child has a turn either to pin them on the line or take them off. The squad finished first wins. All clothespins must stay on the line. If one falls off, the child must return and pin it up again.

VARIATIONS

Give something for them to hang up such as socks or hankies (Kleenex).

ROLL BALL

EQUIPMENT

A golf ball or ping-pong ball for each squad or group. Three blackboard erasers for each squad or a cereal box cut to form an arch.

PLAYERS

Five to six in each group.

DIRECTIONS

Set up an arch about 10 feet in front of each group. Mark a line for contestants to stand behind. The first one in each group has a ball. He endeavors to roll the ball through the arch. He recovers it and tosses it back to the second person and then takes his place behind the last player in his line. Each player rolls the ball in turn and recovers it as the first player did. One point is scored each time the ball passes through the arch. Play for five minutes. The group with highest score is the winner. The game may be repeated.

⤳⤲

I AM TIRED OF STIRRING THE MUSH

FORMATION

Children in seats.

DIRECTIONS

Player who is "It" stands in front of the room pretending to stir a pot of mush. "It" says, "I am tired of stirring this mush." The class asks: "Why?" "It" says, "Because (name of a child) won't walk around the room like a dog and bark like a dog." "It" may suggest anything he wants the child to do such as sing, dance, skip, hop, jump, recite, or run. The child called upon does the action and then becomes "It."

VARIATION

"It" may call upon an entire row to perform. The more varied the acts are, the more enjoyable the game becomes. The new "It" would be the person from the row who did the best imitation.

⤳⤲

HAT IN THE RING

EQUIPMENT

Record player; record—a march; an old straw hat or other type of hat.

DIRECTIONS

Divide the class into two groups. The two groups line up facing each other. Each group counts off consecutively from number one on. Group members must remember their numbers.

Each group makes a circle or, if space will not permit, two circles. The groups may follow their leaders around the room or up and down aisles. The old hat is placed in the middle of the room. When the music starts, the players march around either in their circle or up and down the aisles. Suddenly the music stops. Number one from each group runs to try and get the hat and take it back to the place where he was when the music stopped. The one who succeeds scores a point for his group. At the next music break, number *twos* race for the hat and so on. The group totaling ten points first wins.

⤳⤲

CAT AND MICE

FORMATION

Children seated.

DIRECTIONS

One player is chosen to be cat and hides behind or under the teacher's desk. After the cat is hidden, the teacher beckons to five or six other players to be mice. They creep softly up to the desk, and when all are assembled, scratch on it with their fingers to represent the nibbling of mice. As soon as the cat hears this, he or she scrambles out from under the desk and gives chase to the mice, who may save themselves only by getting back to their holes (seats). If a mouse is caught, the cat changes places with him for the next round of the game. If no mouse is caught, a new cat is chosen.

A different set of mice should be chosen each time in order to give all of the players an opportunity to join in the game.

SELECTED REFERENCES

AMES, JOSELYN, *City Street Games,* New York, Holt, Rinehart and Winston, 1963.

ANDREWS, GLADYS, *Creative Rhythms for Children,* Englewood Cliffs, N.J., Prentice-Hall, Inc., 1954.

BANCROFT, JESSIE, *Games* (Revised edition), New York, The Macmillan Company, 1952.

BAUER, LOIS, and BARBARA REED, *Dance and Play Activities for the Elementary Grades*

(Vol. I), New York; Chartwell House, Inc., 1954.

COTTERAL, BONNIE, and DONNIE COTTERAL, *The Teaching of Stunts and Tumbling,* New York, A. S. Barnes and Company, 1943.

GERI, FRANK, *Illustrated Games and Rhythms for Children* (Primary Grades), Englewood Cliffs, N.J., Prentice-Hall, Inc., 1951.

GILB, STELLA S., *Games for the Gymnasium, Playground, and Classroom* (Revised edition), Lexington, Ky., Hurst Printing Company, 1962.

HARBIN, E. O., *Fun Encyclopedia,* Nashville, Tenn., Aburgden, Cokesbury Press Company, 1950.

HUGHES, DOROTHY T., *Rhythmic Games and Dances,* New York, American Book Company, 1942.

HUNT, SARA, and ETHEL CAIN, *Games the World Around; Four Hundred Folk Games,* New York, The Ronald Press Company, 1950.

LASALLE, DOROTHY, *Rhythms and Dances for Elementary Schools* (Revised edition), New York, The Ronald Press Company, 1951.

LATCHAW, MARJORIE, *A Pocket Guide of Games and Rhythms for the Elementary School,* Englewood Cliffs, N.J., Prentice-Hall, Inc., 1956.

PRICE, KATHERINE, *The Source Book of Play Party Games,* Minneapolis, Burgess Publishing Company, 1949.

RICHARDSON, HAZEL A., *Games for the Elementary School Grades,* Minneapolis, Burgess Publishing Company, 1951.

SMALLEY, JEANNETTE, *Physical Education Activities for Elementary Schools,* Millbrac, Cal., The National Press, 1950.

STUART, FRANCES R., and JOHN S. LUDLAM, *Rhythmic Activities* (Series I), Minneapolis, Burgess Publishing Company, 1955.

WILLEE, A. N., *Small Apparatus for Primary School Physical Education,* New York, Cambridge University Press, 1955.

CHAPTER 23

Activities for Middle Childhood,
Ages Nine and Ten

DANCES AND RHYTHMS

Dances and rhythms for the nine- and ten-year-old child include folk dances, square dances, interpretative and creative dances, and mixers.

Today, many companies have records available with accompanying directions. Square dance records are available with specific directions and calls on one side for teaching. The actual dance music and calls are on the reverse side of the record. Names and addresses of some record companies are listed in Appendix A.

The following dances are recommended for this specific age group. Sources for procuring the records and the country from which the dance originates are given to assist the teacher with correlation to other parts of the curriculum.

Steps for this group include the waltz, polka, pivot, bleking, promenade, step-hop, draw step, and the touch step. These dance steps are defined as follows:

WALTZ STEP (¾ TEMPO)

Count 1: Step forward on left foot.
Count 2: Move right foot forward to the right side.

Count 3: Bring left foot to the right and take weight on left foot. Repeat three counts starting with right foot.

POLKA STEP (⅖ TEMPO)

Count 1: Hop on right foot.
Count 2: Step forward on left foot and bring right foot up to left. Hop, step together, hop is the sequence.

PIVOT STEP (⅖ or 4/4 TEMPO)

A pivot step is used that is much the same as though a person is riding a scooter. The weight is on one foot and the free foot pushes the person around. The foot with the weight is lifted slightly on each push.

BLEKING (⅖ TEMPO)

Bleking is a hop step in which the free foot is extended forward with the heel touching the

306

floor. A quick change brings the forward foot back for the hop and extends the opposite foot forward.

PROMENADE (4/4 TEMPO)

The promenade step is used by couples in American square dances to move around their set. It is a shuffle step smoothly performed as a step-together step.

STEP HOP

Count 1: Step on left foot.
Count 2: Hop on same foot raising right knee forward.

DRAW STEP

The draw step is a sideward step with one foot followed by a "draw" which brings the other foot over to the one used for the sideward step.

TOUCH STEP (2/4 TEMPO)

Count 1: Raise left foot forward and touch the floor with the toes.

Count 2: Raise left foot and step forward on it. Repeat counts one and two with the right foot.

Basic forms for the American folk dance include circle, progressive circle, quadrilles, and line or contra sets.

Circle type sets call for partners to form a double circle with the lady on the gentleman's right. All couples face in the same line of direction. An example of this type is the favorite "Here We Go Round the Mountain."

The *progressive circle* formation places two couples facing each other. They dance specific calls together and then on command each couple moves in the opposite direction to meet a new couple.

The *quadrille* formation is a hollow square made by four couples facing each other. The couple with their backs to the music are always known as the head couple. If "head couples" are called for, the couple facing the head is the additional one. Side couples are the partners on the other side of the square. If a quadrille calls for couple number one, this means the head couple. In sequence, couple number two is to the right of couple one, number three is to the right of two, and number four is to the right of number three.

Line or contra sets are formations that usually call for from four to eight couples facing each other in two straight lines. The couple nearest the music is the head couple and those at the opposite end are the foot couples.

TABLE 23–1. *Folk Dances*

Dance	Nationality	Record
Ace of Diamonds	Danish	Folkraft 1176
Bleking	Swedish	Folkraft 118
Bingo	English	Victor 45:6169
		Folkraft 1189
Captain Jinks	American	Victor 45:6172

Dance	Nationality	Record
		Folkraft 1240
Children's Polka	German	Folkraft 1187
Csebogar	Hungarian	Victor 45:6182
		Folkraft 1196
Donkey Dance	Mexican	Burns and Evans Album 123
Dutch Couples	Dutch	Burns and Evans Album 333
German Clap Dance	German	Burns and Evans Album 333
Gustof's Skoal	Swedish	Victor 45:6170
		Folkraft 1175
Hansel and Gretel	German	RCA Folk Dance Record
Kerry Dance	Irish	Educational Record Sales #6
Nixie Polka	Swedish	
Norwegian Mountain March	Norwegian	RCA Folk Dance Record
		Educational Record Sales #5
Patty Cake Polka	American	Folkraft 1124
Ribbon Dance	English	Victor 45:6175
Sellengers Round	English	Folkraft 1124
Seven Jumps	Danish	Methodist 108
		Victor 45:6172
Swedish Clap Dance	Swedish	Victor 45:6171
		Folkraft 1175
Virginia Reel	American	Folkraft 1141
		Victor LPA 4138
		Victor 45:6180
Yankee Doodle	American	Windsor A-751

DEVELOPMENTAL ACTIVITIES

Developmental activities started in previous grades should be continued. As children grow older and stronger they are capable of and interested in doing more difficult types. The following are recommended.

⚜

PULLUPS—(BOYS)

EQUIPMENT

A bar, of sufficient height, comfortable to grip.

STARTING POSITION

Grasp the bar with palms facing forward; hang with arms and legs fully extended. Feet must be free of floor. The partner stands slightly to one side of the pupil being tested and counts each successful pullup.

ACTION

1. Pull body up with the arms until the chin is placed over the bar.

2. Lower body until the elbows are fully extended.

3. Repeat the exercise the required number of times.

Figure 23–1. Developmental activities.

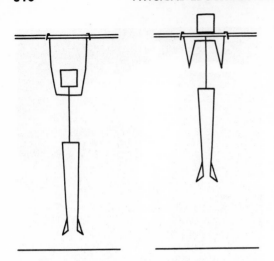

Figure 23–2. Pullups for boys.

RULES

    1. The pull must not be a snap movement.

    2. Knees must not be raised.

    3. Kicking the legs is not permitted.

    4. The body must not swing. If pupil starts to swing, his partner stops the motion by holding an extended arm across the front of the pupil's thighs.

    5. One complete pullup is counted each time the pupil places his chin over the bar.

EQUIPMENT

    Any bar adjustable in height and comfortable to grip. A piece of pipe, placed between two stepladders and held securely, may be used.

STARTING POSITION

    Adjust height of bar to chest level. Grasp bar with palms facing out. Extend the legs under the bar, keeping the body and knees straight. The heels are on the floor. Fully extend the arms so they form an angle of 90 degrees with the body line. The partner braces the pupil's heels to prevent slipping.

ACTION

    1. Pull body up with the arms until the *chest* touches the bar.

    2. Lower body until elbows are fully extended.

    3. Repeat the exercise the required number of times.

RULES

    1. The body must be kept straight.

    2. The chest *must* touch the bar and the arms must then be *fully extended*.

    3. No resting is permitted.

    4. One pullup is counted each time the chest touches the bar.

MODIFIED PULLUPS—(GIRLS)

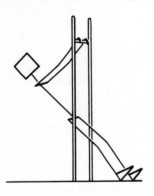

Figure 23–3. Modified Pullups for girls.

PUSHUPS

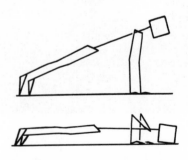

Figure 23–4. Pushups for boys.

STARTING POSITION

Boys: Extend arms and place hands on the floor, just under and slightly to the outside of the shoulders. Fingers should be pointing forward. Extend body so that it is perfectly straight. The weight is supported on the hands and toes. See Figure 23–4.

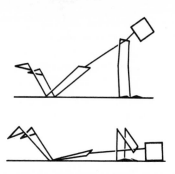

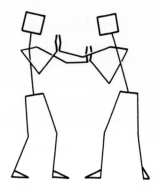

Figure 23–6. Sawing Wood.

ACTION

With a vigorous action, pupils pump the arms alternately as if they were sawing wood. (See diagram.)

Figure 23–5. Modified Pushups for girls.

Girls: Extend arms and place hands, fingers pointing forward, on ground just under and slightly outside of the shoulders. Place knees on floor and extend body until it is straight from the head to the knees. Bend knees and raise the feet off the floor. The weight is supported by the hands and knees. (Also for boys who cannot do regular pushups.) See Figure 23–5.

ACTION

Count 1: Keeping body tense and straight, bend elbows and touch chest to the floor.

Count 2: Return to original position. (The body must be kept perfectly straight. The buttocks must not be raised. The abdomen must not sag.)

WING STRETCHER

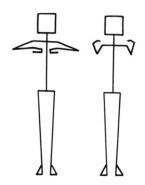

Figure 23–7. Wing Stretcher.

STARTING POSITION

Pupil stands erect. Raise elbows to shoulder height, fists clenched, palms down, in front of chest.

ACTION

Thrust elbows backward vigorously and return. Be sure head and neck remain erect.

SAWING WOOD

STARTING POSITION

Pupils pair off, face each other, and grasp hands with fingers interlaced.

HEAD UP

Figure 23–8. Head Up.

STARTING POSITION

Pupil lies on back, knees bent, feet flat on floor close to buttocks, hands clasped behind neck, elbows on floor.

ACTION

Tighten abdominal muscles. Raise head and press chin to chest. Keep the lower back flat and arms on floor.

THE SCISSORS

Figure 23–9. The Scissors.

STARTING POSITION

Pupil sits against wall, legs extended with knees straight. Hips, back, shoulders, and head touching wall.

ACTION

Raise and lower legs alternately in a scissors fashion. Gradually increase the tempo of the movement.

BEAR HUG

Figure 23–10. Bear Hug.

STARTING POSITION

Pupil stands, feet comfortably spread, with hands on hips.

ACTION

Count 1: Take a long step diagonally right, keeping left foot anchored in place; tackle the right leg around the thigh by encircling the thigh with both arms.

Count 2: Return to the starting position.

Counts 3 and 4: Repeat to the opposite side.

SIDE FLEX

Figure 23–11. Side Flex.

STARTING POSITION

Pupil lies on side, arms extended over head. The head rests on the lower arm. Legs are extended fully, one on top of the other.

ACTION

Count 1: With a brisk action, raise the topmost arm and leg vertically. Attempt to make contact with hand and foot, without bending elbow or knee.

Count 2: Return to starting position.
Repeat for several counts, then change to other side.

GAMES OF LOW ORGANIZATION, INCLUDING RELAYS AND PRELIMINARY AND LEAD-UP ACTIVITIES

PASS AND SHOOT

EQUIPMENT

Two basketballs and two basketball goals.

PLAYERS

Two teams.

DIRECTIONS

Divide the class into two teams. Each team has a ball and lines up in front of the baskets. The ball is passed back through the legs of the team members. When the last person in line receives it he dribbles the ball to the front and shoots at the basket. After each person receives his shot he runs to the front of his line and passes the ball back through his legs. This continues until the leader of each team returns to his original position. Each basket made scores two points. The team with the most points at the end of a set time is the winner.

RACE THE BALL

EQUIPMENT

One volleyball or inflated ball of that size.

PLAYERS

Two teams, an equal number on each.

DIRECTIONS

Children are arranged in two circles of equal size. The game is started by the captain of the passing team. He throws the ball to number *one* in his circle. Number *one* catches it and

Figure 23–12. Race the Ball.

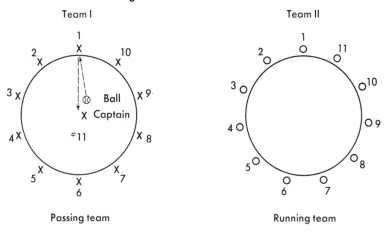

Passing team　　　　Running team

————— = Flight of ball

returns it to the captain who passes it to number *two*, receives it from him, and so on, until the captain has passed the ball to each of his players. As soon as the passing team throws the ball, number *one* of team two starts running around his circle. When he returns to his place, he tags number *two* who runs around. On his return he tags number *three*. Team two keeps running until the captain of team one has passed the ball to each member of his team. The captain then calls "Stop!" Team two counts its score. Every runner who made a complete trip around his circle scores one point for his team. Team two now receives the ball and team one becomes the scoring team. When the ball changes teams, the next runner to start is the one next to the last runner. For example, if number *four* was running when "Stop" was called, number *five* would be the first runner in the next inning.

☙❦

JUMP THE SHOT

EQUIPMENT
A rope about 12 feet long to which a bean bag or an old sneaker has been attached.

FORMATION
Single circle facing inward, one player within the circle.

DIRECTIONS
The odd player swings the object around the circle and the players jump over the rope. The rope should not be more than one foot above the ground. Whoever misses his jump and stops the rope changes places with the center player.

VARIATIONS
1. Use a long pole instead of rope.
2. Players walk or run about the circle, either in the same direction or the opposite

direction to that in which the rope is moving.

☙❦

RAPID TRANSIT

EQUIPMENT
Two objects for throwing—balls, bean bags, or erasers.

PLAYERS
Two teams of six to twelve each.

DIRECTIONS
Each team forms a column in back of the team line. Opposite the first player for each team is the catcher facing his team at a distance of 10 feet or more from the team line. The first player holds the ball. At the signal "Go"

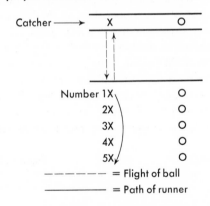

Figure 23–13. Rapid Transit.

the first player throws the ball to his catcher, who throws it back to him. When he receives it, he runs to the back of his team and passes the ball, with both hands overhead, from the rear to the front of the line. When the ball reaches the front, the second player throws it to the catcher who returns it to him and he repeats the action. The game continues in relay form, until the catcher has received the ball ten times. The first catcher who calls out ten is the winning team.

CLOTHESPINS AWAY

EQUIPMENT

Three boxes for each squad; three clothespins for each child.

PLAYERS

Two squads or more.

DIRECTIONS

Players are arranged in squads behind a starting line. Each player is given three clothespins. At the command "Go," the first player in each squad runs to a given point, trying to drop a clothespin in each of the three boxes which are distributed along the running path. He returns to the starting line, tags the next person, and goes to the end of his line. The next player does the same, and so on, until all have had a chance to run. Five points are given to the squad finishing first and one point for each clothespin in the boxes.

CIRCLE RELAY

EQUIPMENT

Two large rubber balls.

PLAYERS

Twenty children or more; two teams.

DIRECTIONS

The group counts off so each person has a number. Those persons having odd numbers make up team A and those with even numbers constitute team B. They form a circle and face the center. Two players, one from each team, stand in the circle, each holding a large rubber ball. They may be children who are not able to participate in strenuous physical activity, or any two team members. The A team member calls odd numbers, and B calls even numbers. A

may call three, and B will quickly call six. As they call the numbers they throw the balls in the air. The students whose numbers are called run to catch the ball. Each one then returns to his place in the circle, lays the ball down, and runs around the circle. The first player back to his place scores a point for his team. These two players are the next to toss the balls and call the numbers. The team that scores ten points first wins the game.

BALL ROLL

EQUIPMENT

Two soccer balls, volleyballs, or basketballs.

PLAYERS

Two teams.

DIRECTIONS

Each team has a ball. Team players line up behind each other. Team one rolls first. As the first player of team one rolls the ball, the first player of team two rolls his and endeavors

Team I	Team II
X	O
X	O
X	O
X	O

Goal line

Figure 23–14. Ball Roll.

to hit team one's ball. If the ball is hit, there is no score. If number one's ball crosses the goal line without being hit, his team scores a point. Each person in team one rolls for a goal, while each in team two endeavors to hit their ball. Then the play is reversed.

MEDLEY RELAY RACE

EQUIPMENT

The amount of equipment depends on the number of teams. Each team needs a tenpin, a block of wood, a ball, and a stick.

PLAYERS

Unlimited number of teams. Four or eight players on a team.

DIRECTIONS

Players line up in straight lines with a tenpin, 20 to 30 feet in front of each. The leader of each team puts a block of wood on his head and runs around the tenpin, returns, and gives it to the next player in line. If he drops it, he must stop, replace it and continue. Each player has a turn. When the leader is again at the front of his line, he dribbles the ball around the tenpin and back. Each player does the same. The third time the leader is in front, he hops on one foot up to the club and back. All players have their turn. The fourth time the leader uses the stick and ball. He hits the ball with the stick up around the club and back. Each player follows suit. The first team to finish the entire activity wins.

WICKET BALL

EQUIPMENT

A croquet ball for each team. One mallet for each team. Five wickets for each team. Old hockey balls or softballs may be used, and hockey sticks may be used in place of mallets.

PLAYERS

Four to eight on a team. Divide large groups into more teams.

DIRECTIONS

Set up the wickets in straight rows about 3 feet apart. Each player hits the ball through each wicket on the way down to the goal line

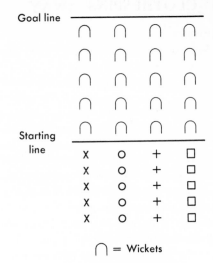

∩ = Wickets

Figure 23–15. Wicket Ball.

and back to his team. The ball must go through each wicket. Each player in line takes his turn and the team through first wins.

CROWS AND CRANES

FORMATION

Large rectangular area with a goal line at each end.

DIRECTIONS

The players are divided into two teams. One team is the Crows and the other is the Cranes. The players of both teams are lined up on their own goal line. They move toward each other walking, running, jumping, or skipping, as directed by the leader. The teacher stands at the center of the area and calls either "Crows!" or "Cranes!" If the teacher calls "Crows!" the Crows run home chased by the Cranes. A Crow tagged by a Crane before he reaches safety behind his own goal line scores a point for the Cranes. The Cranes are chased by the Crows when the teacher calls "Cranes!" The team which has the highest score at the end of the playing period is the winner.

VARIATIONS

1. Permit children to cross into each other's half of the playing area.

2. Change movement to hopping, walking, skipping.

3. Do not call each name in sequence. Call Crows several times before Cranes. However, give each team an equal number of times to tag.

4. Try to trick children by calling Crabs or other names beginning with cr. Those who run score points for opponents.

DARE BASE

FORMATION

Rectangular area.

DIRECTIONS

A rectangular playing space with a goal marked off across each end is used. The class is divided into two equal teams, A and B, and each team takes its place on its own goal. Each group selects a name for identification.

Three players from team A step forward and dare three specific players from team B to tag them. Approximately one minute is allowed for the chase and each player caught scores a point for team B. If a player has not been tagged when time is called, he returns to his own team. Tagged players also return to their original goal. The game continues with team B daring three other members of team A. This alternates back and forth until the end of the playing time. The team having the greater number of points at that time wins the game.

CIRCLE TOUCH BALL

EQUIPMENT

One ball.

FORMATION

Circle.

DIRECTIONS

Players stand in a circle, several feet apart, with an odd player in the center. He tries to touch the ball, which is tossed rapidly from one circle player to another across the circle in any direction. Should he be successful, the one who last touched the ball changes places with him.

CATCHING AND THROWING RELAY

Refer to Chapter 10.

HOT POTATO

Refer to Chapter 10.

DOG CATCHER

Refer to Chapter 14; instructions and diagram appear on pages 165–166.

INDIVIDUAL AND DUAL ACTIVITIES

Children of this age group continue an interest in Hopscotch, Jump Rope games, Marbles, and Throwing and Catching games involving specific skills. They gain great enjoyment in challenging themselves to improve.

Additional games of this type follow.

⚹⚹

TETHER BALL

EQUIPMENT

In a circle 3 feet in radius, mount a pole 10 feet high with a 7.5-foot cord or rope attached to the top of the pole. Paint a 1-inch line 4 feet from the top of the pole. This pole may be attached to a broad base so that it will stand safely, or it may be anchored in the ground. A ball is attached to the rope. This may be a volleyball or a tennis ball in a sack or net. Two paddles are needed if a tennis ball is used. A court diagram is included in Appendix C, Figure C-8.

DIRECTIONS

Players stand on a line which bisects the circle and extends beyond it. One player stands on the line outside the circle and hits the ball, endeavoring to wind it around the pole above the painted line. If a volleyball is used, it is served with the hand; if a tennis ball is used, each player uses a paddle and serves the ball by hitting it with the paddle. As soon as the ball is hit (serve), the opponent tries to hit it and send it back so it will not wind around the pole. Neither player may step into the circle. A game is won when a player is successful in winding the rope completely around the pole above the painted line. The loser serves first in the second game. The greatest number of games won out

of three, five, or seven games, as agreed on before play, wins.

⚹⚹

BALL PITCHING

EQUIPMENT

One old tire, a rope, and a ball. Attach the tire to the rope and fasten the rope to a horizontal bar or tree limb so that it hangs down. The height of the tire may differ depending on age and size of participants.

DIRECTIONS

Mark distances of 10, 15, and 20 feet on the ground on each side of the tire. A football, volleyball, softball, or basketball may be used. One child stands on a line with the ball and attempts to throw it through the tire. Throws may start either underhand or overhand. The second player stands on the opposite side of the tire to catch the ball. A point is scored for each successful throw through the tire. The highest number of points wins.

⚹⚹

SHUFFLEBOARD

EQUIPMENT

Eight discs, 6 inches in diameter and 1 inch thick. Four of the discs are painted one color, and the other four another. Four cues and a marked court are also needed. A court diagram is shown in Appendix C, Figure C-8.

DIRECTIONS

Two or four may play. If two, then each stands at the same end of the court and takes

Figure 23–16. Shuffleboard.

turns sliding the discs to the opposite court, endeavoring to dislocate their opponent's discs and to keep theirs in the scoring area. If four play, partners are at opposite ends of the courts. Discs start from within the "10-off" area. Discs which remain entirely within a marked area, not touching a line, score the points marked in that area. If they remain in the 10-off area, 10 must be deducted from the score. The score of a game may be set at 50, 75, or 100 points. This should be decided before play begins.

JACKS

EQUIPMENT

Six to 12 jacks and a small semihard rubber ball the size of a golf ball. Children use six jacks to start. As they develop and grow older, as many as 12 jacks may be used.

DIRECTIONS

A smooth surface is needed to play on. There are many different ways to play Jacks. Each is discussed under its name.

RULES

Fouls are the same for each type and are as follows:

1. Switching hands to catch the ball.
2. Failure to pick up number of jacks required in the game.
3. Catching ball with two hands.
4. Dropping either the jack, or jacks, or ball.
5. Hitting a jack other than the ones supposed to be picked up.
6. Double bounce of ball before catching.

BABY GAME—ONES

Scatter all jacks upon the playing surface with a single movement of the right hand. Toss the ball, pick up one jack, and, after the ball has bounced once, catch the ball in the same (right) hand. Transfer the jack to the left hand and proceed as before until all six jacks are in the left hand.

TWOS

Jacks are picked up by twos; otherwise, proceed as in Ones.

THREES

Jacks are picked up by threes; otherwise, proceed as in Ones.

FOURS

Jacks are picked up four and then two, or two then four; otherwise, proceed as in Ones.

FIVES

Jacks are picked up one and then five, or five then one; otherwise, proceed as in Ones.

SIXES

Jacks are picked up all at once; otherwise, proceed as in Ones.

DOWNS AND UPS

All jacks and ball in right hand. Toss ball upward, lay down all jacks, and catch ball in right hand. Throw ball up again, pick up all jacks, and catch ball in right hand.

EGGS IN THE BASKET

Scatter jacks, toss ball, pick up one jack, using only the right hand, and while the ball bounces once, transfer jack to the left hand, then catch ball with the right hand. When all jacks have been picked up and transferred to the left hand, the jacks are all put in the right hand and scattered again. Proceed through twos, threes, fours, fives, and sixes.

CRACK THE EGGS

Scatter jacks with right hand. Toss ball with right hand and while ball bounces once, pick up one jack with right hand, "crack" (tap) it on the playing surface, and catch ball in right hand, which is still holding the jack. Transfer

the jack to the left hand and proceed as before until all jacks are picked up. Scatter again and proceed by twos, threes, and so on, through sixes.

DOWNCAST

Scatter jacks with right hand. Toss ball with right hand, pick up one jack with right hand, and catch the ball in the right hand after it has bounced once, as was done in the Baby Game. Bounce the ball downward and transfer the jack to the left hand, then catch the ball with the right hand. Proceed through sixes.

DOUBLE BOUNCE

This is played the same as the Baby Game, but ball must bounce twice before it is caught. Play through sixes.

BOUNCE, NO BOUNCE

Scatter jacks with right hand. Toss ball upward, pick up one jack while ball bounces once, and catch the ball in the right hand. With jack still in right hand, toss the ball upward with the right hand, transfer the jack to the left hand, and catch the ball in the right hand without allowing it to bounce. Continue until all jacks have been transferred to the left hand, then scatter them again and proceed by twos, threes, and so on, through sixes.

CROQUET

EQUIPMENT

Croquet set, grass plot.

PLAYERS

Two or four.

DIRECTIONS

Each player drives his own ball with his mallet through the arches in the prescribed manner (see Figure 23–17) and reverses it to come home. The first player to reach home and hit the goal with his ball is the winner.

Each player has one shot to start and gains an immediate additional shot each time he makes a successful shot through a wicket. He also gains two additional shots if he is able to hit an opponent's ball. If a player wishes, he may use one of his strokes gained by hitting an opponent's ball with his to knock the opponent's ball further away from the playing area. This is accomplished by placing his ball so it touches his opponent's, holding his ball with his foot, and hitting his ball with the mallet. This causes an indirect hit to his opponent's ball and sends it away. One must be certain that his foot holds his own ball securely or else it, too, will roll far away from the playing area.

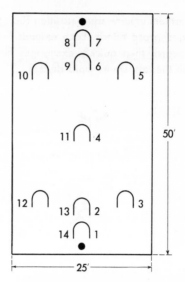

Figure 23–17. Croquet.

SELF-TESTING ACTIVITIES

BEAR DANCE

Figure 23–18. Bear Dance.

Squat position with arms folded across chest. Jump and extend the right foot forward, quickly bring it back, and extend the left foot forward at the same time.

HEAD PUSH

Stand about 2 feet from a wall, place

Figure 23–19. Head Push.

hands and head against the wall. Remove hands and come to erect position without using them.

COUPLE BEAR DANCE

Figure 23–20. Couple Bear Dance.

Partners assume squat position facing each other and grasp hands. Each extends his right leg forward, then quickly exchanges his right leg with the left. Do in rapid rhythm.

HEEL JUMP

Figure 23–21. Heel Jump.

Assume a squat position. Fold arms across chest. Spring quickly, placing weight on heels in a stride position. Return to squat. Repeat rapidly.

TOE KICK

Figure 23–22. Toe Kick.

Stand in a straight position, both feet together. Jump and raise feet forward touching toes with hands.

TWISTER

Partners face each other and join right and left hands respectively. One steps over the joined hands with left foot and the other does

Figure 23–23. Twister.

the same with his right. This brings them back to back. The first puts his right foot over the joined arms, the other one his left foot. They should now be facing each other as when they started.

RING CHAMPION

Figure 23–24. Ring Champion.

Players stand on one leg in 5- or 6-foot circles with arms folded across chest. They challenge another player and endeavor to make him lose his balance or leave the circle.

ROOSTER FIGHT

Figure 23–25. Rooster Fight.

Partners assume a squat position in a circle about 5 or 6 feet in diameter. Arms are folded across their chests. They move in this position endeavoring to force one off balance or push him out of the circle.

SIAMESE HOP

Figure 23–26. Siamese Hop.

Partners stand with backs together. Each grasps the ankle of his partner's left foot. Couples hop on right foot to a given distance.

TEAM GAMES

CENTER CATCH BALL

EQUIPMENT
Two balls.

DIRECTIONS
Divide the group into two teams. Each team stands in a circle. One player from each is chosen to stand in the center of the other circle. Each ball is passed back and forth across each circle. The center player tries to intercept. When he succeeds, he runs back to his team and the next player takes his place in the other circle. Winner is the first team to "play around."

CORNER SPRY

EQUIPMENT
Four balls.

DIRECTIONS
Mark a circle about 10 feet in diameter in the center of a rectangular playing area. Four teams of equal number play. A captain is chosen for each team. One team is in each corner of the playing area and the captains take their places in the circle. Each captain has a ball (see Figure 23–27, page 324).

At a signal, the captain of each team starts passing the ball to each member of his team in succession from one to the last number. As each player receives the ball, he tosses it back and squats. When the captain tosses the ball to the last player in the group he calls, "Corner spry," and runs to the head of the team as all members stand up. The last player runs to the circle and becomes captain and repeats the performance. This is done until all members of the team have been captain. The team whose original captain first returns to the center wins.

BEAT THE BALL

EQUIPMENT
One volleyball.

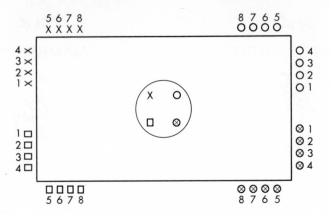

Figure 23–27. Corner Spry.

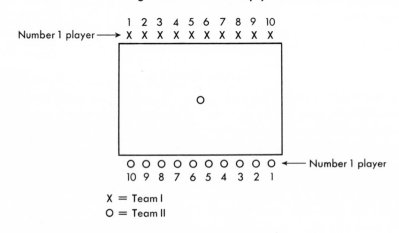

X = Team I
O = Team II

Figure 23–28. Beat the Ball.

PLAYERS

Ten to 30 children.

DIRECTIONS

Two teams of equal number line up facing each other about 30 to 60 feet apart. This distance varies depending on the abilities of the children. Draw a circle in the middle of the area about 3 feet in diameter. Team one has the ball. Number *one* rolls the ball forward. It must roll through the circle. If it does not, he is out. If successful in his roll, he runs and touches the circle with one or both feet and returns to his starting position. Number *one* of the receiving team recovers the ball *after* it has rolled through the circle. He may not leave his starting position until the ball has gone *through* the

circle. He attempts to hit the running player before he returns to his position. Each player of the rolling team who crosses the safety line without being hit scores a point. Each hit constitutes an out. The receiving side becomes the rolling side after there are three outs. The game is played in innings. Change distances and the size of the circle to meet the needs of the children.

HIT THE MALLET OR BAT

EQUIPMENT

One softball and one mallet or one softball and bat.

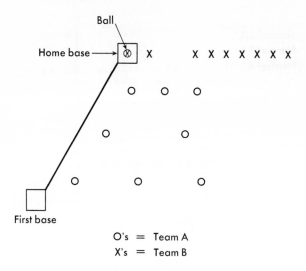

Figure 23–29. Hit the Mallet.

DIRECTIONS

Fielders from team A scatter in the playing area and one child from team B is up at home base. The ball lies on the home base. The playing area is the size suited to the class. One home base and one first base are all the markings needed. The first player of the batting team hits the ball out in the field, lays the mallet down on the home base, and attempts to run to first base and return home before a fielder can recover the ball and roll it *from where it was fielded* to home base and hit the mallet. If the fielder succeeds in hitting the mallet before the runner gets home, the runner is out. If the runner beats the ball, he scores a run. The game is played by innings. If the ball misses, another player may run and get the ball and attempt another roll at the mallet or bat. The game may be played for five, seven, or nine innings. High score at the end of the last complete inning is the winner.

WARM-UP

EQUIPMENT

One basketball, volleyball, soccer ball, or large rubber ball.

DIRECTIONS

Two teams consisting of an even number of players. Playing area is diagramed in Figure 23–30. Distance of goal line from team A may vary depending on children's ability. Team A has the ball. Number *one* throws it out in the field toward the team B players. He immediately runs to the goal line and returns to his original place, tags number *two*, and so on. The object is for as many members as possible of team A to run across the goal line, one at a time, before team B calls "Stop." Each one who succeeds scores a point for team A. Any member of team B recovers the ball as soon as possible and stands still. All of his teammates run and line up behind him. The ball is then passed back to each person in line. When the last player receives it, he runs to the front of his line and calls "Stop." The team A player who is running stops where he is. A's score is counted. Each person who ran to the goal line and back scores a run. Team B scatters and number *two* of team A throws the ball. The runner is the next one in line after the one running when B called "Stop." If number *three* was running when team B called "Stop," number *four* would be the first runner after number *two* throws the ball. The game continues until three team A players have had a chance to throw the

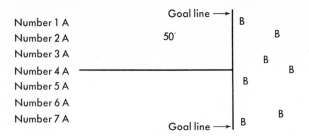

Figure 23–30. Warm-Up.

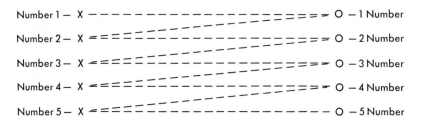

Figure 23–31. Stop Ball.

ball. This is one half an inning. It is then team B's turn to throw and team A is in the field. The highest score of the last complete inning wins.

VARIATIONS

Variations may be made in the way the fielding teams move the ball back to the last player. A caught fly may be considered an out or not, depending on the class.

⚮

STOP BALL

EQUIPMENT

One volleyball, or a rubber ball of about that size.

DIRECTIONS

Two teams or squads line up facing each other. The distance between the two depends on the ability of the children. Number *one* of team X is given the ball. At the signal "Go" he passes it to number *one* of team O. This number

one passes it across to number *two* of team X, and so the ball continues. (Dotted line shows the direction of the ball.) The teacher or leader, with her back to the group so she does not know who has the ball, suddenly calls out "Stop!" The ball must be held by the person until the signal "Go" is given again. If an X player has the ball the O team scores one point, and if the O team holds the ball the X team scores. The class and teacher may decide before starting how many points will win a game.

VARIATIONS

Various methods of passing may be used, such as the two-hand chest pass, one hand throw, and the bounce pass.

⚮

BAT BALL

Refer to Chapter 10 for complete directions.

KICK BALL

Refer to Chapter 10 for complete directions.

DODGE BALL

Refer to Chapter 14 for complete directions.

UNDER LEG BALL

EQUIPMENT

Softball and four bases.

FORMATION

Two teams with positions as in softball. Teams may vary in number from eight up. If space is limited, base lines may be as short as 20 to 25 feet.

DIRECTIONS

The pitcher pitches the ball underhand. The batter catches the ball. If he misses, it is counted as one strike. If the batter fails three times to catch the ball, he is out. When the batter catches the ball he throws it under his leg and runs the bases as in regular baseball. Fouls and outs are the same as in regular baseball.

PIN SOCCER

EQUIPMENT

Two or four Indian clubs and one soccer ball.

FORMATION

A court 20 feet by 30 feet with one or two Indian clubs, each standing in a 3-foot circle drawn at each end of the court. Two teams of five to eight players are scattered in their halves of the court.

DIRECTIONS

One player of each team stands at the center with his foot on the ball. At the signal, the two center players suit the action to the words, "Ground, ball; ground, ball; ground, ball; kick," whereupon play begins.

Each team attempts to knock over the pin in their opponent's court by kicking the ball. They may not go over the center line. The ball may not be caught. When a ball goes out of bounds, the opposite team throws it in to start play. One point is scored each time a pin is knocked over by a legal kick.

TRACK AND FIELD EVENTS

In working with track and field events, children need to be taught the correct form for each event and then should be permitted to practice in small groups of from four to eight children. No competition should be planned until enough time has been spent in practice to assure one that each child is in condition for it.

Each event gives a child opportunities to improve if he or she keeps a record at the beginning of participation and again at the end. A dash need not be run in competition.

A stop watch used by a classmate or a teacher will check the time for the dash. This may be recorded by the child. Six weeks later, after much participation, a second check can be made on speed. Such individual improvement checks may be used for all track and field events with great enjoyment and much physical growth.

STANDING BROAD JUMP

EQUIPMENT

A line can be marked on the ground, or a take-off board 6 or 8 inches wide and at least 2 inches deep may be sunk firmly in the ground. Either the line or board serves as a scratch line. A jumping pit from 5 to 6 feet wide and 25 to 30 feet long is dug in front of the scratch line and filled with sand or sawdust.

DIRECTIONS

The contestant stands on the take-off board or line, bends his knees, and sways his body and arms backward and forward to get impetus. He may not lift his feet until he takes off. He should land on both feet.

The measure of the jump is taken from the front edge of the take-off board or line to the first break the child has made in the sawdust with his feet or any other part of his body.

THREE STANDING BROAD JUMPS

This event is exactly like the Standing Broad Jump, except that instead of stopping when he lands, the contestant jumps again immediately, making a second and then a third jump. He may not stop between jumps even for any of the preparatory movements made before a first jump. The jump is made with both feet and the measurement is made from the outer edge of the take-off board or scratch line to the heel mark made on the last jump, unless some other part of the body has touched the ground nearer to the take-off. All rules and fouls are the same as for Standing Broad Jump.

RUNNING BROAD JUMP

The Running Broad Jump requires a long runway, a take-off board, and a jumping pit. There is no rule limiting the distance of the preliminary run. The jump is made at the finish of the run and is a spring on one foot from the forward edge of the take-off. For the foot to touch the ground in front of the take-off as the jump is made counts as a foul. The jump is measured to the first mark the jumper makes in the pit. The jumper should have good balance in landing and fall forward to avoid lessening the measurement of his jump. Each contestant is given three or four trial jumps.

RUNNING HOP, STEP, AND JUMP

The Running Hop, Step, and Jump is exactly like the Running Broad Jump except that the first leap is a hop, followed without stopping by a step, and then by a jump. All rules, fouls, and procedure are the same as for the Running Broad Jump.

The landing from the first spring is made on the foot that made the take-off—the hop. The second landing is made with the opposite foot—the step. This step should be as long as possible, propelled by the foot that remains on the ground. The spring to the third and final effort (the jump) is made from the one foot then on the ground, but the landing is on both feet. There must be no stop between any of the three efforts.

The measurement is made from the scratch line or forward edge of the take-off board to the final mark of the heels, unless the body has fallen backwards and made other marks closer to the scratch line.

HIGH JUMP

EQUIPMENT

Jump standards and a line or light stick for a bar, and a pit filled with sand or sawdust.

DIRECTIONS

Distance is needed for the contestant to run at least 20 feet. The bar is raised after each successful jump in competition. However, as a child practices, he may wish to keep it at the same level for several tries.

JUMP AND REACH

EQUIPMENT

A wall and piece of chalk.

DIRECTIONS

The child holds a piece of chalk and, jumping as high as possible, either from a crouch or a standing position, marks the wall.

STEP JUMP

From a standing position the child steps with one foot as far as possible and then jumps from both feet.

SOCCER KICK FOR DISTANCE

The ball is placed on a baseline and the player may make a standing or running kick. The distance is marked from the baseline to the point where the ball first touches the ground.

In competition, the play may be between individuals or teams.

BASKETBALL THROW FOR DISTANCE

EQUIPMENT

A basketball.

DIRECTIONS

Mark a starting line. Players may stand at or start back and move up to the line. The ball is held between the hand and arm. Measure the distance from the starting line to where ball first hits the ground.

SOFTBALL THROW FOR DISTANCE

EQUIPMENT

A softball.

DIRECTIONS

Both underhand and overhand throws may be used and recorded in the same fashion as the basketball throw.

DASHES

EQUIPMENT

A flat, stoneless area is needed. A string is held by two people at the end of the measured distance.

DIRECTIONS

Distances recommended: (1) grade four— boys, 30 yards; girls, 30 yards; (2) grade five— boys, 45 yards; girls, 40 yards.

WALKING RACES

Arrangements for Walking Races are the same as those for Dashes, except, of course, that students walk the distance. Start with short distances and gradually increase.

CLASSROOM ACTIVITIES

SITTING BALL GAME

EQUIPMENT

A softball or similar size ball for each squad, a chair for each person.

PLAYERS

Two or four squads of equal number.

DIRECTIONS

Divide the group into two or four squads and place the rows of chairs so that contestants will be facing each other. Contestants fold their arms and extend their legs out straight in front of them, feet off the floor. The ball is placed on the legs of the first person in each row, close to the ankles. Without the use of his hands or having any help whatsoever, each player tries to place the ball on the next contestant's legs, and so on down the row. If the ball falls off it must be picked up and started where it fell. All teams play at the same time. The first team to pass the ball to its last player is the winner.

This and the other games described in this section may of course be repeated as often as time and interest permit.

RUBBER HEELS

EQUIPMENT

Three rubber heels for each group.

PLAYERS

Groups of four or five each.

DIRECTIONS

If tiled floor is available use six blocks for each group; if not, the target may be drawn with chalk on the regular floor. Number the blocks from one to six. Players stand on a line 6 to 10 feet from the target area and toss the rubber heels one at a time. Their score is determined by where the heels fall. A plywood or wallboard target may be used with numbers painted in the squares. If enough targets are available, the game may be played outside. Chalk-marked targets may also be made outside on concrete or asphalt pavement. Bean bags may be substituted for the heels if necessary.

VARIATIONS

Toss clothespins into numbered boxes. Toss spools into old shoes which are numbered.

NUMBERS ARE FUN

EQUIPMENT

None.

PLAYERS

Two teams. One team is designated *number one* and one *number two.*

DIRECTIONS

Two teams are formed and stand back to back. One person in team one calls out a number in a false voice. Then he changes his place in line and in a different voice calls out his number again. The first person on team two tries to guess who called the number. If he succeeds, his team scores a point and may guess again. If he fails, the play is reversed. The team with highest score wins.

FINDING URANIUM

(ADAPTATION OF HUCKLE
BUCKLE BEANSTALK)

EQUIPMENT

Small pebble or stone.

PLAYERS

Entire class.

DIRECTIONS

One child is chosen to be "It" and leaves the room. The class agrees on a hiding place for a small pebble which represents the uranium ore. When "It" comes into the room, the class makes a slow clicking noise with their tongues. They increase the speed of the "Geiger counter" as "It" gets closer to the uranium. When he is far away it becomes a very slow tick, barely audible. The point of the game is to develop the hearing sense of "It," so that he can find the uranium when the "Geiger counter" reaches its highest speed. When "It" finds the uranium, he may choose the next "It."

TRAVELING

EQUIPMENT

Chalk and blackboard.

DIRECTIONS

Teams work according to the rows in which they are seated in the classroom. Each must have an equal number. Each team chooses the name of a car. The names of these cars are written on the board in front of each row. The children in each row join hands. All children except the leader in each row put their heads down on the desk so they may not see the blackboard. The teacher or leader writes a number on the blackboard which represents the miles the cars are to travel. The leader passes this number to the one holding his hand by squeezing his hand the number of times that corresponds to the number on the board. If they are to travel six miles he squeezes his hand six times. The second child squeezes the hand of the third and so on down to the last person in the row. As soon as the last person receives the number, he goes to the blackboard and under his team's car writes the number of miles. The first row finished with the correct number of miles wins the race. The teacher needs to stress quietness in this game. Naturally, if a child tells the number of miles to anyone, there is no game. There must be absolutely no talking until all cars have registered mileage. If the row finished first has the incorrect mileage, the winner will be the next with the correct mileage. Change leaders for each successive game. For mileage of double numbers, i.e., 62, the number 6 would be passed then there would be a pause—then 2. Thus the last one would read the mileage 62, not 6 plus 2, or 8.

COFFEE, TEA, AND MILK

EQUIPMENT
None.

DIRECTIONS

On the floor mark three or more spaces each about 3 square feet. Mark one with a "T" for tea, one "C" for coffee, and the third "M" for milk. All children start moving around the room in a line, varying their steps as the teacher or a leader directs. They may walk in giant strides, tiptoe, hop on both feet, hop on one foot, skip, and so on. The direction around the room is changed frequently. All aisles or parts of the room should be used. The teacher or leader does not watch the children. At various times he or she claps. This is the signal for the children to stop. Children standing in the area marked "M" for milk get one point; children standing in coffee or tea areas have a minus one. All children remain in the game until it is over. The child with the highest score wins. Children must be sure to stop immediately when the clap is heard. As soon as the teacher claps, he or she turns around. Children caught moving may also have a minus one score. The reason the teacher has his or her back to the class when he or she claps is so that he or she will not know where any child is and thus no one will feel that the teacher has been unfair. More areas may make the game more fun.

FOX AND RABBIT

EQUIPMENT

Clean blackboard erasers or similar objects. If there are six teams or rows of children,

three erasers would be left as is and three would have some identifying mark.

DIRECTIONS

The leader of row one is given a plain unmarked eraser. This is the rabbit. The leader of row two receives a marked eraser which is the fox. Each two rows are competitors. The object is for the rabbit to catch the fox or vice versa. The eraser is passed back over the head of each child to the last one in the row, who places it on the desk of the row with which he is competing. If the fox is placed on the last desk in the rabbit row before the rabbit is on the last desk of the fox row, the fox wins. If six rows are competing there would be three winners. Teams or rows may wish to change from fox to rabbit. At the end one can determine if the foxes or rabbits (all totaled scores) won.

VARIATIONS

Require the fox and rabbit to travel up and down a designated number of times.

HANDWRITING IDENTIFICATION

EQUIPMENT

Chalk and blackboard.

DIRECTIONS

One child is chosen "It" and is seated in the back of the room with his eyes closed. A leader points to a child who goes to the blackboard and writes a word. All children then exchange seats so "It" may not be able to tell who wrote the word from the mere direction of sound. "It" is then asked to turn, look at the word, and identify the writer. He has three guesses. If he guesses correctly, he is "It" again. If he does not, the writer is the new "It."

SELECTED REFERENCES

See the end of Chapter 24.

CHAPTER **24**

Activities for Middle Childhood,
Ages Eleven and Twelve

DANCES AND RHYTHMS

Continued use of steps learned in the previous grades give greater opportunities to learn and enjoy dances of a more complicated nature.

This age group is often interested in some social dances as well as the others already discussed. Boys particularly enjoy very strenuous dances such as the Russian Bear Dance and girls are ready for the basic steps of the modern dance plus a continuation of creative dance.

Records and numbers are given ror each dance. The addresses of the record companies are given in Appendix A.

TABLE 24–1. Dances

Folk Dances		
Bager Gavotte	American	Folkraft 1094
Bow Belinda	American	Folkraft 1189
Celito Lindo	Mexican	Folkraft
Crested Hen	Danish	Victor 45:6176
		Folkraft 1194
Glow Worm	American mixer	Imperial 1044
Highland Schottische	Scottish	Victor 45:6179
Heel-Toe Polka	American	Folkraft 1166
Irish Lilt	Irish	Burns Albums B, 348, and J, 555
La Raspa	American mixer	Folkraft 1119
Maypole Dance	English	Folkraft 1093
Mexican Waltz	American	Folkraft 1093
Minuet	French	Folkraft 1179
Military Schottische	American	Folkraft 1101
Portland Fancy	American	Folkraft 1243
Tantoli	Swedish	Victor 45:6183

333

Folk Dances

Tarentella	Italian	Folkraft 1173
Troika	Russian	Folkraft 1170
Varsouiennie	Swedish	Folkraft 1130
		Decca 3131A

Waltz Dances

Black Hawk Waltz	Russian	Folkraft 1107
Circle Waltz Mixer	American	Folkraft 1046
Mexican Waltz	American	Folkraft 1093
Rye Waltz	American	Folkraft 1103

Couple and Ballroom Dances

Boston Two-Step	English	Folkraft 1158
Call to the Piper	Scottish	Folkraft 1065
Glow Worm Gavotte	American	Folkraft 1158
Progressive Two-Step	English	Folkraft 1161
Put Your Little Foot	American	Folkraft 1165
Russian Two-Step	Russian	Folkraft 1096

Dances for Special Events

Festival Professional		Folkraft 1179
Maypole Dance	English-American	Folkraft 1178
Minuet	French	Folkraft 1179
Swedish Weaving Dance	Swedish	Folkraft 1172

DEVELOPMENTAL ACTIVITIES

SQUAT THRUST

STARTING POSITION
    Pupil stands at attention.

ACTION
    Count 1: Bend knees and place hands on the floor in front of the feet. Arms may be between, outside, or in front of the bent knees.
    Count 2: Thrust the legs back far enough

Figure 24–1. Squat Thrust.

so that the body is perfectly straight from shoulders to feet (the pushup position).

Count 3: Return to squat position.

Count 4: Return to erect position.

⋙⋘

KNEE RAISE (SINGLE AND DOUBLE)

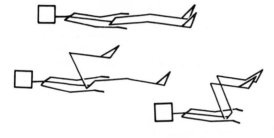

Figure 24–2. Knee Raise (single, center left; double, below right).

STARTING POSITION

Pupil lies on back with knees slightly flexed, feet on floor, arms at sides.

ACTION

Count 1: Raise one knee up as close as possible to chest.

Count 2: Fully extend the knee so the leg is perpendicular to the floor.

Count 3: Bend knee and return to chest.

Count 4: Straighten leg and return to starting position.

Alternate the legs during the exercise. The double knee raise is done in the same manner by moving both legs simultaneously.

⋙⋘

PULL STRETCHER

STARTING POSITION

Two pupils sit facing each other, legs apart and extended, so that the soles of their feet are in contact. Pupils grasp hands with fingers inter-

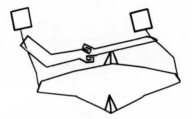

Figure 24–3. Pull Stretcher.

locked and take alternate turns pulling each other to a bending and an erect position.

⋙⋘

LEG EXTENSION

Figure 24–4. Leg Extension.

STARTING POSITION

Pupil sits, legs extended, body erect and hands on hips.

ACTION

Count 1: With a quick, vigorous action, raise and flex the knees by dragging feet backward toward the buttocks with the toes lightly touching the ground.

Count 2: Extend the legs back to the starting position.

The head and shoulders should be held high throughout the exercise.

⋙⋘

UP OARS

STARTING POSITION

Pupil lies on back with arms extended behind head.

Figure 24–5. Up Oars.

RECLINING PULLUPS

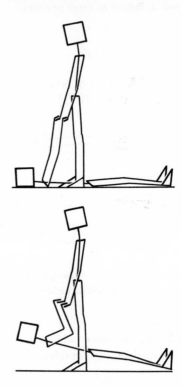

Figure 24–7. Reclining Pullups.

ACTION

Count 1: Sit up, reach forward with the extended arms, meanwhile pulling the knees tightly against the chest. Arms are outside the knees.

Count 2: Return to starting position.

The exercise is done rhythmically and without breaks in the movement.

HEAD AND SHOULDER CURL

Figure 24–6. Head and Shoulder Curl.

STARTING POSITION

Pupil lies on the back with hands clasped, palms down, behind the small of the back.

ACTION

Count 1: Lift the head and pull the shoulders and elbows up off the floor. Hold the tense position for four counts.

Count 2: Return to starting position.

Repeat the exercise.

STARTING POSITION

One pupil lies on back. His partner stands astride of him, looking face to face, feet beside reclining pupil's chest. Partners grasp hands, with fingers interlocked. Reclining pupil's arms are fully extended.

ACTION

Count 1: Pupil on floor pulls up with arms until chest touches partner's thighs. His body remains straight, with weight resting on heels. The standing partner supports but does not aid action.

Count 2: Return to starting position.

GAMES OF LOW ORGANIZATION, INCLUDING RELAYS AND PRELIMINARY AND LEAD-UP ACTIVITIES

Teachers should analyze each team game to determine what specific skills are needed for its enjoyment and success. These skills may be practiced many times in game formations known as relays or preliminary and lead-up activities. For example, in analyzing Kick Ball, one finds that the skills needed are catching, throwing fast and accurately, running fast, and kicking a stationary ball. In Volleyball the skills needed are serving and volleying. Practice situations may well be planned by teachers and children. Many games formulated by combined thinking serve practice needs well and develop the skills desired.

SQUEEZE OUT

FORMATION

A double circle is formed, with partners facing each other. There are two extra players, the chaser and the runner.

DIRECTIONS

The chaser and runner run around or through the circle. The runner is safe if he stops between the members of a couple. When the runner stops, he stands with his back to one of the players. This player is "squeezed out," and he becomes the chaser, while the former chaser becomes the runner. If the runner is caught, the chaser becomes the runner and the runner the chaser. Encourage the players to keep the game moving by not running too long, and to make surprise stops between the couples.

BROAD JUMP RELAY

FORMATION

Several teams with equal numbers of players.

DIRECTIONS

Teams are in single lines behind a starting line. Mark off a space 1 yard wide a good running distance away from the starting line. About 20 feet beyond this, mark off an end line. The first player in each line runs forward, jumps over the area marked off, runs to the end line, and returns to his starting place repeating the actions. He tags the second player and so on. The first team finished wins. Should a player fail to jump the marked area he must repeat his run.

KEEP IT UP

EQUIPMENT

One volleyball for each team.

DIRECTIONS

Teams of eight to 10 players. Each team forms a single circle facing inward. One player in each team starts the play. The ball is volleyed from player to player, the object being to keep it in play. One point is counted for each successful volley and one point deducted for each miss. The team having the highest score in a given time wins. Score is kept aloud.

THREE DEEP

FORMATION

Double circle facing inward, one player standing directly behind the other. One player is chosen to be "It" and another to be the runner.

DIRECTIONS

The runner may save himself by stepping in front of any two players; the rear player of the three then becomes runner. The runner should not run for a long period before stepping in front of a player. If there are many players, several runners and Its may be chosen. Runners may run in any direction and through the circle.

CIRCLE PURSUIT TAG

FORMATION

Players form a single circle facing counter-clockwise. Players should not be closer to each other than eight feet.

DIRECTIONS

At a signal, all start to run following the general outline of the circle. Each tries to tag the runner directly in front of him. Each player tagged drops out of the game and starts a new circle and another game as soon as there are three or four tagged. The last player tagged in the first circle wins. At a signal from a leader or teacher, the circle faces about and runs in the opposite direction. As this reverses the relative position of runners who are gaining or losing ground, it is a feature that may be used by a judicious leader to add much merriment and zest to the game.

VARIATION

Form the players in a large circle facing toward the center and count off by fours. The number ones then take two steps backward and

face to the right. Upon command these pupils (the ones) run forward, each one trying to tag the one in front of him. As soon as one is tagged he must step into the circle. Continue until only one is left. Repeat with "twos," "threes," and "fours," and finally with the four winners.

ARCH GOAL BALL

EQUIPMENT

A ball or bean bag and a basket or box for each team.

FORMATION

Two or more teams of equal number, in columns, with a basket or box placed 15 feet in front of the first pupil of each team.

DIRECTIONS

The first player in each team has a ball or bean bag. At the signal "Go," he throws for the basket or box. Regardless of whether his throw is successful he retrieves the ball, runs to the rear of his team and passes the ball overhead to the player in front of him. The ball is passed on to the front pupil who repeats the action. The race is finished when all have had a turn and the ball has been returned to the first player in line. The team making the greatest number of successful pitches at the basket or box wins. Each successful toss counts one point.

SQUARE RELAY

EQUIPMENT

Four Indian clubs or milk cartons for each team.

FORMATION

Four Indian clubs are placed in position to

form a square. The players are divided into two teams. The teams are in single file each facing a square. The distance the teams are from the clubs differs according to the space available.

DIRECTIONS

At the signal "Go," the first runner of each team starts and runs around the clubs. He must circle each club. Each runner upon completing his run touches off the next runner. The first team to finish wins.

KANGAROO RELAY

EQUIPMENT

An eraser, bean bag, volleyball, or basketball for each team.

FORMATION

Divide players into two or more equal teams. These teams line up in columns behind a starting line drawn on the ground. On the playing space draw another line parallel to the starting line 10 to 20 feet from it.

DIRECTIONS

The first player of each team places a volleyball (or whatever is used) between his knees and at the starting signal jumps to the line on the other side of the playing space, keeping the ball between his knees without touching it with his hands. If the ball falls out he must pick it up and replace it at the point in his running space where he dropped it. Upon reaching the line he takes the ball in his hands and runs back to the starting line, where he gives it to the next player on his team who should be toeing the starting line. He then takes his place at the rear of his team. This mode of playing continues until all players have run. The winning team shall be the one that has each one of its members complete the run and is standing at attention first.

BASKETBALL RELAY

EQUIPMENT

One basketball for each team. Basketball goal for each two teams.

FORMATION

Teams of equal numbers lined in single file, twenty feet from the goal.

DIRECTIONS

Teams are in basic relay formation facing a basketball goal. On the signal "Go," the first player dribbles up to his basket and attempts a shot. He recovers the ball and throws it back to the next player in his line. He then runs to the end of his starting line. Each basket made counts a point for the team.

SOCCER-DRIBBLE RELAY

EQUIPMENT

One soccer ball for each team.

FORMATION

Teams of equal numbers in file formation. One line 20 feet from starting line.

DIRECTIONS

Players stand in a basic running-relay formation. The first player in each team has a soccer ball in front of him. At the "Go" signal, the first player dribbles the ball with either foot to the turning point and back. The second player in line may not start until both ball and player have crossed the finish line. The use of hands is prohibited.

FIVE TRIPS

EQUIPMENT

Two balls, any size desired by class or

teacher. If more than two groups are used, more balls will be needed as each group needs two. Balls should be approximately the same size but should be easily distinguishable. One white volleyball and one red rubber ball would be an example of this.

DIRECTIONS

Groups line up as shown in Figure 24–8. Number one of each team has a ball. At the signal "Go," he passes the ball to the opposite person on his team. Dotted line shows the path of the ball for team X. The ball travels down

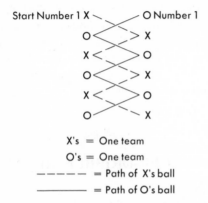

Start Number 1 X   O Number 1

X's = One team
O's = One team
– – – – – = Path of X's ball
————— = Path of O's ball

Figure 24–8. Five Trips.

the entire line in zigzag formation and comes back to the starter. This makes one trip. The leader calls "One" out loud so all may hear. He immediately starts the ball on its second trip and so it continues until the ball has made five trips and is back in the leader's hands. Both teams pass their balls at the same time. This will work well if one leader is designated to make the first pass low while the other is asked to pass it high. From then on no one need worry about the passes. Distances between lines depend on the ability of the children and the type of pass used. Various types may be used. If a ball is lost the person who missed it recovers it and starts it again from his place in line. The number of trips may be varied by the teacher and pupils.

CLUB SNATCH

EQUIPMENT
One Indian club.

DIRECTIONS

A goal is marked off across each end of the playing area, 50 to 100 feet apart. An Indian club is placed midway between the goals. (A stone or dumbbell laid on the ground may be substituted.)

The players are divided into two equal teams and are distributed, one half standing on one goal line and the other half on the other. Each member has a number, from one up. Each must remember his number. The object of the game is for the runners whose numbers are called to snatch the club and return to the goal before they are tagged by a runner from the opposite goal. Both runners leave their starting bases at the same time when their number is called. Should one succeed in reaching the goal with the club before the other player can tag him, his team scores one point. Should he be tagged before he can return with the club, there is no point. The club is replaced after each run. Both players return to their original teams.

The team wins which has the highest score at the end of the playing time. It adds fun to the game to call out two numbers at one time.

INDIVIDUAL AND DUAL ACTIVITIES

DECK TENNIS

PLAYERS

The game may be played as either singles (two players) or doubles (four players).

EQUIPMENT

The doubles court is 40 feet long and 20 feet wide. It is divided across the middle by a net, the ends of which are attached to posts standing one foot outside of the court on either side. The width of the court is divided into half by a line drawn the full length of the court, thus forming the half courts. A neutral ground is marked off by lines drawn parallel to, and two feet from, the net.

The singles court is 40 feet long and 15 feet wide. It is divided the same as the doubles court. The court may be marked out with tennis marker or tapes cut to the proper lengths.

The net is 22 feet long and 36 inches wide with a 2-inch top binding of white canvas. The height of the net is 6 feet at the posts. A rope may be substituted for the net.

The ring shall have a 4.5-inch inside diameter and 7-inch outside diameter. It is made of soft molded rubber. A rope ring may be substituted.

OBJECT

The game is similar to tennis except that a ring is tossed, instead of a ball being batted back and forth.

RULES

1. Choice of sides and the right to serve in the first game shall be decided by toss.

2. The players shall stand on opposite sides of the net; the player who first delivers the ring shall be called the server and the other the receiver.

3. When serving, the server shall stand behind the base line and within the limits of the half court. The server's partner and the receiver's partner may take any position in their own court.

4. The service shall be delivered from the right and left courts alternately, beginning from the right in every game. The ring served shall drop within the half court line and the side line of the court which is diagonally opposite to that from which it was served, or upon any such line. Each player serves a game.

5. The ring must always be played or served with an upward tendency no matter whether the ring be taken high or low. No balking or hesitating is allowed.

6. Either forehand or backhand play is allowed, except the serve, which must be forehand.

7. A ring touching the net in going over during the service is a "let" and the service is taken over.

8. The ring must be caught with only one hand and delivered with the same hand immediately.

9. Scoring is like tennis.

QUOITS (OUTDOOR)

EQUIPMENT

One set (four) of quoits or horseshoes and two metal pegs. Level area 50 feet by 10 feet.

PLAYERS

The game may be played singles (two

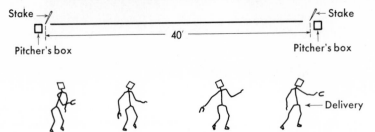

Figure 24–9. Quoits.

players) or doubles (four players). In doubles one player of each team pitches from each peg.

RULES

1. The standard distance apart for pegs is forty feet. For younger players the distance may be shortened. Pegs shall extend 6 inches above the ground.

2. When pitching, contestant's forward foot shall be in the rear of the peg and within 3 feet of either side.

3. At the beginning of a game the contestants shall toss a coin for first pitch, the winner having his choice of first or follow pitch.

4. At the beginning of any game other than the first, the loser of the preceding game shall have first pitch.

5. Except at the beginning of a game, the winner of the preceding pitch shall have first pitch.

SCORING

1. A regulation game shall consist of twenty-one points and the contestant first scoring this number shall be declared the winner.

2. The most points a contestant can score in a single game are 21. Therefore, if a contestant has 19 points, he cannot get full credit for a ringer, but only the necessary points required to bring his total up to 21. Should he make a ringer, in that case it would count only two points.

3. The closest shoe to the peg shall score one point. If both shoes are closer than either of an opponent's they shall score two points.

4. A ringer shall score three points. To be

a ringer, a shoe must encircle the peg far enough to permit a straight edge to touch both calks and clear the peg.

5. A leaner shall score two points. To be a leaner, a shoe must be supported by the peg, and more than one-half of it should be clear of the ground.

6. Two ringers is the highest score a pitcher can make with two shoes and shall count six points.

7. All equals shall be counted as ties. That is, if both contestants have one shoe each, equal distance from the peg or against it, they are tied, and the one having the next closest shoe shall score one point.

⊁⊱

FLOOR OR BEACH TENNIS

EQUIPMENT

A tennis ball or sponge rubber ball.

FORMATION

Mark on the floor or ground a rectangle 6 feet by 12 feet. No net is needed. Draw a line across the court dividing it into two equal parts.

DIRECTIONS

The game is usually played by two players (singles). It may be played by four (doubles). The player starts the game by batting the ball with his hand to his opponent. It is played with the open hand. Players must remain outside of the marked area and make each play by reaching in. Winning score may be set at 13, 15, or 21 points.

HANDBALL

EQUIPMENT

One small rubber ball.

PLAYERS

Two to four players constitute a team.

FIELD

Flat piece of ground 20 feet deep in front of a wall 10 feet wide and 10 to 15 feet high. (Mark off with line on brick wall of a building or wall of gymnasium.) Line drawn on the ground parallel to the wall and 8 feet from it called the *short line*.

DIRECTIONS

To start the game, a player from team A steps up to the short line, bounces the ball on the ground, and bats (serves) it with his hand against the wall so that the ball rebounds beyond the short line, and within the playing area. He has two chances to do this. If on the second trial the ball falls short of the short line, hits the player, or goes outside the playing area, he is out and another member of team A serves.

As soon as a member of team A succeeds in batting the ball so that it rebounds beyond the 8-foot line, the ball is considered in play and a member of team B must return it before it has bounced twice.

RULES

1. The ball must be batted first by a member of one team and then by a member of the opposing team.

2. Failure to return the ball scores one point for the serving team.

3. If the serving team fails to return the ball, it makes an out.

4. Two outs put the side out.

5. Twenty-one points constitute a game.

PADDLE BADMINTON

EQUIPMENT

One paddle for each player, one shuttlecock, one net. Area 25 feet by 50 feet with a net 4 or 5 feet in height attached to poles outside the court.

PLAYERS

Two or four.

DIRECTIONS

A player from one side serves the shuttlecock from behind the end line into the court across the net. Play is then started and the object is to hit the shuttlecock back and forth from one side to the other, keeping it within the bounds of the court. If doubles are being played, alternate hits must be by partners.

One point is scored when a player:

1. Hits the shuttlecock out of the court.

2. Fails to return it to his opponent.

3. Hits the net with his paddle or his body.

The same player serves as long as his side or he, as an individual, scores. If he or his partner fails to score or to return the shuttlecock, hits the net, or hits the shuttlecock out of bounds, his serve ends and the opponent becomes the server. The serving side is the only side which can score a point. Partners alternate services. Points may vary for winning a game. They may be 13, 15, or 21, as set before play.

TABLE TENNIS

EQUIPMENT

One table tennis table, one paddle for each player, three balls, and one net.

PLAYERS

Two or four.

DIRECTIONS

One player serves the ball across the net

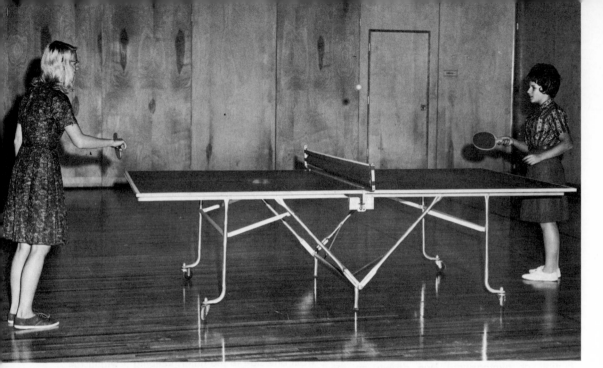

Figure 24–10. Table Tennis.

to his opponent. The ball is served as in tennis except that it must bounce on the server's side of the net before crossing onto the opponent's half of the table. The object is to hit the ball back and forth across the net keeping it on the table. The same player serves until five points have been scored. Service then changes sides. Points are made when a player:

1. Hits the ball off the table.
2. Fails to serve the ball correctly in two turns.
3. Hits the table with his body.
4. Fails to return the ball to his opponent.

The winning score of a game is 21 points.

SELF-TESTING ACTIVITIES

COFFEE GRINDER

Figure 24–11. Coffee Grinder.

Assume a deep knee bend position and place the left or right hand on the floor by the side of the body. Keep the elbow stiff and place weight on the arm. Extend both legs either to the right or left depending on which arm is used. Use the arm as a pivot and walk in a circle.

ANKLE JUMP

Feet together. Grasp ankles with hands.

Jump as far as possible. May be done from a squat or standing position.

Figure 24–12. Ankle Jump.

ANKLE TOSS

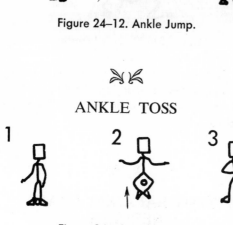

Figure 24–13. Ankle Toss.

Hold a tennis ball or bean bag between ankles. Jump and toss it so you may catch it.

CRANE DIVE

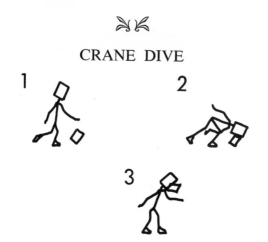

Figure 24–14. Crane Dive.

Stand a piece of paper on the floor about 4 inches to 6 inches in height. Stand in front of it. Balance on one foot, raise the other to the back. Place arms sideward for balance. Bend forward and pick up paper with teeth.

FISH HAWK DIVE

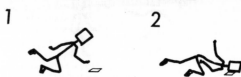

Figure 24–15. Fish Hawk Dive.

Kneel on one knee. Stand a folded paper about the size of an envelope on the floor. Raise one leg backward, balance on the knee, bend forward, and pick up the paper.

HAND WRESTLE

Figure 24–16. Hand Wrestle.

Partners stand facing each other with right hands joined. Their right feet are placed against each other's foot. They endeavor to make each other lose his balance by moving one or both feet from the floor.

HEEL CLICK

Stand erect, both feet together. Jump in the air and endeavor to click heels together two or three times before landing back on the floor.

Figure 24–17. Heel Click.

JUMP THE STICK

Figure 24–18. Jump the Stick.

Hold a broomstick or wand in both hands and jump over it without releasing either hand. Try this forward and backward.

KANGAROO FIGHT

Figure 24–19. Kangaroo Fight.

Each partner stands with a tennis ball or folded newspaper between his knees. Arms are folded across chests. Each endeavors to make the other drop the object by bumping shoulders.

KNEE WRESTLE (MATS NEEDED)

Figure 24–20. Knee Wrestle.

Partners assume a kneeling position on the mat and face each other. They hold right hands and endeavor to push or pull each other off balance.

SITTING BALANCE (MATS NEEDED)

Figure 24–21. Sitting Balance.

One player lies on his back, bends his knees to his chest, and extends his feet. The second child stands with his back to him and sits on the soles of his feet. The first lifts him by straightening his knees upward.

TANDEM

Figure 24–22. Tandem.

Three players stand one behind the other. The last one assumes a semisquat position. The one in front sits on his knees. They walk forward using left and right feet together.

Figure 24–23. Individual Forward Roll.

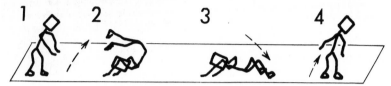

TEAM FORWARD ROLLS (MATS NEEDED)

Three or more people stand at the edge of mats and do forward rolls at the same time endeavoring to keep in rhythm.

TEAM GAMES

Achievement Skills and Tests for Various Team Games

The following will suggest a number of tests to use in determining individual skills:

1. Baseball activities: (a) baseball throw for accuracy, (b) baseball throw for distance, (c) baseball batting for accuracy, (d) fielding grounders and fly balls.

2. Basketball activities: (a) basketball throw for distance; (b) basketball goal throwing—free throw, goal in one minute, goal throw for accuracy; (c) relays to help develop skills—shuttle, dribble and shoot, dribble.

3. Soccer activities: (a) soccer kick for goal, (b) soccer kick for distance, (c) soccer kick for accuracy.

4. Touch football activities: (a) drop kick for goal, (b) punting for distance, (c) forward pass for distance and accuracy.

5. Volleyball activities: (a) serving for accuracy, (b) return for accuracy, (c) volleying with a partner across a net, (d) volleying against a wall to oneself.

BUNT SOFTBALL (OUTDOOR)

Bunt softball is played exactly the same as baseball except for two rules: (1) six men on a side, eliminating the outfield; (2) the batter may do nothing more than bunt; if he swings at a ball, he is out whether he hits it or not.

This game will develop real bunters.

PADDLE BASEBALL

EQUIPMENT

A wooden paddle, similar to a ping-pong paddle, a tennis ball or rubber ball, a diamond marked like a baseball diamond only smaller, depending on the children.

DIRECTIONS

This game is played like softball and may be played in a smaller area and in areas where rules do not permit baseballs or softballs to be used. If boys hit too hard they may be required to bat the opposite way from their regular way of batting. (A left-handed batter would bat right-handed and vice versa.)

PUNCH BASEBALL

EQUIPMENT

One volleyball or a rubber ball of approximately the same size and a baseball diamond sized to meet the children's ability.

DIRECTIONS

The directions are the same as for softball. The pitcher pitches the ball and the batter *punches* it. This is a *must* so the child does not hurt his arm or hand. Children may play this game in a smaller area than softball, get much

Figure 24–24. Team games.

enjoyment, and satisfy the desire for a team game in the spring when area and regulations will not permit softballs to be used.

BASEBALL NEWCOMB

EQUIPMENT

Softball and volleyball net, the top 10 feet from the ground.

FORMATION

An area 30 feet by 60 feet divided into two courts by the net. One team on each side of the net spaced as in volleyball.

DIRECTIONS

A server pitches the ball underhand, over the net. The ball is caught and returned by the receiving side and the play continues until a miss occurs. Players may not run with the ball. Each player should keep his own position on the court. The ball must always be pitched underhand.

SCORING

One point for the opposite side when (1) the ball is improperly thrown; (2) the ball is missed; or (3) the ball is thrown into the net or out of bounds.

BAND BOX BALL

EQUIPMENT

One volleyball and four Indian clubs.

DIRECTIONS

Two teams of five each, divided in three forwards and two guards. More players may be used by enlarging the playing area and using more than one goal. The game is played on a

rectangle. The size will depend on the ability of the children. The ball is put in play by jumping it at center between an A and B player. Forwards try to score a point by knock-

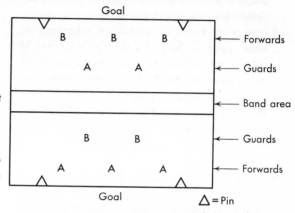

Figure 24–25. Band Box Ball.

ing down their opponent's pins. Guards attempt to intercept and pass the ball to their forwards. If the ball rolls over the band area, the team responsible for it must give their opponent a point. Two points are scored when a forward succeeds in knocking over the Indian club in the goal. They may either throw or roll the ball. Balls which go out of bounds are thrown in by the team not responsible for causing it to go out of the playing area. Balls may not be knocked from an opponent's hand. If this occurs, a forward may have a free shot at his opponent's goal. Teachers and pupils may set the number of points for a game, or it may be played by a time limit in quarters or halves.

LONG BASE

EQUIPMENT

Softball bat and a softball.

FORMATION

The softball area may be used for the area

of this game. To the right of the pitcher's box and 65 feet away from home plate is marked a square; this is the long base. The pitcher's box is marked 30 feet away from home plate. The players, preferably from eight to 12, are divided into two equal groups. The players on each of the teams are numbered in consecutive order. Each of the teams chooses a pitcher, a catcher, and a long-baseman. The remainder of the players are the fielders or the batters, depending upon the playing position of the team. The teams alternate their positions when three outs are declared.

DIRECTIONS

The first batter of the batting team stands at home base and attempts to hit the ball thrown underhanded to him by the pitcher. If the batter hits the ball, it is fair no matter where it goes. The batter runs to the long base and may return to home base. If the batter does this successfully without being tagged by one of the fielders, he scores one run. If a batter reaches the long base safely, he may remain there until another batter of his team hits a ball. During the process of the game, several batters may stand on the long base at once. Once the ball is hit by the batter, the fielders try to tag the batter before he reaches long base or throw the ball to long base before the runner reaches it. All of the fielders, including the pitcher and the catcher, may move anywhere on the field. When the batted ball is retrieved by one of the fielders, he may throw the ball to any fielder who is closer to home base or long base. The team at bat remains at bat until three outs are declared. An out occurs when the fielders catch a fly ball, when the ball beats the runners to long base or a runner is tagged with the ball, when the batter is not within the area of long base and is tagged with the ball, and when the batter throws his bat instead of dropping it as he runs to long base. The game consists of seven innings. The team having scored the largest number of runs wins the game.

KICK BASEBALL

Refer to Chapter 11 for complete directions.

KICK PIN BASEBALL

Refer to Chapter 11 for complete directions.

SCRAM

EQUIPMENT

One volleyball and individual markers for one team.

PLAYERS

From ten to 30 children.

DIRECTIONS

Players take their places in a rectangular playing area sized according to age level. A suggested size is 50 by 40 feet. One player from each team comes to the center of the area,

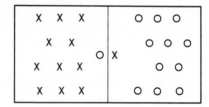

Figure 24–26. Scram.

faces his teammates, and attempts to tap a ball which is tossed straight up in the air by the leader. When the ball is tapped, anyone may catch it and players are then free to move in both courts. The object is to hit players on the opposite team below the waist with the ball. Each hit scores a point for the throwing team. However, *if the opponent can catch the thrown ball, there is no score and he in turn throws it back at his opponents.* Rebounds do not count as hits. Anyone may pick a ball up off the floor and throw it. No one may run or step with the ball. To aid players in knowing teammates, one team should wear markers of some kind. When a player is hit he goes to the side of the court and rests until another of his teammates is hit and comes out; then he returns. This helps to make scoring easy and also enables a child to rest for a few seconds which is often necessary during this game. When a class plays this well, two balls may be used. The game is played in quarters of three, five, or six minutes each, depending on the children.

NEWCOMB

EQUIPMENT

Volleyball, junior-sized basketball, or an 8-inch or 10-inch playground ball.

FORMATION

A court 25 feet by 50 feet in size is marked on the playing area. A net or rope 7 feet from the floor is stretched across the center of the playing area, dividing the court into two equal parts. The players are divided into two equal teams. Eight to 12 players are recommended for each team although the game may be played with smaller or larger numbers.

DIRECTIONS

One player is designated to throw the ball across the net. The game continues with the object being to throw the ball over the net, to catch the ball, and to continue throwing and catching the ball back and forth across the net. Any player may catch the ball. The ball may be relayed among team members. The play continues until one point is scored. Points are

scored when the following occurs: the ball drops to the ground on the opponent's side; the ball hits the net, rope, or standards holding the net; the ball is thrown under the net by a player; the ball is thrown outside the playing area; the ball is held for more than ten seconds. After a point has been scored, the ball is immediately thrown by the side in possession and the game continues as before. The game is played in two 10-minute periods or may be played for points.

SIMPLIFIED VOLLEYBALL

EQUIPMENT

Volleyball and net.

FORMATION

Teams of six to 10 players on either side of the net as in volleyball. Each player should be assigned a position.

DIRECTIONS

Regular volleyball rules should be followed with the following exceptions:

1. Two serves are allowed.

2. An assist on a serve is allowed.

3. Any number of players may play the ball before it goes over the net.

4. A player may hit the ball twice in succession but may not hold it.

5. For very small players the ball may be allowed to bounce once after passing over the net.

6. Any one or all of these exceptions may be allowed.

MASS VOLLEYBALL

EQUIPMENT

Volleyball, giant volleyball or cage ball, and net.

FORMATION

As many players as can be accommodated on the court, one team on either side of the net as in volleyball.

DIRECTIONS

The ball is thrown or batted over the net. As many as can are allowed to play on the ball in succession or at the same time. The objective is to keep the ball in play and to get it back over the net. Players are not allowed to hold the ball. When the ball hits the ground or is knocked out of bounds a point is scored.

SQUARE SOCCER

EQUIPMENT

Soccer ball.

FORMATION

The players are divided into two teams, each team occupying the two adjacent sides of a large square, with clearly marked boundary lines. A soccer ball is placed in the center of the square.

DIRECTIONS

At the leader's command the player at the right end of each team runs to the center and endeavors to kick the ball through the opposing side. The players on the lines stop the ball with hands or body, throwing or kicking it back to the center, or, if possible, through the other team, the two center players assisting. If the ball is kicked over the heads of the players on the line, the opposing center player is given a free kick from the center of the square, the other center standing in back of him. After a team scores a point, the center players take their place at the foot of their teams, and two new players enter the square. One point is scored each time the ball is kicked through the opposing team; the team wins that first scores 21 points.

SOCCER KEEP-AWAY

EQUIPMENT

One soccer ball.

FORMATION

A playing area 25 feet by 50 feet is marked on the playground or gymnasium floor. Across this area are marked parallel lines at 10-foot intervals; five zones are thus formed. The zones at each end are called *end zones*. The middle zone is named the *center zone* and the other two zones of each court are the *neutral zones*. Players are divided into three teams: A, B, and C. One team, B, occupies the center zone, the second and third teams, A and C, occupy the end zones. The neutral zones are unoccupied. One of the team A players in the end zone has possession of the ball at the beginning of the game.

DIRECTIONS

The end zone team A players, with the ball, attempt to kick the ball through the neutral zones and the center zone to team C stationed in the end zone at the opposite end of the playing area. If successful, the kicking team scores one point, and the game is started by team C. After each point has been scored, sides and players on the team alternate in kicking the ball through the center zone. If team B players, stationed in the center zone, stop the ball, the team B player closest to the ball gives it to the end zone team that did not kick the last ball. Each time the center players intercept the ball, one point is scored for their team. If a team player kicks the ball over the heads of both the center zone and the opposite end zone players, both of the latter teams score one point. The end zone teams may score one point each if the center players step into the neutral territory. If the players in any of the zones touch the ball with their hands, the other two teams each score one point. The team having scored the greatest number of points within a designated playing time is declared to be the winner of the game.

☙ ❦

CAPTAIN BALL

EQUIPMENT

Basketball, volleyball, or soccerball.

FORMATION

A playing area is marked as diagramed in Figure 24–27. Each of the circles is approximately 2.5 feet in diameter. Fourteen players are divided into two teams. Each team is made up of three circle players, or forwards, who stand within the three circles of their side of the playing area, three guards who stand outside the opponents' circles, and one player who is designated as the center and who stands behind the center line within the center circle facing his forwards. The captain of each team is the forward player who is stationed in the circle that is farthest away from the center line. The players who serve as jumping centers face each other as the teacher holds the ball between them.

DIRECTIONS

The referee tosses the ball into the air be-

tween the two jumping centers. They attempt to bat the ball to one of their own guards, who in turn attempts to throw the ball across the center line to one of his team forwards. If a forward player secures the ball, he attempts to throw it to his forward captain. All of the circle forwards are guarded by the opponents' guards. The guards may intercept the ball at any time and then throw it to one of their forward players. A point is scored each time the captain receives a throw from one of the forward players. No points are scored if the guards or the jumping center throws the ball directly to the captain. The game is played in two halves of 10 minutes each. At the beginning of the second half the guards and forwards exchange positions so that all players have an opportunity to receive experience in playing the various positions. After the toss up, the running centers cross the line and assist the guards of their own teams. The guards may not step on or inside the circle lines, and the forwards may not step on or outside the circle lines; if this foul is committed, the ball is given to the opposite jumping center who takes it to the center line and resumes play by throwing the ball to a guard on his own team. The team with the highest number of points at the end of the playing time is declared to be the winner of the game.

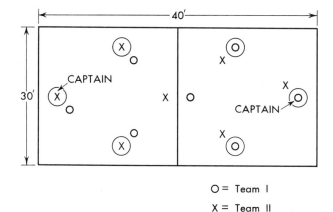

O = Team I

X = Team II

Figure 24–27. Captain Ball.

⊰⊱

TALLY BASKETBALL

EQUIPMENT

Basketball goal, basketball, or volleyball.

FORMATION

If the game is played out of doors, a playing area about the size of a standard basketball court is marked on the play field. If the gymnasium is used, the basketball court lines serve as boundary lines. A center circle is marked in the center of the play area. The game is played by two teams composed of six to 10 players per team. One half of the team players are forwards and the other half are guards. The players are arranged in couples on the court. The forwards of one team remain in one court, and the guards of the same team are stationed in the opposite court; each of the guards has one forward to guard. The same procedure applies to the opposite team.

DIRECTIONS

The referee awards the ball to a forward who stands in the center circle of the playing area. This forward passes the ball to a teammate. This pass may not be intercepted. After the first pass from the center, the forwards, as they receive each pass, call out "One," "Two," and so on, for each completed pass until five consecutive passes are made. The guards may intercept the ball at any time during these passes and pass it to their own team forwards, the guards' passes are not counted. When a forward receives the first pass from another forward, he starts counting in a manner similar to that of the opponent team. When a team has made five consecutive passes, one point is scored. The player who is credited with the fifth consecutive pass walks to the basket and attempts to make a basket. The player may select his own place on the floor from which to shoot. If he scores, one additional point is given. Whether he makes the basket or not, the ball

is dead, and the referee gives the ball to the center forward of the team which did not score. The game is played in four quarters of five minutes each. Teams receive the ball alternately from the referee for a center throw after a point has been scored. The team that has gained the greatest number of points at the end of the playing time is the winner. A rest period of two minutes is given between each of the quarters. Fouls occur if the players walk or run with the ball, push or hold a player, or hand the ball to a teammate. A free shot at the basket is granted for a foul which involves personal contact; other fouls are penalized by not counting the passes made. If two opposing players are holding the ball simultaneously, the referee calls a "tie ball," and the ball is thrown up between the two players for a jump ball.

VARIATIONS

Change number of passes to 10 before scoring.

⊰⊱

RECEIVE AND RUN

EQUIPMENT

A junior football or substitute.

FORMATION

Two teams of six to 20, each on each half of the rectangular playing field. Goal lines marked at the ends of field. Suggested size of field is 40 feet by 70 feet.

DIRECTIONS

One team throws a forward pass from the middle of the field. If playing on a small field it may be thrown from the end instead of the middle.

The opposing team receives the ball and attempts to run forward. They may pass the ball in any direction at any time. No tackling or blocking is allowed. The ball is dead when the player carrying the ball is tagged by a member of the opposing team.

The ball is returned to the facing team and passed again from the point at which it was declared dead. After a second pass, the ball goes to the other team.

A point is scored if the ball is carried over the goal line.

FORWARD PASS BASEBALL

EQUIPMENT
Junior football.

FORMATION
Baseball diamond with baselines of approximately 50 feet. There are two teams of eight to 12 players each. One team is "up," the other in the field. The team in the field consists of a catcher and fielders. There are no basemen or pitcher.

DIRECTIONS
The player who is up throws a forward pass, then runs the bases. The fielders retrieve the ball and pass it to the catcher. When the catcher has the ball and has his foot on home plate, any runner off a base is out. The runner may not take a lead off bases. His foot must be in contact with the base until the next ball is thrown. Note that on all plays the ball is thrown to the catcher.

A thrower is out on a caught fly and all runners must return to their bases.

A ball thrown outside the base lines is a foul. Two fouls constitute an out.

FLAG FOOTBALL

Flag football is a variation of varsity or touch football. Rules should be adapted to suit the needs and safety of the participants (number of players, size of field, length of game, and so on).

KICKOFF
The kickoff should be made from the kicking team's equivalent of the 20-yard line of a regulation field. (*Examples:* 75 yard field, kickoff from 30-yard line; 50 yard field, kickoff from the goal line.)

SCORING
Six points for a touchdown.

SCRIMMAGE
There shall be no tackling of ball carrier, passer, kicker. (Penalty, 15 yards enforced from spot of foul.) The man carrying or in possession of the ball is considered down when the flag has been removed from his back belt area. There shall be no strenuous or violent blocking, such as leaving the feet. (Penalty, 15 yards enforced from spot of foul.) Blocking in line play is permissible.

DOWNS
There shall be four downs required in a series of downs. Option 1: If a team fails to score after a series of downs the ball shall be turned over to the defensive team. Option 2: If a team completes three out of four passes it may be awarded another series of downs. Option 3: A predetermined distance of ball advancement may be considered necessary before a new series of downs is awarded.

FORWARD AND LATERAL PASSES
Forward and lateral passes are permissible exactly as in regular football. Forward passes behind the line anywhere are permissible, but only one to a play. A forward pass thrown beyond the line of scrimmage is illegal. (Penalty, loss of 5 yards from spot of foul.) All men on playing field, both offensive and defensive, are eligible to receive passes at all times. Lateral passes recovered by the defense may

be advanced farther than point of recovery only when the ball has not touched ground. Offensive players may advance their own fumbled lateral at any time.

DEAD BALL

When a player in possession of the ball steps out of bounds the ball is dead. The ball is declared dead when a defensive player succeeds in obtaining the flag from the back belt area of the offensive player carrying the ball. Whenever the whistle blows, the ball is dead.

FLAGS

Flags can be easily made of heavy cloth and should be worn so all players have the same amount of cloth exposed.

ADVANTAGES OF FLAG FOOTBALL

Flag football eliminates much of the roughness which often takes places with either one- or two-handed tagging in touch football. It eliminates any indecision as to whether the offensive player was actually tagged, since the defense must actually have the evidence in his hand—the opponent's flag.

TRACK AND FIELD EVENTS

Events worked on in the previous age group continue to be challenging with the eleven- and twelve-year-old child; see pages 327–330.

Different distances are recommended for dashes: (1) grade six—boys, 60 yards; girls, 50 yards; (2) grades seven and eight—boys, 75 yards; girls, 60 yards.

CLASSROOM ACTIVITIES

CIRCLE PUSH

EQUIPMENT

Yardsticks, broomsticks, wands or similar sticks, and blackboard erasers. One stick and one eraser for each team or squad.

DIRECTIONS

A circle is drawn on the floor in front of each team or squad. Each is the same size. Inside of each circle two smaller circles are drawn. Each circle is numbered. A straight line is drawn in front of each team. The eraser is placed on this line. The leader of each team is given a stick which he uses as a pusher. His object is to push the eraser with his stick so it

goes to and remains in the circle. He scores according to which circle it remains in. He gives

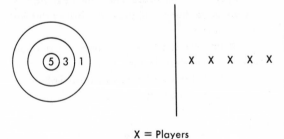

X = Players

Figure 24–28. Circle Push.

his stick to the next person in line, recovers the eraser, and tosses it back to the starting line. He then takes his place at the blackboard and records his points and the points of each succeeding player of his team. Each succeeding player, as he has his turn, recovers the eraser, tosses it to the next player, and then goes to the rear of the line. The line or team scoring the most points wins the round. As many rounds may be played as time and interest permit. The team which has the highest score at the end of the playing time is the winner.

VARIATIONS

Many variations exist using this idea. Bean bags may be used for tossing into these circles without the use of sticks for pushers.

IN THE BOX

EQUIPMENT

Three or four rolled-up socks for each group.

PLAYERS

Three or four squads.

DIRECTIONS

A box is placed 6 to 10 feet in front of each squad. Members line up behind a leader. Each person takes a turn and endeavors to toss the socks in the boxes. Every time a player succeeds he scores one point for his squad. After each person tosses his three socks, he retrieves them and throws them to the next player in his line. Number *one* is score keeper. At the end of a specified time the team with the highest score wins.

CLASSROOM GOLF

EQUIPMENT

Indoor golf ball. Yardstick, broomstick, wand, or golf club cut out of plywood. Objects to be used as obstacles on the course may be

blackboard erasers, pencils, a pencil box with the two ends cut out for a tunnel, pieces of colored paper, lines drawn on the floor, or any available object that would be appropriate and not take up too much room. Set up the course in the back of the classroom or in the recreation room.

PLAYERS

Two or more depending on the space available and ability of children to control their own activity.

DIRECTIONS

Play as miniature golf.

CROSSING THE BROOK

EQUIPMENT

Four or six paper plates for each team.

PLAYERS

Four teams. Seven or eight players in a team.

DIRECTIONS

Lay the brook out as in Figure 24–29, page 358. Use paper plates for stones. At the word "Go," the first person on each team steps from rock to rock crossing the stream to the far goal line and returns the same way. This is played as a relay, each person having a turn. The winning team scores 10 points; second team, seven points; third team, five points; last team, three points.

WORD GAME

EQUIPMENT

Pencil for the leader of each squad, team, or unit. Piece of paper on the first desk in each row or on a table or desk placed in front of each row of children.

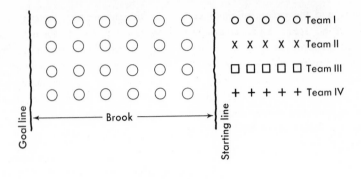

 = Paper plates

Figure 24–29. Crossing the Brook.

DIRECTIONS

The group is divided into as many equal squads as the teacher wishes. Each squad lines up behind its leader. Each leader is given a pencil. A piece of paper is placed on the desk in front of him. At the signal "Go," the first person in each group writes a word on the paper. He takes the pencil and runs to the back of his line and passes the pencil down the line to the first person. When he receives the pencil he writes another word on the paper, goes to the rear of the line, passes the pencil forward, and so the game continues until the captain is again in front of the line. The team finishing first with no misspelled words is the winner. No word may be repeated. All must be legible.

VARIATIONS

This game may be varied many ways. A specific number of letters may be required for each word; numbers may be used; initials of children; states; rivers; proper names; countries; and the like. Children may walk, hop on one foot, skip, or vary the method of reaching the end of the line.

UPSET THE UNION

EQUIPMENT

None.

DIRECTIONS

Each child selects the name of a state. One child is "It." The only seats used in the game are the ones occupied by the children at the beginning of the game. Extra seats must be marked in some way so they are not used. "It" calls the names of two states. These two must change seats while "It" tries to get one of the seats. If "It" succeeds, the player with no seat becomes "It." More than two states may be called. This is up to the leader or to "It." If "It" wishes all children to move, he calls "Upset the Union." Winners of this game will be those who were never "It." This challenge makes "It" always trying for a seat and thus keeps the game very active.

VARIATIONS

Many variations are possible for this game. For example, names of cars, flowers, birds, rivers, and cities may be used.

OVER AND UNDER RELAY

EQUIPMENT

One ball or bean bag for each team.

FORMATION

Even number of children standing in relay formation.

DIRECTIONS

Teams stand in lines of equal numbers. The first player in each line holds a ball or bean bag. At the signal "Go," he passes it over his head to the second player. The second player passes it between his legs to the third player. The object continues to be passed alternately over and under until it is received by the last player in line. When he has the object he runs to the front of the line and restarts it always *over the head*. When each person has had a turn to be the leader and the original starter is at the head of the line the game is over. The first team to complete this is the winner.

TELEGRAMS

FORMATION

Even number of children in each row. They may be sitting or standing. Each holds the hand of the person in front and back of him.

DIRECTIONS

All students must close their eyes except the first one in each line. The teacher writes numbers on the board corresponding to his or her wishes, e.g., 4–7–6. As soon as all *number one* players see it, the teacher erases it. Each number one passes the telegram to the corresponding number two by squeezing his hand as follows: four squeezes, then a pause, seven squeezes, a pause, and six squeezes; then each number one unclasps his hand from number two. Thus the telegram is passed from one to the other in this manner. When the last person receives the telegram he runs to the blackboard and writes it on the board. Then he must decipher it. Each number means the letter of the alphabet, i.e., 4 = D, 7 = G, 6 = F. From the coded letters he must write a message, e.g., *Don't go fast*. The first to finish with the correct answer wins the game.

VARIATIONS

All variations must be written on the board by the leader.

1. *Long and short codes*, e.g., 6–7. Six is a long, even squeeze. Pause. Seven is a rapid, light squeeze. Answer is read "six long and seven short."

2. *Addition*: Two or more numbers sent as directed. Last person adds them and gives the sum.

3. *Multiplication*: Two numbers sent. Last person multiplies them and gives the product.

4. *Fractions*: Addition or subtraction, whichever is directed.

5. *Division*: Two numbers sent. Last person divides and gives the quotient.

NOTE

After each game, the last child should move to the front of the line and be the new starter.

BIRD, BEAST, AND FISH

FORMATION

The entire class is divided in two equal sections.

DIRECTIONS

One person on each team is selected to be the score keeper. The teacher may be "It" until the class learns the game. "It" points to a student and calls either "Bird," "Beast," or "Fish." "It" immediately starts to count aloud, 1–2–3–4–5–6–7–8–9–10, as rapidly as possible. The student whom "It" selected must give the name of whichever group "It" called for. For "Bird" the response may be "robin." For "Fish" the response may be "bass." For "Beast" the response may be "horse." If the selected player cannot say a name before "It" reaches 10, a point is scored for the opposite side. The game may be set for five points or more depending on interest. No duplication may be used.

VARIATIONS

As the class becomes accustomed to the game it may be made more challenging by adding various categories. For social studies ask for rivers, mountains, states, capitals, and so on. For nature ask for trees, flowers, stones, and so on. In a general category often called "the sky is the limit," the leader, or "It," is privileged to call for anything. Examples are makes of cars, modes of travel, holidays, and Presidents' names.

SELECTED REFERENCES

FISCHER, HUGO, and DEAN SHAWBOLD, *Individual and Dual Stunts*, Minneapolis, Burgess Publishing Company, 1950.

HARRIS, JANE A., ANNE PITTMAN, and MARLYS S. WALLER, *Dance Awhile* (Second edition), Minneapolis, Burgess Publishing Company, 1955.

HINDMAN, DARWIN A., *Handbook of Active Games and Contests*, Englewood Cliffs, N.J., Prentice-Hall, Inc., 1951.

LATCHAW, MARJORIE, and JEAN PYATT, *A Pocket Guide of Dance Activities*, Englewood Cliffs, N.J., Prentice-Hall, Inc., 1958.

MASON, BERNARD S., and ELMER D. MITCHELL, *Social Games for Recreation*, New York, A. S. Barnes and Company, 1938.

ROGERS, MARTIN, *A Handbook of Stunts*, New York, The Macmillan Company.

STUART, FRANCES R., and JOHN S. LUDLAM, *Rhythmic Activities* (Series II), Minneapolis, Burgess Publishing Company. 1955.

CHAPTER 25

Activities for Parties and Special Occasions

Parties and special occasions are often headaches for teachers. Yet, they are a valuable part of the social life of each child and provide valuable learning experiences.

If parties involve refreshments, the preparation and planning of them may have an interesting and valuable correlation with health. Committee work brings in our democratic idea of working together. Finances may be used as part of the math work. If the party involves invitations, programs, and the like, the language arts are used.

Teachers should remember that the names of games and activities may be changed to suit special holidays and occasions. As their programs progress, they will think of many games to use. Children are eager to accept the challenge of making up new games, individually or in groups. One idea may often result in several different activities. Do not be afraid to use ingenuity. The following is appropriate to encourage ideas:

Ideas have much in common with rubber balls. The way they bounce depends on where they start from; the force with which they are thrown, dropped, tossed or pushed; the character of the surface on which they hit; the "texture" of the ball or idea itself; the ambient temperature in which the bounce takes places. All of these influence the bounce of a ball—and the rebound of an idea.

—*Norman G. Shidle*

HALLOWEEN ACTIVITIES

The names of games and characters can be changed to suit the occasion. For examples, Brownies and Fairies can be called Witches and Goblins.

BLACK MAGIC

See Latchaw, pp. 293–294.[1]

[1] See Selected References, page 371.

NUMBER MAGIC GAMES

See Mason and Mitchell, p. 176.

PUMPKIN STEM

Draw a pumpkin minus the stem and fasten it on the bulletin board. Blindfold children, one at a time. Give each a pumpkin stem and have him try to pin it to the pumpkin.

DRAWING CONTEST

Each child is given paper and a crayon. Within a specified time, they must draw a witch or a goblin. The winners may be those who draw the ugliest or prettiest witch or goblin, whichever has been decided before the start of the game.

FINDING PARTNERS

To group couples, print a familiar saying such as, "A stitch in time saves nine," on a paper witch. Cut the witch into two pieces so that part of the saying appears on each half of the witch. Place each piece in a separate box. The number of pieces must correspond with the number of persons present. Each person draws a piece from a box and then endeavors to locate his partner. This method may be used to pair children for refreshments or games. Use one box for boys and one for girls.

SEED GUESSING

Place pumpkin seeds in a jar. Have the children guess the number in the jar and write it on a piece of paper on which they have also written their names. Prizes may be given to the person who guesses the nearest correct number and a booby prize to the one who was farthest off.

BLINDFOLDED ARTIST

Blindfold certain children. Give them paper and a crayon. Instruct them to draw pictures of ghosts, goblins, black cats, corn shocks, or anything appropriate for Halloween. Much fun will result when the art is exhibited.

OLD MOTHER WITCH

This is a group game with a verse to chant. See Chapter 21.

CAT ON THE FENCE

Organize the children in squads or groups. Draw a line on the floor the length of the room in front of each squad. Each child who can walk the line by measuring his feet (place each heel of advancing foot against the toe of the other foot) scores a point for his group.

BLACK TOM

See Chapter 22.

WITCH RELAY

Ride a broom to a given goal and return. Give the broom to the next person. The group which completes the ride first is the winner.

RHYTHMS AND DANCES

1. Broom Dance. See Stuart, p. 11.

2. Pussycat. See Stuart, p. 78.

3. Imitations and impersonations of witches and goblins.

4. Black cats and ghosts for creative rhythms.

THANKSGIVING ACTIVITIES

CORN GAME

Give ears of corn to certain children or to each child. In a given time limit, see who can shell off the most kernels. They must count their kernels. The winner is the one with the highest number of kernels. Use the kernels for Bingo-type games. They may also be used for a kernel hunt.

TURKEY

Play this the same as Bingo, except the winner must have six numbers or names in a row not five and must call "Turkey" not "Bingo." Kernels left from the corn game may be used for this game. Cards may easily be prepared by folding sheets of paper to make the squares. Each person may write his own numbers in each square, or cards may be prepared in advance.

TURKEY PASS

Cut small turkeys out of paper. Divide the group into squads. Give each person a straw. Give the leader of each squad a paper turkey.

He must hold the turkey on the end of his straw by sucking in. At the signal "Go," he transfers it to the next person's straw and so on until the last person in line has the turkey. No one may use his hands in this game. The winning group is the one which succeeds in passing the turkey to each child.

TURKEY GUESS

This game is played like blindman's buff, except "It" asks, "Where is a turkey?" and the person must gobble like a turkey in reply.

STUFF THE TURKEY

Use a box to represent the turkey. This may be done by pasting a large picture of a turkey on the side next to the group. Organize the children into groups. Give each person one ingredient which is used to stuff a turkey. Ingredients may be drawn in the art class or may be cut out of magazines—for example, pictures of bread, salt, pepper, celery, oysters, etc. The children line up an equal distance from the turkey. At a signal, each one runs up and drops his paper in the box to stuff the turkey. Play this in relay formation.

THANKSGIVING WORDS

Twelve children are placed on each team. Give the first person on each team a piece of paper and a pencil. At the signal "Go," he must write a word starting with the letter T. He then passes the paper to the next person who writes a word starting with the letter H. This continues down the row until all the letters in *Thanksgiving* have been used. The first line finished with all words correctly spelled wins. The length of words may be specified if desired. For example, they may be only five-letter words. The number of letters for each word would depend on the grade level and the ability of the group.

CHRISTMAS ACTIVITIES

HERE WE GO ROUND THE CHRISTMAS TREE

Tune: "Here We Go Round the Mulberry Bush." Use toys and pantomime actions of them using the same directions as "Here We Go Round the Mulberry Bush."

SANTA'S TOYS

Pantomime the actions of dolls, soldiers, tops, and all toys.

JINGLE BELLS

See Stuart, p. 41.

UPSET THE FRUIT BASKET

Rename it Santa's toy pack and give each child the name of a toy instead of a fruit.

REINDEER

One child is Santa. He goes to the front of the room and calls the names of his reindeer. As he calls each name, he beckons a child to come up. When he has called all of his reindeer, each child reindeer places his hands on the shoulders of the one ahead. Santa is in the back. He gives the signal for them to walk by saying "Get Up!" They move around the room. When Santa calls "Merry Christmas" they must run to their seats. The first one to sit down is the new Santa.

CHRISTMAS ORNAMENTS

Make different ornaments out of paper. On the back of each one place a number. Fasten these ornaments on the wall, on a string, or place all of them in a box. Organize the children in several groups. Each child may choose one ornament at a time. The group adds up the numbers on the back of the ornaments and the group with the highest score wins. A variation of this game may be played by blindfolding different children and letting them try to find ornaments which have been placed around the room. They add their scores when time is called. The highest score declares the winner.

PIN THE WHISKERS ON SANTA

A large picture of Santa is on wall. Children are blindfolded, one at a time, and given whiskers which they pin on Santa. The person whose whiskers are nearest the correct place on Santa's face wins the game. Transparent tape may be substituted for pins.

SANTA CLAUS GUESSES

Same as blindman's buff. Santa is "It" and asks, "What do you want for Christmas?" The person answers a present of his choice and Santa tries to guess who is speaking.

INTERPRETIVE DANCES

1. All toys in Santa's pack.
2. Santa's reindeer.
3. Skaters' waltz.

VALENTINE'S DAY ACTIVITIES

WALKING ON HEARTS

Divide the group into equal teams. Two hearts drawn on 9-inch by 12-inch construction paper are needed for each group. At the signal "Go," the first person in each group lays one heart on the floor and steps on it, then he lays the next heart down and steps on it. He picks up and lays down the hearts until he reaches a goal. He may not walk on any part of the floor except the hearts. When he reaches the goal, he picks up both hearts, runs back, and gives them to the next player in his group who repeats the action. The first group finished wins all the hearts.

AUTOGRAPH ARTIST

Give several children a heart (6 inches by 9 inches) with one side uncolored. Give each child a pencil. At the signal, "Go," they begin collecting autographs. At a given signal the one with the most legible signatures wins.

THE MISSING HEART

Fasten fewer hearts upon the walls of the room than there are children participating. Play the game like Going to Jerusalem, except when the music stops, children must put one hand on a heart to be safe. The winner is the one never left without a heart during the playing time. No one is eliminated.

VALENTINE HUNT

Send the group to another place in the

building. Hide small hearts all over the room. These may be the small commercial paper hearts which are purchased to stick on envelopes or used in making valentines; they may be tiny hearts cut out of red construction paper; or they may be candy hearts. When the group returns the game is played like Peanut Hunt. The one who finds the most hearts in a specified time wins the game.

If moderately-sized paper hearts are used, this game may be varied by putting a number on the back of each heart and determining the winner by adding.

FILL THE CUP

Each child has a little paper cup, a straw, and 25 or 30 little red candy hearts. The hearts are placed on a napkin beside the paper cup. Each person endeavors to fill his cup with the candy hearts, picking them up on the end of his straw by drawing in on the straw which is in his mouth. They may not use their hands. The first one to succeed stands up and is the winner.

EASTER ACTIVITIES

PIN THE TAIL ON THE RABBIT

A large picture of a rabbit is fastened on the wall. Children are blindfolded and given a bunny's tail, which they endeavor to pin on the rabbit. The one who pins it nearest the proper place for the tail is the winner. Transparent tape may be substituted for pins.

EASTER RABBIT

All children form a circle. One child is the Easter rabbit and has a plastic Easter egg. He runs around the outside of the circle and drops the egg in back of a child. He then weaves in and out among the children hopping like a rabbit. The player who picked up the egg follows in the same manner and tries to tag the Easter rabbit before he returns to the runner's place. If successful, he is the new Easter rabbit;

if not, the original "It" chooses a new rabbit.

EGGS IN THE BASKET

Use an empty Easter basket or box covered with Easter paper. Three paper eggs are needed for each player. Golf balls or ping-pong balls may be used. Place the box in the center of the floor and line the children up around it in a circle. They must all be an equal distance from the box. Each one attempts to toss his three eggs into the basket, one at a time. The winner is the first person to do so. Children may recover eggs which missed the basket and throw again after they have returned to their starting place.

EGG WORDS

Each player must give three words, each

starting with the letters in *egg*. For example: *Everyone goes gunning*. At the beginning of the game, players need not be required to form a sentence. As the game progresses, especially for more mature groups, there is more fun and challenge if players are required to make a complete sentence. This game may be played orally to see who can make the funniest sentence, or it may be used in a relay with each player required to write a sentence and pass the paper to the next one, and so on, until each person has written a sentence. A variation may be had by using the letters in the word *Easter*. Each person may be asked to give only one word. The first person would use a word which starts with *E*, the second a word beginning with *A*, and so on.

A DOZEN EGGS

Divide the players in groups of twelve each. Give the first person in each group a large piece of paper and a crayon. The game is started with this rhyme:

> Draw an egg,
> Draw it fast,
> So your team,
> Won't finish last.

The first player of each group draws an egg, colors it, and passes the crayon to the next. Each person must repeat this. The team who completes the dozen eggs first is the winner.

EGGS IN THE BASKET

Two large Easter baskets are drawn on oaktag or wrapping paper and fastened to the wall. The children line up in two even groups the same distance away from the baskets. The first person in each group has a crayon. At the signal "Go," he runs to his basket, draws an egg, returns, and gives the crayon to the second player, and so on. The team which has the best looking basket of eggs wins.

DUCKS AND CHICKS

This game is played like Crows and Cranes, or Brownies and Fairies. Players are either ducks or chicks.

BARNYARD SQUABBLE

Hide candy Easter eggs (jelly beans) all over the room. Divide the class in four groups. One group is chickens, one group ducks, one group geese, and one pigeons. All children join the hunt for the eggs, but only the leader of each group may pick them up. When the chicks find an egg, they peep until the leader comes and picks it up. The ducks quack, the geese honk, and the pigeons coo. A time limit is set and the team with most eggs wins.

BIRTHDAY PARTY GAMES

CUT THE BIRTHDAY CAKE

Arrange the children in a circle with hands joined. The honored guest is "It" and stands in the center. He walks around and cuts the hands of two children. As he does so, he says, "I cut the birthday cake." These two children walk with giant steps, each in the opposite direction, around the circle. The first one back wins and may cut the next piece of cake.

children and give each a paper candle to try and put on the cake. The one coming nearest to the center of the cake wins.

FIND THE CANDLES

Hide small cake candles around the room. Designate one specific colored one as the prize candle. For example, all may be blue except one which is yellow. The yellow one would be the prize candle. Each candle found scores one point for the finder. The prize candle scores 10 points. The person with the highest score wins.

NUMBER GUESSING

Divide the class into four groups. Permit each group to select one number. Each group is given one guess to try for the lucky number. The correct number is the age of the honored guest. If no group guesses it the first time they may have a second try or as many tries as are necessary.

CANDLE PIN

Draw a picture of a large birthday cake on paper and hang it on the wall. Blindfold

GIFT GIVERS

Divide the class into four groups. Show each group a fancy wrapped package. The object is for a group to guess its contents. Each group agrees on one object. Each group is given a turn to guess in rotation. Select a funny article such as a dill pickle, pretzel, or the like, for the package. If the guessing is far from the object, hints may be given, such as the first letter of the article, or the number of letters in the word.

UNWRAP THE PRESENT

The class stands in a circle. Music is played either on a record or piano. A very securely wrapped package tied with several layers of wrappings and string is passed around the circle from one child to the next. Each time the music stops, the child who has the package may unwrap a bit of it. When the music starts again, it must be passed on. Each time the music stops, it is unwrapped a little bit more. Make the stops very short. The player who completely unwraps the present is permitted to keep it.

SUGGESTIONS FOR MAY DAYS AND SPECIAL OCCASIONS

The following suggestions are a few of the many possible topics and themes which may be used for special occasions.

1. Use a circus theme. See: *The Circus Comes to School,* by Tibbetts, New York, A. S. Barnes Company, 1937.

2. Use various countries as the theme. Dances, games, and activities appropriate to these countries, plus costumes and programs with their colors or flags on them, make this a very interesting and educational experience.

3. Each class may show a different part of the physical education program. For example: (a) first grade—dramatizations; (b) second grade—folk dances and singing games; (c) third grade—various types of games; (d) fourth grade—novelty relays; (e) fifth and sixth grades—(girls) Maypole dancing; (f) fifth and sixth grades—(boys) stunts and tumbling.

4. Use an historical theme and carry it through with activities suitable for the period and occasion.

5. Select a favorite story as a theme and plan suitable activities around it.

6. Use the months of the year and have each class depict an activity appropriate for the month.

These are only a few ideas. Teachers will think of many more. May Day may be used to interest parents in the various types of activities their children are taught during the physical education program that are interesting and educational for the children.

Children should help with all of the plans, costumes, invitations, and everything that is to take place during the program. Every child should be given a chance to participate in the day's activities.

May Days may be climaxed with various sports and games. These may fit the theme or not. Refreshments planned to fit the theme tend to add interest.

Figure 25–1. Enjoying the May Pole Dance.

Figure 25–2. The Virginia Reel at May Dance festivities.

Figure 25–3. Crowning the May Queen.

SELECTED REFERENCES

ALLEN, CATHERINE L., *Fun for Parties and Programs,* Englewood Cliffs, N.J., Prentice-Hall, Inc., 1957.

ANDREWS, GLADYS, *Creative Rhythmic Movement for Children,* Englewood Cliffs, N.J., Prentice-Hall, Inc., 1954.

BANCROFT, JESSIE, *Games* (Revised edition), New York, The Macmillan Company, 1952.

BAUER, LOIS M., and BARBARA A. REED, *Dance and Play Activities for the Elementary Grades,* New York, Chartwell House, Inc., 1953.

BUCHER, CHARLES A., *Methods and Materials in Physical Education and Recreation,* St. Louis, The C. V. Mosby Company, 1954.

EISENBERG, HELEN, and LARRY EISENBERG, *The Handbook of Skits and Stunts,* New York, Association Press, 1953.

————, *Omnibus of Fun,* New York, Association Press, 1956.

GERI, FRANK H., *Games, Rhythms and Stunts for Children,* Englewood Cliffs, N.J., Prentice-Hall, Inc., 1956.

HARRIS, JANE A., *File of Fun,* Minneapolis, Burgess Publishing Company, 1962.

HUNT, SARAH, and ETHEL CAIN, *Games the World Around,* New York, A. S. Barnes and Company, 1950.

LATCHAW, MARJORIE, *A Pocket Guide of Games and Rhythms,* Englewood Cliffs, N.J., Prentice-Hall, Inc., 1956.

MASON, BERNARD S., and ELMER D. MITCHELL, *Social Games for Recreation,* New York, A. S. Barnes and Company, 1937.

RICHARDSON, HAZEL A., *Games for the Elementary School Grades,* Minneapolis, Burgess Publishing Company, 1951.

STUART, FRANCES R., and JOHN S. LUDLAM, *Rhythmic Activities* (Series I–II), Minneapolis, Burgess Publishing Company, 1955.

PART TWO   *The Elementary School*

Health Program

CHAPTER 26

The Nature and Scope of the Elementary School Health Program

The World Health Organization defines health as "a state of complete physical, mental, and social well-being, not merely the absence of disease or infirmity." The primary purpose of the school health program, therefore, is to promote the total health of the child. To accomplish this objective there must be adequate supervision of the physical, mental, emotional, and social experiences the child has during the school day. This, in turn, means that courses of instruction must be developed for the teaching of health topics based on the needs and interests of the pupils; the school plant must be a safe and healthful place in which to live; and proper medical services must be offered to improve and maintain the health of the child.

THE IMPORTANCE OF HEALTH IN THE ELEMENTARY SCHOOL

Well-informed teachers know that totally healthy children learn more rapidly, are better adjusted, get along with their classmates, and make teaching a pleasure. Schools should strive to have every student in a state of optimum health.

Many educational organizations have pointed out the school's responsibility in regard to the health of students. In 1918, the report of a commission on education of the National Education Association listed health as its first objective. The Educational Policies Commission, an important policy-making group in education, points out that an educated person understands basic facts concerning health and disease, protects his own health and that of his dependents, and strives to improve the health of the community. The American Council on Education, another policy-making group, states that schools should help pupils to improve and maintain their own health. A White House Conference on Education report stresses physical and mental health as an educational objective.

Specifically, a concern for the health of the elementary school child is important for the following reasons:

1. *The health of the child determines how he will function.*

A child functions physically, mentally, emotionally, and socially. The health of the child will determine not only his physical well-being but, also, how well he concentrates on mental tasks, how capably he controls his emotions, and how easily he adapts socially to his classmates and other people. Health is essential to optimum functioning as a human being. Without it a child is ineffective, sickly, and unproductive. The healthy child is an integrated organism in which all aspects of his growth and development participate in the learning process.

2. *The healthy child has a better chance to be a success in school.*

To be a success in school requires a sound physical base upon which intellectual fitness can operate. The healthy child will be more alert, think more clearly, and enjoy school more than the unhealthy child.

3. *The mental aspects of a child's growth cannot be separated from other aspects of his total development.*

The physical affects the mental—a child with a stomach ache finds it difficult to do his school work. The mental affects the physical—when a child spends all his time studying without regard for physical needs he finds that lack of physical activity, proper rest, and failure to meet physical needs results in harm to his health. The mental, physical, emotional, and social are all closely interwoven into the human being's makeup. One cannot be slighted without harming the other.

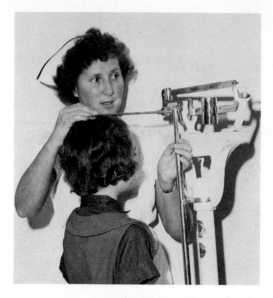

Figure 26–1. Healthy children are successful children.

4. *Education has a legal responsibility to concern itself with the child's health.*

The child is required by law to go to school. As such, the school has the responsibility to provide for the child's health and safety while in school, similar to the way a parent provides for them while the child is at home. Therefore, in addition to being a moral and educational responsibility, health is also a legal one.

FACTORS THAT INFLUENCE THE HEALTH OF THE CHILD

Three factors that affect each child's health are his heredity, the physical, biological, social, and economic environment in which he lives, and the way he lives.

Heredity determines the height of a person, the color of his eyes, the size of his body, the shape of his head, his blood type, the kind of nervous system he has, and many other characteristics. There is nothing that he can do about most of these traits. They are a part of him throughout life. Heredity makes him an individual and education helps him to accept what heredity has given him and make the most of it.

Environment influences a child's health. Although heredity sets the limits of achievement, environment will determine whether or not the potential is achieved. Environmental factors play a part in health and disease. Factors in the physical environment, such as climate and air pollution, affect the child's health. Plants and animals, a part of the biological environment, play a part in the nutritious value of some foods eaten and also are instrumental in the transmission of some diseases. Family, community, church, and other phases of the social environment affect mental, emotional, and social aspects of health. Finally, the economics of the society in which a child lives affects many factors that influence health. Such social-economic factors include housing, food, and medical services.

The way a child lives plays a major role in his health. The daily routine of the child, including the clothes he wears, the sleep he gets, the play he experiences, and the food he eats, will affect his well-being as much as any other factor. It is important, therefore, to note that ways of living can be conditioned by education. A child can be taught to live in certain ways that will be conducive to good health. He can be taught to practice cleanliness of person, to be considerate of others, and to look before he crosses the street. Unfortunately, many older people have poor health habits because they never were taught the harmful implications of such practices as smoking and overeating. As a result, their health has suffered. Society has the obligation to educate young people so they understand why good health habits are important and are motivated to develop them.

HEALTH PROBLEMS OF ELEMENTARY SCHOOL CHILDREN

A few of the health problems of elementary school children are indicated by the statistics in Table 26–1.

Respiratory conditions such as sore throats, colds, influenza, and tonsilitis, infections and parasitic conditions such as measles, mumps, and chickenpox, and injuries and digestive disturbances are the health conditions that most frequently keep children home from school.

More than 9,000,000 children between the ages of five and seventeen have eye conditions needing special care.

About 1,725,000 of the nation's children under twenty-one years of age have orthopedic defects; 335,000 have cerebral palsy, and 325,000 have epilepsy.

From 325,000 to 650,000 children under twenty-one years of age have impaired hearing.

The nation's children just beginning school have on the average, three or more decayed primary teeth.

Accidents are the leading cause of death among school-age children. In a recent year 6,836 children aged five to fourteen were killed by accidents.

A large proportion of the nation's children have been declared physically soft.

Leading causes for death among children five to fourteen years of age for a recent year were accidents, cancer and leukemia, influenza and pneumonia, congenital malformations, heart disease and rheumatic fever, meningitis and meningococcal infection, vascular lesions of the central nervous system, and acute kidney disease.

Health surveys have shown that nutritional inadequacies are common among elementary school pupils.

TABLE 26–1. *Selected Causes of Death Among Persons Aged Five to Nineteen in the United States*[1]

Cause of Death	Total	5–9 Years	10–14 Years	15–19 Years
All CAUSES	28,722	9,163	7,374	12,185
Accidents	13,540	3,687	3,149	6,704
Malignant neoplasms	3,438	1,391	1,024	1,023
Congenital malformations	1,660	777	510	373
Influenza and pneumonia	1,302	590	339	373
Homicide	708	83	90	535
Suicide	568	3	90	475
Chronic nephritis, etc.	349	68	104	177
Chronic rheumatic heart disease	258	25	70	163
Diabetes mellitus	220	50	82	88
Appendicitis	193	68	75	50
Rheumatic fever	177	63	74	40
Acute nephritis, etc.	162	73	43	46
Complications of pregnancy	135		7	128
Tuberculosis, all forms	86	24	21	41
Measles	83	74	6	3
Acute poliomyelitis	71	39	16	16

OBJECTIVES OF THE HEALTH PROGRAM IN THE ELEMENTARY SCHOOL

Specific objectives are frequently listed for the school health program, including the correction of health defects and the reduction of communicable disease. There are four general and major objectives with which the elementary school teacher should be concerned. These are health knowledge, wholesome health attitudes, desirable health practices, and health skills.

Health Knowledge

The teacher in the elementary school has the responsibility of transmitting to the child scientific health information that is readily understood and meaningful at his stage of growth and development. School children should know about such things as how their bodies function, the importance of sanitation, why it is important to eat the right kind of food, and the need for brushing their teeth regularly. This information can be presented in a meaningful manner together with experiences which show the children in the class the importance of living healthfully.

[1] Source: Public Health Service, U.S. Department of Health, Education, and Welfare, *Vital Statistics of the United States*, 1960.

Health Attitudes

Health attitudes are linked to health interests of children and the motives which impel them to act as they do. The health knowledge that is imparted will be applied only if a wholesome attitude exists on the part of the child. This is a challenge to the teacher because in some subjects it is important to get across only facts, but in health the facts are of little value without the interest, drive, or motivating force. The teacher must help the youngster to develop wholesome attitudes toward health, attitudes that should be developed early in life.

Health Practices

Health practices, such as washing hands before eating, drinking milk, wearing proper clothing, and getting adequate sleep and rest, represent the end product of the educational process. If the teaching has effectively imparted the knowledge and has developed the right attitudes toward health, the right health practices will be developed. To have an effective school health program, it is important to recognize the close relationship that exists among health knowledge, health attitudes, and health practices. One contributes to the other.

Health Skills

Another objective of the school health program is the development of skills. In the elementary school such skills might be home nursing and first aid. The teacher has the opportunity to develop some of these skills during the intermediate grades.

DIFFICULTIES IN ACHIEVING HEALTH OUTCOMES

Health teaching is a very difficult job for other reasons than the fact that the teacher must be concerned with knowledge, attitudes, and practices. The teacher is plagued with poor adult health practices, misleading commercial advertising, and lack of visible proof that what she or he is saying is the right thing for children to know, feel, and do.

Poor Health Habits of Adults

Teachers may point out some of the harmful effects of cigarette smoking only to have their youngsters go home and see their mothers and fathers smoking. Teachers may try to have the youngsters identify themselves with the performance of a great athlete only to hear that the home run king smokes a particular brand of cigarettes. The fact that many adults have bad health habits makes it difficult to convince children that such practices are harmful and not in the best interests of health.

Commercial Advertising

Television, newspapers, and magazines frequently show and tell in glowing terms the value and worth of some particular drug, drink, laxative, or other product which may have implications for the health of boys and girls. Children become confused and wonder who is right, the teacher or the man on television. Some teachers have found it effective to bring newspaper and magazine ads and television sets into the classroom where commercials can be evaluated in light of our scientific health information. Although it is difficult, the dedicated and creative teacher will usually find a way to get the accurate information across.

Absence of Immediate, Tangible Results

The child may wash his hands regularly before meals. He may drink his milk three times a day. He may go to bed at eight o'clock each evening. However, there may be no immediate results which convincingly show him these health practices pay rewards. He looks at other children who fail to perform such rituals and doesn't see how he differs from them. As a result, he wonders if it's worthwhile to follow these practices. The inspiring and dedicated teacher will try to show that health habits have long-term rewards for the individual who practices them, rewards which will endure long after formal education ends.

THE SCHOOL HEALTH PROGRAM

The school health program is that phase of the educational process which is concerned with developing an understanding of health and providing those experiences and services which play an active part in maintaining and improving the health of both pupils and school personnel. It includes teaching for health, living healthfully at school, and the supplying of services for both health maintenance and health improvement.

Teaching for health or health instruction refers to those experiences provided for the purpose of imparting knowledge and influencing attitudes and practices relating to both personal and group health.

Living healthfully at school includes providing a healthful physical environment as well as such aspects of the nonphysical environment as teacher-pupil rapport, organization of the school day, and school activities which affect the social and emotional health of pupils.

Services for health improvement refer to the six procedures which are vital to a desirable school health program:

1. Appraisal of the physical, mental, emotional, and social health status of children and school personnel.

2. Procedures used by teachers, physicians, nurses, and others to counsel pupils and parents in regard to health appraisal findings.

3. Follow-through procedures for correcting remediable health defects.

4. Provisions for the exceptional child.

5. Procedures for prevention and control of communicable diseases.

6. Emergency care in cases of sickness and injury.

School Health Councils

School health councils are organized in some schools to meet the health needs of pupils and school personnel. Councils are made up of people who devote their efforts to studying health problems and planning a course of action for their solution. Members of the team include such persons as the school nurse, a dental hygienist, the classroom teacher, the school principal, a physician, the custodian, and others who are interested and can contribute to developing a sound school health program. Table 26–2 gives a diagramatic representation of the school health program.

TABLE 26–2. *The School Health Program*[2]

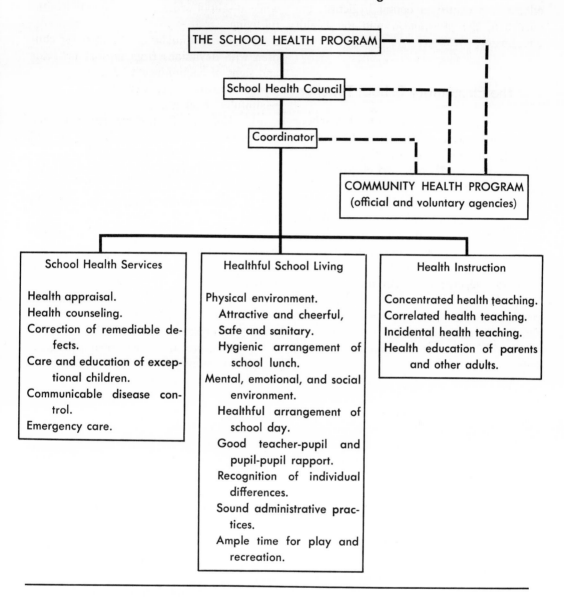

THE SCHOOL HEALTH TEAM

The objectives of the school health program cannot be achieved unless the various members that make up the health team function smoothly and effectively. Some of the important members of this team are the elementary school teacher, the school administrator, the school physician, the family

[2] Charles A. Bucher, *Administration of School Health and Physical Education Programs,* St. Louis, The C. V. Mosby Company, 1963, p. 44.

physician, the school nurse, the physical educator, a dentist, a dental hygienist, the custodian, the nutritionist, and the health coordinator.

The Elementary School Teacher

The classroom teacher is the key school person involved in the health of the elementary school child. The organization of the school with its self-contained classroom enables the teacher to observe the pupils continually and to note deviations from normal. Continuous contact with the same children over a long period of time also makes it possible to know a lot about their physical, social, emtional, and mental health. The classroom teacher can help the pupils develop the right knowledges, attitudes, and practices. Some of the responsibilities which fall to the classroom teacher in regard to the health of his or her pupils are listed below:

1. Possess an understanding of what constitutes a well-rounded school health program and the teacher's part in it.

2. Meet with the school physician, nurse, and others in order to determine how he or she can best contribute to the total health program.

3. Become acquainted with the parents and homes of students; establish parent-school cooperation.

4. Discover the health needs and interests of pupils.

5. Organize health teaching units which are meaningful and are in terms of the health needs and interests of the students.

6. See that children needing special care are referred to the proper place for help.

7. Be versed in first-aid procedures.

8. Participate in the work of the school health council. If none exists, interpret the need for one.

9. Provide an environment for children while at school which is conducive to healthful living.

10. Be continually on the alert for children with deviations from normal behavior and signs of communicable disease.

11. Provide experiences for living healthfully at school.

12. Help pupils assume an increasing responsibility for their own health as well as for the health of others.

13. Set an example for the child of what constitutes healthful living.

14. Motivate the child to be well and happy.

15. If possible, be present at pupils' health examinations and contribute in any way which is helpful to the physician in charge.

16. Follow-through in cooperation with the nurse to see that remediable health defects are corrected.

17. Interpret the school health program to the community and enlist its support in solving health problems.

18. Provide a well-rounded physical education program for the class.

19. Help supervise various activities which directly affect health, such as school lunch, rest periods, and so on

20. Become familiar with teaching aids and school and community resources for enhancing the health program.

21. Be aware of the individual differences of the pupils.

The School Administrator

The school administrator plays a key role in the school health program. To a large degree he will determine how much money is allocated for health purposes, what personnel will be appointed to the faculty to teach health courses, what facilities are available for healthful school living, health instruction, and services, and the degree to which there is public understanding of the health program in the schools. Some ways in which the teacher may help the school administrator to understand the need for and support a better school health program follow:

1. Prepare and submit to him periodic reports on the health needs and interests of the pupils.

2. Utilize some time in faculty meetings to acquaint the administration and colleagues with the job that needs to be done.

3. Requisition supplies and materials to enhance the program.

4. Invite the principal and/or superintendent to speak to the class on some aspect of health.

5. Stimulate the formation of a school health council at which the school administration would be asked to preside.

6. Stimulate interest among citizens' study groups and parent-teacher associations in the school program.

7. Cooperate with community health agencies in interpreting the role of health in the school and community.

8. Work with the school physician, nurse, and school administrator in the work of coordinating school health efforts.

The School Physician

Most school physicians serve under one of two types of appointments: as a full-time school physician employed by the state or local community, or as a part-time practitioner who supervises the health of the children.

The school physician has responsibilities which frequently include administering medical examinations to children, giving advice to parents, having medical control of the teaching staff, maintaining liaison with public health authorities in connection with communicable disease in schools, supervising the health of kitchen personnel, having medical supervision of handicapped pupils, providing medical assistance during the athletic

Figure 26–2. The school administrator plays a key role in the school health program.

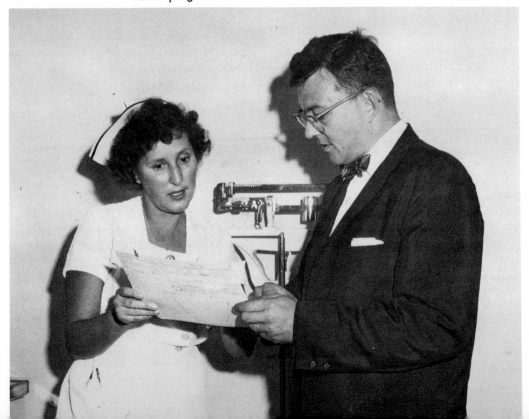

programs, maintaining health records, and preparing reports.

The classroom teacher can work effectively with the school physician through such means as:

1. Attending medical examinations of pupils (with permission of physician).

2. Discussing results of medical examinations with physician.

3. Passing on observations of pupils, especially in respect to any atypical conditions that have been noted.

4. Discussing with physician how she or he can most effectively contribute to the school health program.

5. Orienting the physician about other phases of the educational program.

6. Assisting the physician in following-through to see that remediable defects are corrected.

The Family Physician

In many school systems, the family physician, who knows the child's background, home conditions, and health habits, is in an excellent position to perform some meaningful health counseling. He can also discuss the child's health problems with parents.

The classroom teacher can work effectively with the family physician in much the same manner as she or he works with the school physician.

The School Nurse

The nurse works closely with medical personnel on one hand and with students, teachers, and parents on the other. Some of the duties she performs include the administration of health tests and other forms of measurement, assisting in medical examinations, screening for hearing and vision, holding parent conferences, keeping full health records, teaching health, coordinating school and community health efforts, and helping to control communicable disease.

Figure 26–3. Doctor, nurse, and parents check records after a physical examination.

The classroom teacher can work effectively with school nurses through such means as:

1. Working on the administration of tests of health status.

2. Working cooperatively on health observation techniques.

3. Discussing medical follow-up and health records.

4. Discussing ways to contribute to a more healthful school environment.

5. Cooperating in the health education of parents.

6. Determining what community health resources have value for her or his class.

7. Exploring ways of meeting needs of pupils who have health problems.

The Physical Educator

The physical educator can contribute much to the school health program. His or her training in areas such as first aid and foundational sciences makes such services an important contribution to the team effort. In many school systems physical educators test hearing and vision, weigh and measure the children, teach health, give first aid, and conduct adapted physical education classes for handicapped children.

The classroom teacher can work effectively with the physical educator through such means as:

1. Seeking advice on the best procedures for carrying out the physical education class.

2. Consulting with the physical educator on health problems of children which concern the field of physical education and for which physical educators are qualified.

3. Working with the physical educator on posture and pupils' problems with body mechanics.

4. Developing an adapted physical education program for the handicapped.

The Dentist

The dentist employed to work with school children frequently is involved in such duties as conducting dental examinations of pupils, giving or supervising oral prophylaxis, and advising on curriculum material in dental hygiene.

The classroom teacher can work effectively with the school dentist through such means as:

1. Asking advice on the selection of curriculum material for classroom teaching.

2. Discussing dental problems of students.

3. Inviting dentist to participate in classroom experiences of pupils.

The Dental Hygienist

Dental hygienists usually assist dentists and do oral prophylaxis. The classroom teacher can work effectively with this specialist in much the same way as she or he works with the dentist.

The Custodian

Since the custodian is largely responsible for the cleanliness of the building and a healthful school physical environment in general, he is a member of the health team. He can contribute by regulating lighting, ventilation, and heating and removing any hazards that exist on playgrounds, stairs, and other school areas.

The classroom teacher can work effectively with the custodian through such means as:

1. Calling the custodian's attention to improper heating, ventilation, and other health conditions.

2. Assisting him in helping to have a clean school by having pupils keep their

desks, classroom, and other facilities in good condition.

3. Inviting him to help plan pertinent aspects of health curriculum.

The Nutritionist

The nutritionist's duties include planning school menus and being concerned with the nutritional problems of students.

The classroom teacher can work effectively with the nutritionist through such means as:

1. Asking advice on subject-matter concerning nutrition for the health education program.

2. Inviting the nutritionist into class to speak to students about food and nutrition.

3. Discussing nutritional problems of students and working to see if they can be corrected.

The Health Coordinator

Some schools are fortunate to have a health coordinator whose job is to see that all aspects of the school health program are functioning. He or she assists teachers, works closely with medical and dental personnel, suggests materials for teaching, conducts in-service health education for staff members, coordinates school-community-home relationships, organizes a health council and is an active member thereof, maintains health records, and formulates the policies and the procedures for the total school health program.

The classroom teacher can work effectively with the health coordinator through such means as:

1. Attending meetings which he calls and to which she or he is invited.

2. Having frequent conferences on the health program for her or his class.

3. Asking for advice on teaching aids, methods, and techniques.

4. Discussing health interests and problems of students.

5. Reporting pertinent health observations of pupils.

6. Assisting in the follow-through program.

7. Assisting in the evaluation of the school health program.

THE RELATION OF HEALTH TO PHYSICAL EDUCATION

The layman is sometimes confused about the relationship of health and physical education in the school program. Unfortunately, some educators feel they are one and the same. Although closely allied and concerned with the health of the students, they are separate and distinct subject matter fields. Each area has its own specialized subject-matter content, its specialists, and media through which it is striving to accomplish its goals. Physical education at the elementary school level is concerned with the many physical activities that are discussed in this book and through which the teacher strives to achieve the physical, mental, and social goals. On the other hand, health education is concerned with imparting knowledge about all phases of health, such as nutrition and communicable disease control, and developing the right attitudes and practices for physical, mental, social, and emotional health.

The elementary school teacher should recognize that she is not meeting all the health needs of the child simply by conducting regular periods of physical activity. This section on school health will help to clarify in the teacher's mind how she can meet the requirements for a program that will be useful to all her pupils.

QUESTIONS AND PRACTICAL PROBLEMS

1. Study the various lists of objectives that have been set forth for education during the last one hundred years. Determine how many refer to health as an objective.

2. Describe a physical education program and a health program, showing their similarities and differences.

3. Make a chart, outlining the three aspects of a school health program. List the components of each phase of the program.

4. Set up a school health council within your class. Have a mock meeting at which the most important health problems in the school are discussed.

5. Visit the local health department and report on the services available to the elementary school child.

6. Visit several elementary schools and prepare a report on the school health programs that exist. Evaluate each one.

7. Define the term *health*.

8. What are some responsibilities of the classroom teacher for the health of her children?

SELECTED REFERENCES

BUCHER, CHARLES A., *Adminisration of School Health and Physical Education Programs,* St. Louis, The C. V. Mosby Company, 1963.

GROUT, RUTH E., *Health Teaching in Schools,* Philadelphia, W. B. Saunders Company, 1963.

IRWIN, LESLIE W., *et al., Health in Elementary Schools,* St. Louis, The C. V. Mosby Company, 1962.

JOINT COMMITTEE ON HEALTH PROBLEMS IN EDUCATION OF THE NATIONAL EDUCATION ASSOCIATION AND THE AMERICAN MEDICAL ASSOCIATION, *Health Education,* Washington, D.C., National Education Association, 1961.

KILANDER, H. FREDERICK, *School Health Education,* New York, The Macmillan Company, 1962.

LASALLE, DOROTHY, and GLADYS GEER, *Health Instruction for Today's Schools,* Englewood Cliffs, N.J., Prentice-Hall, Inc., 1963.

TURNER, C. E. *et al., School Health and Health Education,* St. Louis, The C. V. Mosby Company, 1957.

VANNIER, MARYHELEN, *Teaching Health in Elementary Schools,* New York, Harper and Row, 1963.

WILLGOOSE, CARL E., *Health Education in the Elementary School,* Philadelphia, W. B. Saunders Company, 1964.

CHAPTER 27

The Health Education Program
in the Elementary School

Health education is an important part of the elementary school program because this is where scientific knowledge is imparted to youngsters about their health. Health education is no longer a "sometime" experience, but is, instead, a planned and regular part of the educational program. It should be given equal status with such other subject-matter areas as arithmetic, science, and art.

BASES FOR SELECTING CURRICULUM EXPERIENCES

The Joint Committee[1] on Health Problems of the National Education Association and the American Medical Association stresses that the bases for selecting curriculum experiences should be the *biological needs* of boys and girls such as rest, sleep, and food; the *characteristics of children* at different age levels and their growth and developmental needs; *health problems* as revealed through a study of mortality records by age groups; *health status* by age groups as revealed by health records, accident and illness records, special studies, and surveys; *analysis by age groups* of activities related to health in which the majority of boys and girls engage; *analysis of environmental health hazards* in school, home, and community; *analysis of citizenship responsibilities* relating to health; *analysis of major social trends* relating to health; and *analysis of vocational opportunities* in health education.

HEALTH NEEDS AND INTERESTS OF STUDENTS

Health education in the elementary school should be based to a large degree

[1] Joint Committee on Health Problems in Education of the National Education Association and the American Medical Association, *Health Education*, Washington, D.C., National Education Association, 1961, pp. 126–129.

upon the health needs and interests of the children it serves. There is no single procedure that can be followed or set formula that can be applied to determine the health needs and interests of children. The procedure followed will vary with the particular school and community involved. Some of the procedures for determining children's interests and needs are as follows:

1. *Pupil Observation.* Observing the pupil and watching his habits will reveal his knowledge, attitudes, and health practices.

2. *Records.* Pupils' general health history, attendance, communicable disease, and other health records give information concerning certain diseases, health defects, behavior, and abnormalities.

3. *Tests.* Diagnostic health knowledge, attitude and habit tests, and health interest inventories may be of value for older elementary pupils.

4. *Class Discussions.* Many of the interests and needs of children are revealed during classroom discussions.

5. *Surveys.* Utilizing such instruments as check sheets and questionnaires for school

and community use will give wanted information. For example, a survey of food habits may suggest nutritional needs.

6. *Consultations.* School physicians, family physicians, nurses, parents, public health workers, and others can provide important health information.

7. *Visits.* Observing practices in other schools may indicate needs not previously revealed.

8. *Health Conferences.* Discussions of school health problems in general frequently focus attention on needs and interests that have been overlooked.

9. *Professional Literature.* Examining material concerned with needs and interests of children can be of value.

10. *Parent-Teacher Association Meetings.* Meetings of teachers with parent groups can sometimes provide valuable health data.

GENERAL GUIDES TO HEALTH EDUCATION

Some general guides for the elementary school teacher to keep in mind in teaching health to pupils follow:

1. *Health education must be planned.*

Much thought must be given to the planning process if health education is to be effective. The planning will help in determining such things as the subject-matter to be taught, the learning experiences needed, the methods used, the community and school resources to be tapped, and the health problems to be covered.

2. *Planning for health education should be a total school endeavor.*

Although the classroom teacher will spearhead the planning for his or her own pupils, nevertheless, there must be continuity and progression throughout the various grades and schools in an educational system. To accomplish this, there should be commit-

tees of teachers, specialists, and consultants who plan the overall school program. Units on health problems and topics can be outlined, correlation with other subject-matter areas can be thought through, and curriculum experiences can be explored.

3. *Objectives are important in determining health education experiences.*

The general objectives of the school health program, including knowledge, attitudes, practices, and skills, were discussed in the previous chapter. These need to be reviewed and a further delineation of the knowledges, attitudes, practices, and skills, grade by grade, should be listed. Then, on the basis of the outcomes desired, the program can be planned intelligently and meaningfully.

4. *The community can contribute to health education.*

The health department and other official agenices, the mental health society and other voluntary associations, doctors and dentists and other health specialists, and parents can contribute much to a health education program that recognizes the school as a part of a broader community in which its students live and into which many graduates go.

5. *The classroom teacher is the person responsible for health teaching.*

Although there may be specialists in health education at the elementary level, the classroom teacher is the logical person to handle this specialized experience. The teacher has special preparation in elementary school teaching. The teacher has the opportunity to see students throughout the school day, observing them at play as well as in study. The teacher knows the health problems of her pupils. The teacher works closely with the parents, school nurse, and other persons concerned with health in the elementary school. The teacher is in a position to make a better contribution to the total health of the child than a specialist who may see the children only one period a day. This, however, does not mean that the specialist cannot play an important role. In meetings and consultation with the teacher, materials can be furnished, aids and techniques explored, and discussions held about ways in which health teaching can be made effective.

6. *Health education can be included in any of the variety of curricular pat-*

Figure 27–1. Nutritious lunch is part of total school endeavor in health education.

terns that are followed in elementary schools.

a. Health and safety can be taught as a *separate subject-matter course* like science, art, physical education, or geography. There is a body of subject-matter that fits well into the elementary school curriculum. Such a curriculum pattern would give health its rightful place in school education programs.

b. Health can be *correlated* with other subject-matter courses. For example, the English class could write essays concerned with health, the art class could make posters showing safety precautions at street intersections, the foreign language classes could translate health material into French and Spanish, and the science class could explore the biological foundations of health. The correlated plan, however, is regarded as a supplementary way of presenting health material rather than as a plan whereby all the essential material is covered.

c. Health can be taught in a *core curriculum pattern,* where there is a center, or core, around which many educational experiences are planned. Included in these experiences could be health and safety activities.

There are other ways in which subject-matter may be organized, including the *integrated,* the *areas-for-living,* and the *broad fields* approaches. Regardless of the curriculum pattern followed, health training can be planned in a compatible way.

7. *Incidental health education should be utilized.*

Incidental health education refers to that education which can take place when attention is suddenly focused on some news development or event that is of interest to pupils. Such occasions may arise as a result of a question asked by a student; when a personal health problem confronts a member of the class, a family, or the community; or when a sudden illness, accident, or special event takes place. Incidental health

education represents an opportunity for the teacher, physician, dentist, or nurse to provide information that is educational in nature. It can be planned for in advance. Situations and incidents should be anticipated and utilized to their fullest in the interests of good health teaching.

8. *The time allotment for health education should be in line with that of other subjects in the curriculum.*

Health is as important for the child as other experiences, including arithmetic, social studies, and music. As such, it should be provided for in the school's schedule. At the same time, it should be understood that health instruction in the kindergarten and primary grades is taught in a more informal manner, while in the intermediate grades it is more systematic and should be allotted additional time. Anderson suggests the following principles for scheduling health education.

1. A weekly schedule provides for extended time periods and allows for necessary flexibility.

2. A daily health period is not required for health instruction.

3. Two fairly extended periods per week may be sufficient scheduling for health instruction in the primary grades and three periods a week will serve the intermediate grades.

4. A flexible schedule allows for continuation of an activity which is particularly challenging.

5. Opportunities should be provided for the varieties of activities that health instruction entails.

6. When special health needs or interests require it, the schedule should be rearranged. Extra time invested in health instruction during one week can be followed by incidental instruction in the following week or weeks.

7. Opportunities for incidental and integrated health instruction should not be sacrificed to maintain a rigid schedule.

8. Correlation of health with other areas,

to be effective, must be given a definite place in the organization of health instruction.[2]

9. *Kindergarten and primary grades represent a setting where stress should be placed on the development of wholesome attitudes and habits.*

The early school years are an ideal time to impress upon children the importance of healthful routines, proper attitudes, and habits. Through attention to clothing, cleanliness, ventilation, rest, eating, safety, and other health goals, the foundations of good health for a lifetime can be laid down.

10. *The health education offered through the school should be closely integrated with home conditions.*

If what is taught in the school is not practiced at home and in out-of-school situations, the education has not been meaningful. Furthermore, to have the knowledge gained at school applied at home means working closely with parents and knowing something about home conditions.

PSYCHOLOGICAL PRINCIPLES THAT PROMOTE LEARNING

In order for the elementary school teacher to get health knowledge across to pupils most effectively, a sound psychological approach must be used. A few of the essential principles for effective learning which have implications for the teaching of health follow:

1. *The goals should be clear to the student.*

Learning progresses much more readily when the goals are clear in the student's mind. The student should have a vivid mental picture of which health practices are desirable and which ones are undesirable. The reasons for desirable health practices should be pointed out. If there are certain rules of bicycle safety, for example, with which the pupil should be familiar, then these should be demonstrated and made clear in the student's mind and reasons should be given for using these rules.

2. *Frequency of classes is an important consideration for effective learning.*

Health classes should be held regularly. If classes are held too infrequently, much of the material will be forgotten before the next class is held, requiring much repetition of material. At least two or three classes per week should be scheduled.

3. *The learner must be ready to learn.*

The information that is to be taught must be presented in light of the pupil's level of maturity and past experience. Pupils in the primary grades, for example, cannot be expected to assimilate highly technical health knowledge. They have not matured to the point where they can appreciate and understand such presentations.

4. *The learning experience must be a satisfying one.*

Human beings tend to enjoy and want to repeat those experiences which satisfy them and meet a felt need. This means that materials must be selected and methods used which will help to make health learning an enjoyable educational experience for the students.

5. *Learning takes place more readily when the pupil is involved in doing.*

When the child conducts an experiment to show two different types of diets on white rats, when the child actually sees the results

[2] C. L. Anderson, *School Health Practices,* St. Louis, The C. V. Mosby Company, 1960, p. 274.

of inadequate safety precautions, and when the child administers artificial respiration, much learning takes place—more so than when the child is told about something but is not actually involved in doing it. Wherever possible, the learning situation should be one that involves boys and girls actively in the educational experience.

6. *Each child learns at his own rate of speed.*

To expect each child to progress at the same rate, have the same health interests, and be challenged by the same methods or have similar health needs is wishful thinking. Each person is different and educational programs cannot provide blanket prescriptions. Instead, they must be adapted to the individual.

7. *Pleasant emotions enhance the learning process.*

The fear approach in teaching health is not advocated by most educators. Instead of taking a negative approach and telling youngsters they will die sooner, lose their teeth, contract some disease, or that something very dreadful will happen to them if they fail to follow the teacher's advice, it is better to take a positive approach which emphasizes the good things that will result if wholesome health habits are learned and practiced.

8. *The leadership provided determines in large measure how much learning takes place.*

The dedicated, inspired teacher is the key to a good learning situation. The good teacher who knows his or her subject, understands pupils and has good rapport with them, utilizes proper methods, and plans each lesson carefully will achieve significant results in health education.

9. *Learning takes place more rapidly when the pupil wants to learn.*

Motivation is the key to effective learning. It is a quality imbedded within the student that propels him forward to learn because of some inward drive or desire. Basic psychological needs can often provide this motivation. For example, a desire for self-respect, belonging, recognition, a feeling of worth, security, and for achievement of certain goals in life may be factors the wise teacher will want to consider when trying to spark an individual to learn important material.

10. *Visual aids will aid in presenting a more favorable learning situation.*

In health education there are many movies, slides, pictures, posters, and other visual aids which may be used to help give the student a clearer understanding of the material being covered.

11. *Knowledge of results will provide additional incentive for learning.*

Students should be informed of the progress they are making. This means an evaluation of their progress must be made periodically in terms of knowledge, attitudes, practices, and skills. If practicable, individual teacher-pupil conferences will help each boy and girl to know where he or she is and what improvements can be made.

12. *When effective health teaching takes place there is transference to life situations.*

The field of health education is primarily interested in seeing that the scientific knowledge imparted is translated into good health practices. Therefore, the teaching must make classroom experiences as nearly lifelike as possible, because only under such conditions will transfer of training take place.

THE HEALTH EDUCATION CURRICULUM

Health education at the elementary level is aimed primarily at helping the child to develop good health habits and health attitudes and to live happily, healthfully, and safely. These objectives can be achieved by imparting scientifically-based knowledge adapted to the child and by incorporating good health practices to the regular routine of school and home living. The classroom teacher is the guiding influence and his or her understanding of good health will determine to a great degree the effectiveness of such a program.

The question of what material is to be taught is one with which every elementary school teacher should be familiar. The Arkansas State Board of Health and Arkansas Board of Education recommend that the health content for each grade in their elementary schools be developed around the following basic approaches:

1. *Grade One:* General health habits; care of parts of body.

2. *Grade Two:* Foods and habits of eating; exercise and posture.

3. *Grade Three:* Clothing; sanitation, first aid, and communicable disease.

4. *Grade Four:* Growth and health; foods and habits of eating; elimination of body waste.

5. *Grade Five:* Fresh air, ventilation, and sunshine; eyes; feet.

6. *Grade Six:* The mind and nervous system; sanitation; communicable disease; harmful substances.

The American Association of School Administrators in its *Twentieth Yearbook* states that the health problems which confront and interest children in the primary grades include such topics as: (1) growth and health, (2) nutrition, (3) elimination, (4) exercise, relaxation, rest and sleep, (5) personal hygiene, (6) prevention and control of disease, (7) care of eyes and ears, (8) medical and dental attention, (9) emotional and social adjustment, and (10) safety. These various subjects must, of course, be adapted to the individual child. At the intermediate level health problems may cover many of the same topics with more information and experiences being adapted to the child's level of understanding. Specifically, topics that are appropriate for the intermediate grades include: (1) growth and health, (2) nutrition, (3) exercise, relaxation, rest, and sleep, (4) personal hygiene, (5) care of eyes and ears, and (6) prevention and control of disease.

The Norfolk, Virginia, public schools list 14 basic areas of health instruction for the elementary school: (1) play and physical education, (2) social hygiene, (3) mental and emotional health, (4) personal hygiene, including diet, rest, sleep, exercise, clothing, elimination, handwashing, and exposure, (5) experiences in healthful living, (6) communicable diseases, including diseases listed under health service, (7) nutrition, (8) dental hygiene, (9) eye hygiene, (10) posture education, (11) safety education, (12) first aid, (13) experiences in health service, and (14) foot hygiene.

Kilander has listed eleven major health areas to be covered throughout the elementary and secondary school levels and the relative emphasis to be placed on each. His table is presented to give the elementary school teacher an appreciation of how the emphasis on various health topics varies throughout the school years and how each of the educational levels fits into the total picture.

TABLE 27–1. *Recommended Relative Emphasis on Health Knowledge, Attitudes, Practices, and Skills by Grade Levels for the Major Health Areas*[3]

Health Areas	Preschool Level	Grade 1	Grades 2–3	Grades 4–6	Grades 7–9	Grades 10–12
1. Personal health	XX	XX	XX	XX	XXX	XX
2. Nutrition	XX	XX	XX	XX	XXX	XXX
3. Community health and sanitation	X	X	X	XX	XXX	XX
4. Consumer health			X	X	XX	XXX
5. Mental health	X	X	X	XX	XX	XXX
6. Stimulants and depressants			X	X	XX	XXX
7. Family life	X	X	XX	XX	XXX	XXX
8. Safety education	X	XX	XX	XX	XXX	XX
9. First aid		X	X	XX	XXX	XXX
10. Home nursing			X	X	XX	XXX
11. Driver education				X	XX	XXX

Note: XXX—Major emphasis on this area at this grade level.
   XX—Moderate emphasis on this area at this grade level.
    X—Some attention, particularly to attitudes and practices rather than to knowledge.
Blank:—No attention to this area at this grade level.

The authors' college classes have suggested the following as some of the important health topics and experiences for consideration in the elementary school:

Kindergarten

1. Getting acquainted with school nurse, doctor, and dietitian.

2. Location and proper use of school facilities (bathrooms, drinking fountains, and lunch room).

3. Safe practices in classroom and playground.

4. Safety procedures to and from school.

5. Learning skills of handwashing, toothbrushing, and use of handkerchief.

6. Wearing appropriate clothing for different weather conditions.

Primary Grades, One–Three

1. Social and mental adjustment to school life (sharing with others, and so on).

[3] H. Frederick Kilander, *School Health Education,* New York, The Macmillan Company, 1962, p. 290.

2. Need for cleanliness and good grooming (eyes, ears, hair, teeth, clothes, and so on).

3. Nutrition (eating habits, kinds of foods, manners, and so on).

4. School safety and accident prevention (fire drills, crossing streets, and so on).

5. Growth (height and weight).

6. Communicable diseases and infections (colds, wounds, immunization, and so on).

Intermediate Grades, Four–Six

1. Learning body structures and systems.

2. Posture and body control.

3. Relation of rest, exercise, and relaxation to health.

4. Essential food elements for a balanced diet.

5. Relation with peers.

6. Safety and accident prevention.

7. Personal appearance and cleanliness, caring for the eyes, ears, teeth, and so on.

8. Common health disorders (stomachache, headache, and so on).

9. How to cope with and resolve fears and frustrations.

10. Importance of medical and dental examinations.

11. Basic first aid procedures.

12. How the community provides for healthful living.

The type of health program offered should be adapted to the child's level and planned in accordance with his or her interests and needs. It should also be remembered that health education is a continuous process and cannot be completely compartmentalized within a definite subject area or within a specific class period. It should embrace all the activities and subjects that are a part of the child's life.

THE UNIT APPROACH IN HEALTH EDUCATION

Health instruction must proceed in a systematic way if optimum results are to be achieved. This means planning subject-matter areas which are based on the needs and interests of the pupils concerned. Following a textbook, chapter by chapter, will not provide the best type of learning experience for the student. Instead, it is recommended that the classroom teacher plan units of instruction based on health topics and problems of interest that are appropriate for a particular age group or class.

Units in grades one to three, for example, might be developed around such subjects as the following:

1. Developing a liking for new foods.

2. Resting and relaxing as part of the school day.

3. Understanding the importance of brushing the teeth.

4. Using safety rules at all times on the playground.

5. Realizing the importance of washing the hands after going to the toilet.

Units for grades four to six might be developed around such subjects as the following:

1. Understanding how food contributes to a healthy body.

2. Following a well-balanced daily regimen of study, rest, relaxation, play and sleep.

3. Knowing the structure of the teeth and what causes decay.

4. Developing skill in a few simple first-aid measures.

5. Understanding how germs are spread.

A few years ago, approximately 100 teaching units in health from all over the United States were studied. From these units, a committee selected those which they thought were best for illustrating the unit plan in health teaching. The committee also analyzed and set forth a functional procedure for developing health units. In order to acquaint the prospective elementary school teacher with their recommended procedure, the committee's outline for developing health units is given below:

1. *Finding the Problem.* In a brief paragraph, explain how the problems happened to be brought to a focus, or enumerate the methods used for discovering the health needs or problems, such as: (a) observation in the classroom or during play periods; (b) survey of school or community environment; (c) interviews with nurse, parents, and pupils; (d) studying health examination records; (e) accidents or epidemics occurring in school community.

2. *Objectives.* List goals or desired outcomes which were established.

3. *Procedures.* Describe procedures to follow for attaining goals, including such items as: (a) approaches used for arousing pupil interest in the work; (b) list of specific questions or problems selected for study in connection with the list; (c) activities selected and learning situations provided for helping students answer their questions and solve any problems related to the main problem (explaining how activities were selected); (d) other steps taken, if any, for attempting to solve the problem, such as (1) cooperation with the home and community and with other school personnel, (2) examining and improving the daily program, (3) making changes designed to improve the school environment, (4) providing essential materials and equipment necessary for solving the problem.

4. *Teaching Aids.* (a) Reading materials; (b) audiovisual aids (multisensory); (c) resource people; (d) experiments; (e) demon-strations; (f) field trips; (g) work projects; (h) others.

5. *Evaluation.* Describe briefly the outstanding accomplishments which resulted from teaching this unit in terms of original purpose.[4]

Outline for Dental Health Unit

The following is an outline for a unit on dental health for a fifth grade class based on the outline procedure for developing health units.

The Problem

Observation of fifth grade children showed that their permanent teeth were still erupting and their deciduous teeth were disappearing. Children were curious about their teeth, asking where they came from, what their purpose was, why first teeth come out and new ones come in, and why some are crooked and others straight. A survey of the fifth grade class showed an average of three carious teeth to each child. An interview with the dental hygienist at the school showed that many of the children didn't brush their teeth regularly and parents seemed indifferent to the dental needs of their children. The doctor, nurse, and dentist all felt that the children could benefit greatly from health instruction in the care of their teeth.

Objectives

1. Provide pupils with an understanding of the structure and function of their teeth.

2. Develop an appreciation for proper care of teeth.

[4] Committee on Health Instruction of Society of State Directors, "Health Teaching Units, Part 1," *Journal of Health, Physical Education and Recreation,* June, 1953.

3. Acquaint students with the services rendered by the dentist and dental hygienist.

4. Develop skill in how to brush teeth correctly.

5. Familiarize pupils with the relationship of nutrition to healthy teeth.

Procedures

1. Film—"Behind the Smile."

2. Film followed by a discussion of the importance of teeth to appearance and to health in general.

3. Participation of students in planning for unit—what they would like to learn about their teeth and what educational experiences they would enjoy having as part of this unit.

Questions or Problems

1. Why is good dental health important?

2. How many teeth do we have? What is the purpose of each type of tooth?

3. What are the various parts of a tooth?

4. What are the causes of tooth decay?

5. How do we protect our teeth from decay?

6. Why is it important to see the dentist regularly?

7. What is the best diet for good dental health?

Activities and Learning Situations

A committee of students meeting with the teacher and dental hygienist might select these activities to help students answer questions and solve problems:

1. Examining teeth using mirrors.

2. Obtaining a large chart showing the structure of a tooth. Studying the chart.

3. Using a large model, demonstrating and discussing the proper method for brushing teeth. Individual toothbrushes to be brought from home by students to use for personal practice.

4. Reading about the reasons for dental decay.

5. Preparing posters illustrating good dental hygiene.

6. Researching the effectiveness of fluoridation of water supplies for dental health.

7. Doing a case study of a boy and a girl on what they have done for a period of three years to provide for their dental health.

8. Making a graph to show incidence of dental caries among pupils at each grade level (using information provided by dental hygienist).

Other Steps to Solve Problems

1. Working with dental association.

2. Gathering materials from various commercial concerns, such as toothpaste concerns, and evaluating materials.

3. Evaluating toothpaste ads in magazines.

4. Discussing television programs which relate to dental health or advertising.

5. Preparing and presenting student committee reports on such topics as "Should primary teeth be retained as long as possible in order to have good dental health?"

Teaching Aids

1. Reading materials in textbook.

2. Materials obtained from the American Dental Association, 222 East Superior Street, Chicago 11, Illinois.

3. Materials and information obtained from the State Health Department.

4. A class field trip to a local dentist's office (see equipment used, X-rays of teeth, and discuss dental problems with dentist).

5. Dental hygienist to speak to class.

Evaluation

The accomplishments of this unit in terms of original purpose are to be determined by:

1. Giving an examination to pupils about material covered in the unit to see if the children have knowledge of structure of tooth, dental caries, and health practices that promote good dental health.

2. Conducting daily health regimen check lists to see if children demonstrate a continued interest in brushing teeth and provide for their dental health.

3. Carrying out a dental survey of parents to see how many children visit the dentist regularly to have teeth examined and treated.

4. Determining the childrens' skill in brushing teeth through actual practice in the classroom.

5. Having the children write their own evaluation reports on what worth the unit had for them.

METHODS OF TEACHING HEALTH

Methods in health education will determine to a great degree the outcomes achieved. They should be adapted to the group being taught, be compatible with the objectives sought, stimulate interest among the pupils, be capable of being used by the teacher, be adaptable to available space, equipment and time in the school program, and be capable of use with the health activities that comprise the educational offering. Children usually like variety, so several different methods should be used rather than just one. Some of the better-known methods for the elementary school health program are listed below.

Problem Solving. Problem solving is one of the most effective and best methods. It can be utilized with nearly all health topics. An example of a health problem is "What are the effects of smoking on health?" After stating the problem to the class a systematic approach is utilized by the pupils to obtain the answer. For example, a problem could be treated step by step in this manner:

1. Stating the nature and scope of the problem.

2. Defining the various possible solutions to the problem.

3. Collecting scientific information to support each of the various aspects of the problem.

4. Analyzing the information and data gathered as to its source, authoritativeness, date of origin, and other pertinent factors.

5. Drawing conclusions on the basis of the information gathered.

6. Applying conclusions to the solution of the problem.

Class Discussions. Probably the most common method used is class discussion and group interaction on a particular health topic.

Textbook. Assigned readings in a textbook with a discussion based on these readings is a common method.

Construction Activities. In construction activities, students build something which will help enlighten them on health problems. For example, they may build a model of an ideal kitchen showing provisions for proper cooking of food and food handling.

Field Trips. Trips to such places as a dairy, health clinic, hospital, police station, or some other place which has health implications are effective teaching methods.

Demonstrations. Demonstrations can

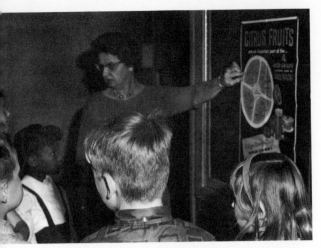

Figure 27–2. Demonstrations are important to health education.

provide a visual picture of certain health and safety concepts. For example, rules of the road could be demonstrated to a class of children who ride bicycles.

Experiments. An example of a common experiment is to see what happens to the growth of animals with different types of diets.

Panels and forums. A panel of students or outside specialists presents reports or discusses some health topic during class.

Class committees. The class is divided into committees and topics are assigned for exploration.

Exhibits. An exhibit of various types of bandages that can be used in cases of first aid is an example of this method.

Dramatizations. A play can be put on by a class, for example, to bring to the pupils' attention the importance of safety on the playground.

Independent Study. Each student might go to the library after being assigned a particular health topic for which he or she is supposed to gather as much information as possible.

Resource People. A doctor, dentist, health commissioner, or some other specialist can be invited to speak to the class.

Audiovisual Aids. Films, tapes, recordings, movies, and other kinds of audiovisual aids can be used for class presentation.

The Joint Committee on Health Problems in Education of the National Education Association and the American Medical Association has listed some of the health instruction activities in which pupils in the intermediate grades can engage:

Conducting animal feeding experiments and experiments to test food nutrients.

Taking field trips to local dairies, markets, restaurants, bakeries, water supply and sewage treatment plants, and housing projects.

Visiting museums.

Preparing charts and graphs for visualizing class statistics, such as absences due to colds or school accidents.

Making pin maps of sources of mosquitoes, rubbish depositories, and slum areas.

Making health posters.

Setting up room and corridor health exhibits.

Preparing health bulletin boards and displays.

Making murals and dioramas.

Maintaining class temperature charts.

Arranging a library corner of health materials on the subject being studied.

Using sources of printed material— reference books, texts, bulletins, newspapers, and magazines—for the study of a particular topic.

Giving reports in various ways—chalkboard talks, dramatizations, role-playing, and panels.

Serving on the safety patrol.

Joining the bicycle safety club.

Participating in a home or school clean-up campaign.

Sharing health programs with primary grades.

Planning menus.

Preparing meals for class mothers or other guests.

Securing a health examination.

Having all dental corrections made.

Taking innoculations.

Keeping records of growth through charts or graphs.

Keeping diaries of health practices.

Studying texts or references to find answers to problems.

Thinking through solutions to problems.

Applying in daily practices health principles learned.[5]

MATERIAL AIDS FOR HEALTH TEACHING

There are many material aids for health teaching. The elementary school teacher should be familiar with these various pictures, charts, films, and other materials that can be obtained from governmental sources, health agencies, professional societies, business groups, and other organizations. This section provides a brief discussion of the various aids that are available and where they can be obtained. The teacher should use material aids that are adapted to her students' interests, age, and experience and which help to clarify the health material covered.

Textbooks, Encyclopedias, Study Guides, Workbooks, and Printed Matter. Textbooks and other printed materials used in the elementary school must be selected with care if they are to be an effective teaching aid. It would be wise for the elementary teacher to review with the state education department the list of criteria they have developed for the adoption and use of textbooks. Also, some professional associations have prepared such criteria. The criteria commonly applied to the selection of printed materials include content which is scientifically accurate, good organization of material, material related to age group and needs of children, interest appeal, attractive presentation, and a layout that includes type which is easy to read with good paper stock and illustrations.

Posters, Flash Cards, and Flip Charts. There are many posters available for health teaching about various topics that are related to the elementary level. Such posters should be accurate in content, be simple, have appeal, possess balance, attract atten-

tion, and, of course, convey a message which is necessary for the child. Flash cards which can be used to flash certain information before the pupils and flip charts on nutrition and other such topics also have a place in the classroom.

Still Pictures. Still pictures include such illustrative material as filmstrips, lantern slides, charts, and prints. They are readily available from a number of sources for use in the schools. Filmstrips are increasingly being produced by professional health agencies as well as many commercial agencies. They are convenient, require little equipment, and usually carry 20 to 50 pictures on a strip, which makes it possible to cover considerable material. In connection with still pictures, the opaque projector has great value since charts, graphs, reports, and other materials can be projected on a screen in the classroom for all to see.

Motion Pictures. The motion picture attracts much interest among persons of all ages. The action that can be presented and the material covered has great value if proper pictures are selected. Films can motivate, inform, and educate youngsters in regard to health. They are available from state departments of health, university film libraries, commercial houses, and various health agencies. Furthermore, the *United States Office of Education Film Library Directory* lists a great many excellent films.

[5] Joint Committee on Health Problems in Education of National Education Association and American Medical Association, *Health Education,* Washington, D.C., National Education Association, 1961, pp. 187–188.

Flannelboards, Bulletin Boards, Chalk-boards, and Magnetic Boards. A piece of velvet cloth stretched over a piece of wood or masonite provides an excellent place to attach pictures and other materials for use in the classroom. A bulletin board is also a suitable place to post materials that have been clipped from newspapers, magazines, and various periodicals. Furthermore, chalk-boards always provide an accessible spot in the typical classroom to record meaningful health material. Magnetic boards are also available to many teachers.

Radio and Television. Radio and television have many possibilities for the health education program. Radios in the classroom are very inexpensive and there are many programs that feature health lectures and other programs worth listening to. Furthermore, there are many opportunities to broadcast school programs to the community at large. Television for health purposes has been enhanced by the great number of educational television channels that have been activated throughout the country. Furthermore, closed-circuit television has possibilities in many school systems that use it. Through such a medium, outstanding resource people and other programs can be utilized which otherwise might not be possible.

Recordings. Recordings on both phonograph records and tape have proved to be of value to health teachers. There are many fine records which are on the market and suitable for classroom work. Also, tape recordings can be made of speeches, radio programs, or special presentations and later played back to a class.

Collections. A health class can collect such things as insects, frogs, pictures, plants, teeth of animals, bones, and other items which have health implications. For children to see, at first hand, various animate or inanimate objects which have health implications makes it possible for them to identify much more readily with these objects.

Models. Models play a very important part in health instruction. To have a model of the human body that shows the various muscles and vital organs makes it much more interesting and understandable for children. There are other models which relate to health that can be made by the children themselves, such as houses, filtration plants, and traffic situations for safety purposes.

Stick Drawings, Cartoons, Sketches, and Related Materials. Many times, visual aids in the forms of cartoons, drawings, and sketches make it possible to present health material in a much more vivid form than would otherwise be possible. Such materials can be found in magazines, newspapers, and other periodicals or they can be made up by the school art department, teachers, or the pupils themselves.

Miscellaneous Materials. Some other materials not mentioned which may be used in health education are scrapbooks, pamphlets, manikins, mobiles, question boxes, food samples, first-aid supplies, mirrors, microscopes, comics, puppets, health records, bicycles, museums, and writing pads.

SOURCES OF HEALTH MATERIALS

There are many agencies, business concerns, health departments, and other organizations where free or inexpensive health materials may be procured by the elementary school teacher. It would take up much valuable space to list all these sources. Instead, a partial listing of where such materials are available is given. The teacher should investigate further if the list does not meet his or her needs.

Schools and Universities. The teacher should explore his or her own school library and public library. These settings often have needed materials or will order them upon request. In addition to books and printed materials, many libraries stock such items as recordings and films. Any nearby university is an additional source of materials.

The elementary school teacher should make sure to determine the availability of materials from the health education specialist, the health coordinator, the physical education director, and the coordinator of audio-visual materials in the local school system.

Official Health and Educational Agencies. Official health agencies such as the local health department are an excellent source for help and materials. At the county, state, and national levels there are also many official agencies. State departments of education, state health departments, the United States Department of Health, Education, and Welfare, the Public Health Service, the Childrens Bureau, and the United States Office of Education are examples of source agencies that will be helpful in furnishing materials. On the international scene, such agencies as the World Health Organization will be of help.

Professional Societies and Voluntary Health Organizations. There are many professional societies and voluntary health organizations such as the American Dental Association, the American School Health Association, the American Association for Health, Physical Education and Recreation, the American Academy of Pediatrics, the American Hearing Association, the American Public Health Association, the American Association for Mental Health, Inc., and the National Safety Council that will be happy to be of assistance.

Commercial Concerns. Several com-mercial concerns have made it a practice to publish health materials. This is especially true of insurance companies, cereal manufacturers, toothpaste producers, citrus growers, and athletic groups. Such material should be evaluated in light of the commercial and advertising purposes associated with it.

Some Sources of Free or Inexpensive Materials

Free or inexpensive materials are available from the following sources:

American Association for Health, Physical Education and Recreation, 1201 16th Street, Washington 6, D.C.

American Automobile Association, Inc., 1712 G Street, N.W., Washington 6, D.C.

American Cancer Society, 521 West 57th Street, New York 19, N.Y.

American Dental Association, 222 East Superior Street, Chicago 11, Ill.

American Hearing Society, 919 18th Street, Washington 6, D.C.

American Heart Association, 44 East 23rd Street, New York 10, N.Y.

American Medical Association, 535 North Dearborn Street, Chicago 10, Ill.

American National Red Cross, Washington 25, D.C.

American Public Health Association, 1790 Broadway, New York 19, N.Y.

American School Health Association, 515 East Main Street, Kent, Ohio.

Association for Aid to Crippled Children, 345 East 46th Street, New York 17, N.Y.

Athletic Institute, 209 South State Street, Chicago 4, Illinois.

Bristol-Myers Company, Educational Service, 45 Rockefeller Plaza, New York 20, N.Y.

Cereal Institute, Inc., 135 LaSalle Street, Chicago 3, Ill.

Child Study Association of America, 132 East 74th Street, New York 21, N.Y.

Equitable Life Assurance Society of the United States, 1285 Avenue of Americas, New York 19, N.Y.

Joint Committee on Health Problems in Education of the National Education Association and the American Medical Association, 1201 16th Street, Washington 6, D.C.

Metropolitan Life Insurance Company, 1 Madison Avenue, New York, N.Y.

National Association for Mental Health, 10 Columbus Circle, New York 19, N.Y.

National Dairy Council, 111 North Canal Street, Chicago 6, Ill.

National Education Association, 1201 16th Street, Washington 6, D.C.

National Foundation, 800 Second Avenue, New York 17, N.Y.

National Safety Council, 425 North Michigan Avenue, Chicago 11, Ill.

National Society for the Prevention of Blindness, 1790 Broadway, New York, N.Y.

National Tuberculosis Association, 1790 Broadway, New York 19, N.Y.

Parke-Davis Company, Detroit, Mich.

Public Affairs Pamphlets, 22 East 38th Street, New York 16, N.Y.

Science Research Associates, Inc., 57 West Grand Avenue, Chicago 10, Ill.

Some Publishers of Textbooks for Elementary School Health Education

The following publish textbooks for elementary school health education:

American Book Company, New York, N.Y.

The Bobbs-Merrill Company, Inc., Indianapolis, Ind.

Ginn and Company, Boston, Mass.

Laidlaw Brothers, River Forest, Ill.

Lyons and Carnahan, Chicago, Ill.

The Macmillan Company, New York, N.Y.

Scott, Foresman and Company, Chicago, Ill.

The L. S. Singer Company, Syracuse, N.Y.

The John C. Winston Company, Philadelphia, Pa.

EVALUATION

There should be periodic evaluation of the school health program. Such evaluations assist the teacher in determining knowledge achieved by the students, whether the students' needs are being met, if objectives are being realized, marks for grading purposes, if certain methods are effective, the need for curriculum revision, if the teaching is effective, strengths and weaknesses of the program, and the value and importance of the health in the educational program. They

also motivate the students to greater effort.

The Joint Committee on Health Problems of the National Education Association and the American Medical Association has listed some instruments that can be used in the evaluation process.[6] These may be summarized as follows:

[6] Joint Committee on Health Problems in Education of the National Education Association and the American Medical Association, *Health Education,* Washington, D.C., National Education Association, 1961, pp. 342–343.

1. Observations of students in respect to their behavior and skills.

2. Surveys of health conditions.

3. Questionnaires and checklists which are submitted to students and parents to determine their knowledge about health matters.

4. Interviews with such people as pupils, parents, teachers, and various school personnel.

5. Diaries and other records kept by pupils.

6. Health and growth records of students.

7. Records of other health conditions or improvements such as vital statistics from the local health department, or improvements in school's health conditions.

8. Samples of pupils' work, such as charts, models, exhibits, and reports.

9. Case studies of individual pupils.

10. Health knowledge tests, both oral and written.

It is important to recognize that many factors need to be evaluated to appraise the entire school health program. In addition to health knowledge, there are health attitudes and health practices. Furthermore, it is important also to evaluate the school environment and school health services.

QUESTIONS AND PRACTICAL PROBLEMS

1. What are ten bases for the selection of curriculum experiences for the elementary school health education program? Discuss how each may be used.

2. Prepare a health unit for the teaching of nutrition to a third grade class.

3. What are some psychological principles that could be applied in the teaching of health in the elementary school?

4. Write to ten national health organizations and collect materials for the elementary school health program from each. Prepare a file of materials according to a topical index.

5. Survey ten state departments of education and obtain their courses of study for teaching health in the elementary school. Analyze the ten reports and prepare a statement of findings.

6. Survey an elementary school class and find out what pupil interests are in the field of health.

7. Interview a dentist, a doctor, and a psychiatrist to formulate a list of health problems that should be covered in the elementary school health education program.

8. Select a health knowledge test and evaluate the health knowledge of a fifth grade class.

9. Prepare a lesson plan for teaching about bicycle safety for a sixth grade class using a problem-solving approach.

10. What are ten sources of health materials for the elementary school?

SELECTED REFERENCES

BUCHER, CHARLES A., *Administration of School Health and Physical Education Programs,* St. Louis, The C. V. Mosby Company, 1963.

GROUT, RUTH E., *Health Teaching in Schools,* Philadelphia, W. B. Saunders Co., 1963.

HARNETT, ARTHUR L., and JOHN H. SHAW, *Effective School Health Education,* New York, Appleton-Century-Crofts, 1959.

IRWIN, LESLIE W., *et al., Health in Elementary Schools,* St. Louis, The C. V. Mosby Company, 1962.

JOINT COMMITTEE ON HEALTH PROBLEMS IN EDUCATION OF THE NATIONAL EDUCATION ASSOCIATION AND THE AMERICAN MEDICAL ASSOCIATION, *Health Education,* Washington, D.C., National Education Association, 1961.

KILANDER, H. FREDERICK, *School Health Education,* New York, The Macmillan Company, 1962.

LASALLE, DOROTHY, and GLADYS GEER, *Health Instruction for Today's Schools,* Englewood Cliffs, N.J., Prentice-Hall, Inc., 1963.

TURNER, C. E., *et al., School Health and Health Education,* St. Louis, The C. V. Mosby Company, 1957.

VANNIER, MARYHELEN, *Teaching Health in Elementary Schools,* New York, Harper & Row, 1963.

WILLGOOSE, CARL E., *Health Education in the Elementary School,* Philadelphia, W. B. Saunders Company, 1964.

CHAPTER **28**

Environment and Services for Healthful School Living

ENVIRONMENT FOR HEALTHFUL SCHOOL LIVING

The school should be conducive to healthful living. First of all, this means that the physical environment is attractive, sanitary, and functional. The buildings have been constructed with health and safety standards in mind. Secondly, the mental and emotional environment is conducive to good health. This is as important as the physical environment. These two phases of living healthfully at school are discussed in this chapter.

The Physical Environment

The elementary school classroom teacher should be familiar with certain aspects of the physical environment.

1. *School Site.* In urban communities the school should be situated near transportation facilities, but at the same time away from industrial plants, railroads, noise, heavy traffic, fumes, and smoke. It should be attractive and well landscaped. In rural communities the school should be located in an attractive setting where the physical environment is conducive to healthful school living.

2. *Play and Recreation Area.* Standards recommend at least 5 acres of land for elementary schools. Play area should consist of a minimum of 100 square feet for each child.

3. *Buildings.* There is a trend toward one-story construction, where possible, with stress on functional planning rather than ornamental structure. In addition to an adequate number of classrooms, school buildings should contain such facilities as health suite; special rooms for activities like music, dancing, arts, crafts; gymnasium; cafeteria; and, if possible, a swimming pool.

4. *Lighting.* It is important to conserve vision, prevent fatigue, and improve morale. Light intensity in most classrooms varies from 15 to 50 foot-candles. Most authorities recommend between 20 and 40 foot-candles for reading and close work.

5. *Heating and Ventilation.* Heating standards vary according to the activities and the clothing worn by the participants. The following specifications are generally accepted. Classrooms, offices, and cafeterias: 68–72° F (30 inches above the floor); kitchens, closed corridors, shops, and laboratories: 65–68° F (60 inches above floor); gymnasiums and activity rooms: 55–65° F (60 inches above floor). Ventilation should provide from 8 to 21 cubic feet of fresh air per minute per occupant. The recommended humidity ranges from 35 to 60 per cent. The type and amount of ventilation will vary with

the specific needs of the particular area to be served.

6. *Furniture.* Seats and desks which are adjustable and movable are recommended by most educators. Desks should be of proper height and adjusted to fit the pupil comfortably and properly. This helps to avoid fatigue and faulty posture habits.

7. *School Plant Sanitation.*

a. Water supply should be safe and adequate. One authority suggests that at least 25 gallons per pupil per day is needed for all purposes.

b. Drinking fountains at various heights should be recessed in corridor walls. Approximately one drinking fountain should be provided for every seventy-five pupils. The stream of water should flow from the fountain in a manner that does not require the drinker to get his mouth too near the opening.

c. Water closets, urinals, lavatories, and washroom equipment such as soap dispensers, toilet paper holders, waste containers, mirrors, bookshelves, and hand-drying facilities should be provided as necessary.

d. Waste disposal should be adequate.

8. *Other Essentials for a Healthful Environment.*

a. A well-planned school lunch program should include good, wholesome food, adequate time for eating, and a pleasant, quiet, attractive atmosphere.

b. Necessary custodial help and cleaning supplies should be secured for maintaining sanitary conditions in all classrooms, lavatories, gymnasiums, cafeterias, and so on.

c. Safe, uncrowded transportation to and from school and on all trips sponsored by the school should be provided.

d. Special arrangements should be made for handicapped children, such as seats near the front of the room for auditory handicapped individuals.

Mental and Emotional Environment

The mental and emotional environment is equally important if pupils are to live healthfully at school. Some of the factors that the elementary school teacher should recognize as contributing to good mental and emotional health are as follows:

1. The teacher, school officials, and pupils work harmoniously and happily together.

2. The teacher exemplifies good physical, mental, emotional, and social health.

3. The educational curriculum is adapted to the needs and interests of the child.

4. An atmosphere of friendliness and consideration of the rights of others exists in all personal school relationships.

5. The teacher gives each child a feeling of belonging and security.

6. The teacher does not use sarcasm or ridicule children.

7. Frequent opportunities are provided for relaxation and play.

8. Pupils are encouraged to improve themselves rather than to excel over their classmates.

9. A permissive climate prevails.

10. Pupils help in making decisions.

11. A variety of teaching methods is used.

12. Individual differences are recognized.

13. The length of the school day is in conformance with the age of the child.

14. Classes are scheduled in a way that does not result in excessive fatigue.

15. Excessive emphasis is not placed on marks.

16. School attendance is not overemphasized to the point of disregarding the health of the individual.

17. As much freedom as possible is given to the pupils.

18. The teacher takes a personal interest in and loves each child.

19. The teacher has a pleasing personality.

20. There is good rapport between the teacher and the parents of each child.

SERVICES FOR HEALTH IMPROVEMENT

Health services represent a very important part of the total school health program. In this section, each of the six areas of the health service program will be discussed in light of the elementary school teacher's responsibilities.

Health Appraisal

Health appraisal is that phase of the school health service program which is concerned with evaluating the health of the whole child, through examinations, observations, and records.

The aims of health appraisal have been well stated by the American Association of School Administrators in their *Twentieth Yearbook:*

1. To identify pupils in need of medical or dental treatment.

2. To identify pupils who have problems relating to nutrition.

3. To identify pupils who are poorly adjusted and in need of special attention at school or of treatment by a psychiatrist or a child guidance clinic.

4. To measure the growth of pupils and to assist them in attaining optimum growth.

5. To identify pupils with nonremediable defects who may require modified programs of education—for example, the crippled, partially sighted, hard-of-hearing, mentally retarded, and those with speech defects.

6. To identify pupils who need a more thorough examination than is usually provided at school—for example, X-ray examination, examination by a specialist, or a laboratory examination of one kind or another.

7. To identify pupils who may be cared for best apart from the regular school situation —for example, the blind, deaf, and tuberculous.

The classroom teacher's responsibilities in regard to health appraisal include the following:

1. To weigh and measure children periodically when it is requested or desired.

2. To give screening vision and hearing tests where required or desired.

3. To orient children as to the nature and purpose of medical examinations.

4. To be present at medical examinations to give the physician further health information on pupils and also to provide various health records for physician's information.

5. To help to make the medical examination and other forms of appraisal a worthwhile educational experience for the child.

6. To be familiar with the health history of the student.

7. To refer pupils needing special medical or psychological help to the proper clinic.

8. To help in dental examinations.

9. To know the various physical and behavior conditions that have implications for children's health for which the teacher should be alert.

10. To be observant in noting digression

from normal health appearance or behavior in children.

11. To keep health appraisal findings in strict confidence.

Health Counseling

In light of the findings gathered through appraisal techniques, health matters should be discussed with pupils and parents. Such problems as the need for medical and dental treatment, better health practices, diagnostic examinations, special services, and analyzing behavior problems require such conferences. Through such counseling procedures a better understanding of the health of children can be achieved. Some of the teacher's responsibilities in respect to health counseling follow:

1. To work closely with the nurse and other school officials on counseling problems.

2. If he or she is requested to do counseling, to get to know the pupil and parents well enough to do effective counseling.

3. To have face-to-face conferences rather than writing letters or using the telephone.

4. To understand desirable health counseling procedures.

5. To have all necessary records at hand.

6. To have a knowledge of health defects and proper action that needs to be taken, plus an understanding of the problems surrounding the particular pupil in question.

7. To be sympathetic and understanding of both the pupil's and the parents' points of view (a friendly atmosphere is necessary for good results).

8. To be a good listener.

9. To refrain from talking down to pupils or parents.

10. Not to divulge, except to proper persons, results of counseling conferences.

11. To understand that the success of the counseling conference will depend on the counselor's skill and the degree to which he or she has planned for the conference.

12. When the conference is concluded, to arrive at a common understanding with pupil and parent concerning the next step to be taken in the elimination of health problems.

Correction of Remediable Defects

After health appraisal and health counseling have been carried out, there must be a follow-through to see that remediable defects are corrected. The teacher can help by:

1. Continually being informed and keeping accurate records as to the status of her pupils' remediable defects, both those that have been corrected and those still needing correction.

2. Constantly encouraging pupils and parents to correct remediable defects.

3. If lack of money or some other insufficiency is responsible for failure to correct defects, trying to remedy the problem (in most communities there are charitable organizations, civic groups, or others who are ready to help such cases).

4. Visiting the home if this is essential for getting better results.

5. Tapping community resources (public clinics, welfare agencies, and voluntary organizations should be utilized; a list of hospitals, specialists, and clinics for various types of treatment should be provided when parents want additional information).

Care and Education of Exceptional Children

The term *exceptional* refers to those children who are handicapped mentally, physically, socially, or emotionally, and also to those who are gifted intellectually or in other ways.

The elementary teacher can help these children by:

1. Developing a planned procedure for determining those pupils who are exceptional.

2. Knowing the exceptional children and their needs.

3. Adapting the educational program wherever possible to help meet the needs and interests of the exceptional.

4. Referring for special services those exceptional children who need such care.

5. Observing children closely—through continuous observation, deviations from normal behavior may be identified.

6. Treating exceptional pupils as individuals and giving individual consideration in every case, rather than viewing children as groups with similar characteristics. (Whether or not the exceptional child should be a part of the regular group in the school situation, a part of a separate group, or a separate school will depend upon the individual. The decision should be in favor of the situation which will allow the greatest possibility for improvement of the child's condition and for his total growth and development.)

7. Providing an adequate supervisory program in connection with special classes for exceptional children. (Good supervision will insure periodic examinations to determine the status of the individual in respect to his exception, making sure that the program is as much like a regular school program as possible and seeing that the child is returned to the regular class as soon as possible.)

8. Being aware of the many ways that the school can make special provisions for handicapped children, such as scheduling all classes for handicapped on the same floor, providing rest periods for children with cardiac and other impairments, transporting them to and from school, and providing specially constructed chairs and desks.

9. Possessing emotional stability and having the type of temperament that is suitable for working with exceptional children.

Communicable Disease Control

Wherever children congregate there is the possibility of spreading disease. The school, as a place for children and youth to assemble, is unique in that the law requires attendance. Therefore, if school attendance is compulsory, there should be certain protective measures and precautions taken to insure that everything is done to guard the health of the child. This includes the necessary procedures for controlling communicable disease. The teacher can play a very important part by:

1. Knowing the symptoms for various communicable diseases.

2. Being continually vigilant to notice such symptoms, isolating affected individuals immediately, and referring these cases to the school or family physician.

3. Consulting regularly with the nurse and school physician as to what other contributions she can make.

4. Providing a healthful classroom environment which will help prevent the spread of communicable diseases. (This should include proper ventilation and heating, safe running water, cleanliness, use of pasteurized milk as a safeguard against milk-borne diseases, control over readmissions of students who have had communicable diseases, and abandonment of overemphasis on perfect attendance for both pupils and teacher.)

5. Stressing the importance of immunization against preventable diseases.

6. Having a good rapport with parents of children so that unnecessary risks will not be taken.

Emergency Care

The school is responsible for providing each child with the necessary protection and care while the child is at school. The school acts in place of the parent, and it is assumed that the child will receive the same care and protection during the hours of school that he normally would receive at home. Children often become sick or injured during school hours. Therefore, the school must provide the necessary attention until it can be taken over by the parents. The classroom teacher has such responsibilities as the following:

1. Every teacher should have a definite plan to follow in event of emergency. Such a plan should be in writing. There should be an over-all school plan; however, if such a plan does not exist, the teacher should have one of her own. This plan should cover such essentials as first-aid instructions, staff responsibilities, procedures for medical help, transportation, notifying parents, and having supplies, equipment, and facilities available.

2. All teachers should know where the first-aid supplies are and how to use them.

3. Every teacher should be trained in first-aid procedures.

4. Each teacher should have complete personal information on each of her pupils: parent's name, address, and phone number; parent's business address and phone number; family physician's address and phone number; family dentist's address and phone number; parent's instructions in case of emergency; choice of hospital; and all other pertinent information.

5. A complete record should be kept of every accident, including first aid given and emergency care administered in the event of illness.

6. The legal aspects of health problems in regard to emergency care should be understood.

7. Various insurance plans should be discussed at parent-teacher and other school meetings.

8. All teachers should possess foresight —disaster or accidents can happen at any time. Be prepared.

In summary, a point of view is presented which was formulated by a committee of teachers and officers for the guidance of Curriculum Committees in Washington, D.C., and is entitled "Place of Health in the School Program."

1. Health is a way of living.

2. The child's state of health influences all the phases of his existence—physical, mental, emotional, social.

3. Good health is a major basis for school success.

4. The school should be a place for healthful living rather than a place to learn about health.

5. A healthful school environment should be the first responsibility of all who are concerned with children.

6. The teacher should exemplify good physical, mental, and emotional health.

7. The curriculum should emphasize the formation of desirable health habits and attitudes rather than just the acquisition of health knowledges.

8. The school should adapt every phase of its program to meet the individual health needs of children.

9. There should be many opportunities for health experiences in the entire curriculum. These experiences should be so planned that there will be sequential development in many areas.

10. A meaningful school health program for elementary school children should include: (a) healthful school living, (b) health services, (c) health education, (d) wholesale physical activities.

11. Health instruction and health services have value only to the extent to which they favorably influence the everyday living of the child.

12. The materials used for health instruction should be factual, founded on the latest scientific information, and useful for practical living.

13. All those concerned with the development of the child—teachers, administrators, parents, and directors of services—should participate in planning the health program.

14. A health program is successful if (a) the child cooperates in following good health practices even before he understands the reasons, (b) the child grows in comprehension of what constitutes good health, (c) the child accepts personal responsibility for his own health, (d) the child takes active precautions to safeguard the health of others, (e) the home understands and supports this program throughout the child's school years.[1]

QUESTIONS AND PRACTICAL PROBLEMS

1. Write an essay on the subject of "School Health Services." In this essay, list essential services for the elementary school child, and some of the factors involved in the accomplishment of each.

2. What are some of the factors that should be taken into consideration in providing a healthful school environment for children?

3. What are some of the factors that the elementary school teacher should recognize as contributing to good mental and emotional health?

4. Describe what you consider to be an ideal classroom from a physical point of view. In your description include standards for play and recreation area, lighting, heating, ventilation, furniture, and color scheme.

5. Prepare a mock counseling session for your class which will show an elementary school teacher having a conference with a parent on her child's health.

6. What are five ways in which an elementary school teacher can help to prevent the spread of communicable disease?

7. Put on a demonstration for the class showing what you would do if an unconscious child had just been pulled from the swimming pool.

SELECTED REFERENCES

BUCHER, CHARLES A., *Administration of School Health and Physical Education Programs,* St. Louis, The C. V. Mosby Company, 1963.

GROUT, RUTH E., *Health Teaching in Schools,* Philadelphia, W. B. Saunders Co., 1963.

JOINT COMMITTEE ON HEALTH PROBLEMS IN EDUCATION OF THE NATIONAL EDUCATION ASSOCIATION AND THE AMERICAN MEDICAL ASSOCIATION, *Healthful School Living,* Washington, D.C., National Education Association, 1957.

———, *School Health Services,* Washington, D.C., National Education Association, 1953.

KILANDER, H. FREDERICK, *School Health Education,* New York, The Macmillan Company, 1962.

WILLGOOSE, CARL E., *Health Education in the Elementary School,* Philadelphia, W. B. Saunders Company, 1964.

[1] Committee of Teachers and Officers for the Guidance of Curriculum Committees in Washington, D.C., "Place of Health in the School Program," *Journal of Health, Physical Education and Recreation,* **24:**36 (December 1953).

Appendixes

Appendix A

SOME BOOKS, VISUAL AIDS, AND RECORDS

Books

Teachers will perhaps be interested in knowing where to locate various source books for materials in the event that they wish to purchase them for the library. This brief review may assist them. The list is not intended to be complete, but is sufficient to give the teacher a wealth of resource materials. Publishers are not included here if the book is listed as a reference in the text.

Creative Rhythms for Children, Andrews. An excellent practical book to aid the teacher with creative rhythms for children.

Dance a While, Harris, Pittman, and Waller. Handbook of folk, square, and social dances with clear concise directions, but no music.

Dance and Play Activities for the Elementary Grades (2 Vols.), Bauer and Reed. Volume I contains games, rhythms, and self-testing activities for grades one, two, and three. Volume II contains graded activities for grades four, five, and six.

File of Fun, Harris. Excellent source for games and activities for social recreation.

Fun for Parties and Programs, Allen. Scores of popular games and dances with several complete sample party plans.

Fun Around the World, Keene. Activities of various countries and parts of the world.

Games for the Gymnasium, Playground and Classroom, Gilb. Excellent source for all age groups.

Games for Playground, Home, School and Gymnasium, Bancroft. A wealth of materials for all grade levels and suitable for all types of play spaces and areas.

Games and Rhythms for the Elementary School, Latchaw. Pocket guide of games for all grade levels. Well illustrated and contains an evaluation check list for each game.

Games for the Elementary School Grades, Richardson. Card file of graded games. Complete directions and some teaching suggestions for each game.

Individual and Dual Stunts, Fischer and Shawbold. One hundred fifty illustrated stunts.

Official Guides for Basketball, Softball, Soccer, Touch Football, Volleyball for men and boys, Official Sports Library for Men, New York 17, New York.

Official Guides for Basketball, Soccer, Speedball, Softball, Volleyball and Recreational Games, Tennis, Badminton, Archery, Riding, Aquatics, Winter Sports, and Outing Activities for women and girls, National Section for Girls and Women's Sports, 1201 Sixteenth Street, N.W., Washington, D.C.

Omnibus of Fun, Eisenberg, Helen, and Larry. A 640-page book with thousands of ready-to-use, easy-to-use activities for fun, recreation, and relaxation for all groups.

Physical Education for Small Schools. A joint publication of the Department of Rural Education and the American Association for Health, Physical Education, and Recreation, Washington, D.C., 1954.

Physical Education Activities for the Elementary Schools, Smalley. Contains all types of materials suitable for physical education programs in grades one through six.

Rhythms and Dances for Elementary Schools, LaSalle. Dances clearly explained and presented with music for all grade levels, including the fundamentals for the lower grades.

Rhythmic Activities, Stuart and Ludlam (Series I and II). Printed on individual cards. Series I contains rhythms for grades one, two, and three; series II, rhythms for grades four, five, and six. Music, directions, and record numbers are given.

Social Games for Recreation, Mason and Mitchell. Contains materials for social play in parties, clubs, playgrounds, camps, picnics, and homes.

The Source Book of Play Party Games, Price. Complete rhythmic games and dances with music for all grade levels in the elementary school.

Visual Aids

Teachers may wish to know sources of various visual aids useful in physical education programs. Film catalogues are available from some of the following companies. This list is not exhaustive.

Coronet Instructional Films, Coronet Building, Chicago, Ill.

Encyclopaedia Britannica Films, 20 North Wacker Drive, Chicago, Ill.

H. W. Wilson Company, 950 University Avenue, New York 52, N.Y.

National Section on Women's Athletics,

1201 Sixteenth Street, N.W., Washington 6, D.C.

The Athletic Institute, Merchandise Mart, Room 805, Chicago 54, Ill.

United States Government Printing Office, Washington, D.C.

Magnetic boards are of great help as teaching aids for team games. They may be obtained from:

Jaconda Manufacturing Company, Department H8, 5449 Hunter Street, Philadelphia 31, Pa.

Magnetic Bulletin-Board, Novel Novelty Company, New York, N.Y.

Magnetic Sport Board, The Sportswoman, 7848 Wisconsin Avenue, Bethesda, Md.

The Program Aids Company, Inc., 550 Fifth Avenue, New York 36, N.Y.

Records

Records for dances may be secured from the following companies. This is not an exhaustive list.

American Squares, 121 Delaware St., Woodbury, N.J.

Bowmar Company, Inc., 12 Cleveland St., Valhalla, N.Y.

Burns Record Company, 755 Chickadee Lane, Stratford, Conn.

Capitol Records, Sunset and Vine, Hollywood, Cal.

Century Music Publishing Company, 235 W. 40th St., New York, N.Y.

Chartwell House, Inc., Publishers, 112 E. 19th St., New York 3, N.Y.

Columbia Recording Company, 1473 Burnum Ave., Bridgeport, Conn.

Dot Records, Sunset and Vine, Hollywood, Cal.

Electro-Vox, 5546 Melrose Ave., Hollywood, Cal.

Evans Records, Chartwell House, Inc., 280 Madison Ave., New York 16, N.Y.

Evans, Ruth, "Childhood Rhythmic Records," 326 Forest Park Ave., Springfield, Mass.

Folk Dancer, Box 201, Flushing, Long Island, N.Y.

Folkraft Records, 1159 Broad St., Newark 5, N.J.

Henlee Record Company, 2404 Harris Blvd., Austin, Tex.

Honor Your Partner, Teaching Aids, Freeport, Long Island, N.Y.

Kismet Record Company, 227 E. 14th St., New York 3, N.Y.

Methodist Publishing House, 150 Fifth Ave., New York, N.Y.

Rainbow Records, 767 Tenth Ave., New York 19, N.Y.

Record Squares, 152 Swall Drive, Los Angeles, Cal.

Sing 'n Do Company, P.O. Box 279, Ridgewood, N.J.

Sonart Record Corporation, 251 W. 42nd Street, New York, N.Y.

Square Dance Associates, 102 N. Columbus Drive, Freeport, Long Island, N.Y.

Victor Records, Radio Corporation of America, Camden, N.J.

World of Fun Records, 150 Fifth Ave., New York 11, N.Y.

Appendix B

SUGGESTIONS FOR MAKING EQUIPMENT AND FOR VARIOUS FREE OR INEXPENSIVE MATERIALS WHICH WILL AID TEACHERS IN THEIR PROGRAMS

1. Bowling pins may be secured free from your local alley. Contact the local manager and ask him to save those which are not good enough to be refinished. These may be used for many games, for marking playing areas, and so on.

2. If the school is in an area where there are sewing mills or hosiery mills, ask them to save the spindles or cones which the thread comes on for you. They may be used in place of Indian clubs, for bases, for bowling games, and so on.

3. Ask your children to bring in large tin cans. Be sure that they have smooth edges. They may be used for target tossing games in the classroom and on the playground in warm weather.

4. Your school cafeteria or your favorite sweet shop will save the ice cream cartons bulk ice cream is packed in for you. Wash, dry, and have your class paint them. They may be used for games, to store small balls, bean bags, and the like, and to carry outside and mark play areas.

5. Children may bring in ears of dried corn and heavy cloth material to make bean bags under your guidance. They are much

better than those which may be purchased and naturally are cheaper.

6. Ask your children, local farmers, and poultrymen for empty feed bags. Put clean hay, straw, or dry lawn clippings in them. Tie them with binder twine and use them for bases in softball, to mark play areas, and for bases in all other games. Carry them out and in each time so they do not get wet and muddy. They are light, clean, and require little storage space.

7. Use plain paper plates to mark your playing area for running and tagging games. These may also be used for indoor tossing games. A little sand or dirt placed on the center of each will prevent them from blowing away.

8. Ask your children to bring in bottle caps. Use them for target tossing games. Toss them into the tin cans, on marked floor targets, or in the ice cream cartons already mentioned.

9. Make quoits out of rope. The rope must be heavy enough to hold its shape and may be taped with tire tape. These quoits may be used over homemade pegs made by crossing two sticks of wood with an upright

piece in the center, an old bowling pin, or they may ring a person's arm. The human target bends his arm at the elbow, makes a fist, and endeavors to catch the ring on his arm.

10. Volleyball nets are costly. If you have none, use a piece of rope—clothesline will do very nicely. Attach it to two posts or trees. Tie strips of white cloth every few inches on the rope and permit them to hang down 3 or 4 feet. This makes it very easy to ascertain whether the ball goes over or under the rope.

11. Ask your children to bring in smooth pieces of board or ask for them from your manual arts room. They may vary in size from 12 by 12 inches to 24 by 24 inches. Have your children paint circles on them for dart games. Use suction or regular darts.

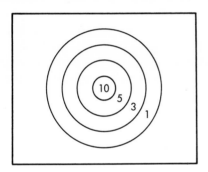

Figure B–1. Dart board.

12. Mark pieces of board of any appropriate size in squares. Paint numbers in each square. Next, drive a nail in each square at an angle. Use mason jar rubber rings for tossing at the board. Rings must hook over nails and remain on. Each person has five turns. His score is then recorded. Make the game any score you desire. See Figure B–2.

13. To mark players for two teams in games where they intermingle, use any colored cloth or red or blue bandanas. Tie on the arm of the players of one team. These may also be used to mark boys or girls in dances where your group is uneven.

6	4	9	14
3	5	6	8
7	1	15	11
12	10	2	13

Figure B–2. Ring Toss board.

14. Cut rings from round cereal boxes. Use them to toss short distances for ring games. They may also be used on the floor or ground to toss bottle caps or pebbles into for target games.

15. Use rolled socks for classroom games so no damage will be done if a child misses it. These socks may be sewn so they do not come unrolled. Mothers or children may knit or crochet a cover and stuff it with socks.

16. Pieces of red material may be fastened on heavy wire or pieces of wood. One end may be pushed in the ground to mark playing areas. See Figure B–3.

17. Use pieces of wall board to make target games of various kinds.

18. Use an old dishpan or round basin. Fill it with wet cement and stand a piece of 2-inch pipe about 12 inches long in the center of it so it will dry there. When it dries you have a standard to hold up nets for Paddle Tennis, Deck Tennis, Badminton, and the like. Insert a 1-inch pipe in this 2-inch pipe and tie the net to it. The cement is a heavy enough base to hold the nets satisfactorily.

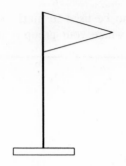

Figure B–3. Playground marker.

19. Collect quart milk cartons. Wash them thoroughly and use them in place of Indian clubs for games. They make fine quiet pins for indoor bowling games. They may be used to mark play areas. If they are partially filled with sand, the wind will not blow them away when used out of doors.

20. Collect cloth salt or sugar sacks and fill them with shredded newspapers. Sew them securely to use for indoor games and activities.

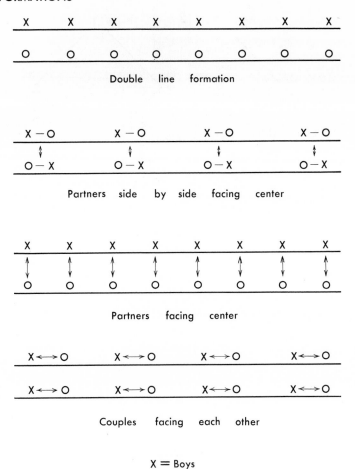

Double line formation

Partners side by side facing center

Partners facing center

Couples facing each other

X = Boys

O = Girls

Figure C–3. Double line dance formations.

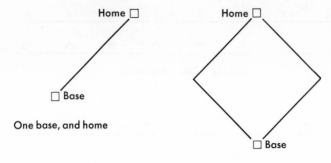

One base, and home

One base opposite home

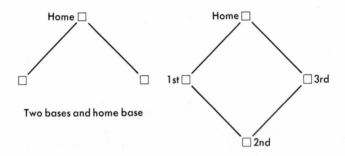

Two bases and home base

Diamond formation, four bases

Figure C–4. Base diagrams for games.

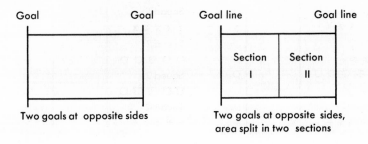

Two goals at opposite sides

Two goals at opposite sides, area split in two sections

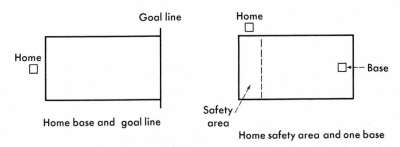

Home base and goal line

Home safety area and one base

Figure C–5. Diagrams of general playing areas.

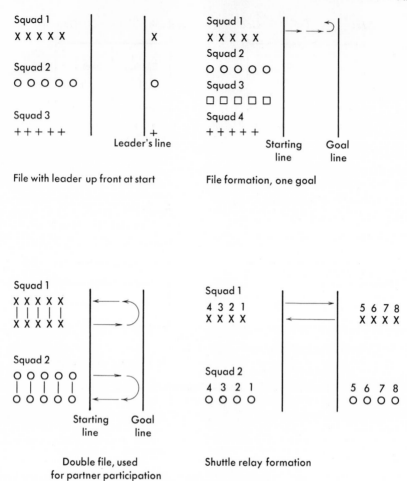

Figure C–6. Relay formations.

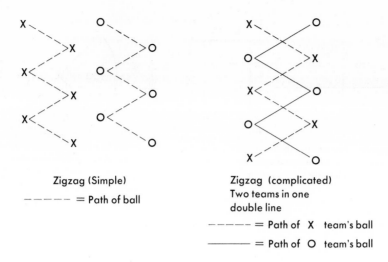

Zigzag (Simple)

— — — — — = Path of ball

Zigzag (complicated)
Two teams in one
double line

— — — — — = Path of X team's ball

——————— = Path of O team's ball

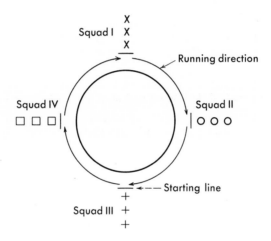

Circle relay with four teams

Figure C–7. Relay formations.

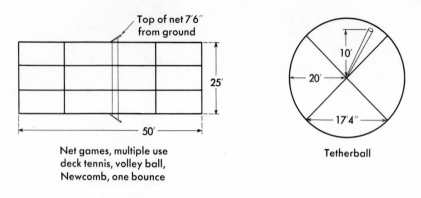

Top of net 7'6" from ground

25'

50'

Net games, multiple use
deck tennis, volley ball,
Newcomb, one bounce

10'

20'

17'4"

Tetherball

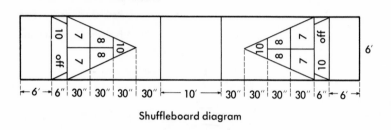

Shuffleboard diagram

Figure C–8. Individual and dual game diagrams.

Appendix D

SOURCES OF EQUIPMENT AND SUPPLIES

Various equipment and supplies may be secured from the following sources. This is not an exhaustive list. Catalogues are available and are great aids for teachers and administrators.

A. G. Spaulding & Brothers, 161 Sixth Ave., New York 13, N.Y.

American Athlete and Educational Supply Co., 13609 Normandie, Gardena, Cal.

Atlantic-Pacific Manufacturing Corp., 124 Atlantic Ave., Brooklyn 1, N.Y.

Creative Playthings, Inc., Edenburg Road, Hightstown, N.J.

The MacGregor Co., Cincinnati 32, Ohio.

Miracle Equipment Company, Grinnell, Iowa.

Nissen Medart Company, Cedar Rapids, Iowa.[1]

Paneltrol, Inc., 9 N. Colonial Ave., Wilmington 5, Del.[2]

Peterson Mat Co., Division of Wayne Iron Works, Wayne, Pa.

Premier Athletic Corp., Riverdale, N.J.

Rawlings Company, St. Louis, Mo.

Safe Fencing Company, 21 Harrison Avenue, Glens Falls, New York.

W. J. Voit Rubber Corp., 45 W. 18th St., New York 11, N.Y.

[1] Manufacturer of the "Physical Educator" portable apparatus.
[2] Manufacturer of the "Challenger" portable gym.

Appendix E: AAHPER YOUTH FITNESS TEST[1]

THE YOUTH FITNESS TEST battery consists of seven test items which are given in the gymnasium or outdoors and three aquatic tests. It is suggested that the pull-up (for boys), modified pull-up (for girls), sit-up, standing broad jump, and shuttle-run be given in one period; the 50-yard dash, softball throw for distance, and 600-yard run-walk in a second period. The aquatic tests could be worked into any existing swimming program.

The pupils should be given reasonable warm-up prior to the testing. A test should not be given to any pupil whose medical status is questionable.

1 pull-up

BOYS, GRADES 5-12

Equipment. A metal or wooden bar approximately 1½ inches in diameter is preferred. A doorway gym bar can be used and, if no regular equipment is available, a piece of pipe or even the rungs of a ladder can also serve the purpose *(Figure 1)*.

Description. The bar should be high enough so that the pupil can hang with his arms and legs fully extended and his feet free of the floor. Use the overhand grasp *(Figure 2)*. After assuming the hanging position, the pupil raises his body by his arms until his chin can be placed over the bar and then lowers his body to a full hang as in the starting position. The exercise is repeated as many times as possible.

Rules. 1. Allow one trial unless it is obvious that the pupil has not had a fair chance.

2. The body must not swing during the execution of the movement. The pull must in no way be a snap movement. If the pupil starts swinging, check this by holding your extended arm across the front of the thighs.

3. The knees must not be raised and kicking of the legs is not permitted.

Scoring. Record the number of completed pull-ups to the nearest whole number . . .

[1] American Association for Health, Physical Education and Recreation, *AAHPER Youth Fitness Test Manual,* Washington, D.C., American Association for Health, Physical Education and Recreation, 1962, pp. 5–13, 18–31. Reprinted by permission.

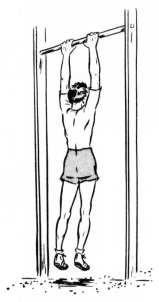

FIGURE 1
Improvised equipment for pull-up—
Doorway gym bar in background,
ladder in foreground.

FIGURE 2
Starting position for pull-up.

modified pull-up

GIRLS, GRADES 5-12

Equipment. A metal or wooden bar approximately 1½ inches in diameter is preferred. A doorway gym bar can be used and, if no regular equipment is available, a piece of pipe can also serve the purpose. In some instances, it is possible to use the aisle between bleacher seats and have the bleachers support the pipe at the desired height *(Figure 3)*.

Description. Adjust the height of the bar so it is approximately at nipple level. Use an overhand grasp. The pupil extends her legs under the bar and extends the arms fully. The arms should form an angle of 90 degrees with the body line, and the body line should form an angle of 45 degrees with the floor *(Figure 4)*. The heels should be braced to prevent slipping; they can be resting on a mat or against an improvised rest, like the scorer's foot, to prevent slipping. From this position the pupil raises her body by her arms until the chest touches the bar, then lowers her body to a full hang. The exercise should be repeated.

Rules. 1. No resting is permitted.

2. No pull-up shall be counted in which the pupil fails to: keep the body straight, come to a full extension of the arms, or touch the chest to the bar.

3. The maximum number is 40.

Scoring. Record the number of completed pull-ups to the nearest whole number, with a maximum of 40.

FIGURE 3
Improvised equipment for modified pull-up—bar supported on bleachers.

FIGURE 4
Starting position for modified pull-up. Note 90° angle from arms to body line, 45° angle from body line to floor.

2 sit-up

BOYS AND GIRLS, GRADES 5-12

Equipment. Mat or floor.

Description. The pupil lies on his back, either on the floor or on a mat, with legs extended and feet about two feet apart. His hands are placed on the back of the neck with the fingers interlaced. Elbows are retracted. A partner holds the ankles down, the heels being in contact with the mat or floor at all times *(Figure 5)*.

The pupil sits up, turning the trunk to the left and touching the right elbow to the left knee, returns to starting position, then sits up turning the trunk to the right and touching the left elbow to the right knee. The exercise is repeated, alternating sides *(Figure 6)*.

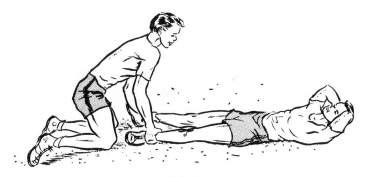

FIGURE 5
Starting position for sit-up.

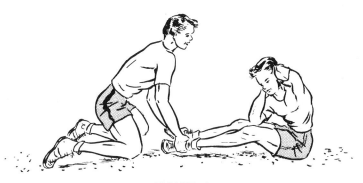

FIGURE 6
Sit-up.

Rules. 1. The fingers must remain in contact behind the neck throughout the exercise.

2. The knees must be on the floor during the sit-up but may be slightly bent when touching elbow to knee.

3. The back should be rounded and the head and elbows brought forward when sitting up as a "curl" up.

4. When returning to starting position, elbows must be flat on the mat before sitting up again.

Scoring. One point is given for each complete movement of touching elbow to knee. No score should be counted if the fingertips do not maintain contact behind the head, if knees are bent when the pupil lies on his back or when he begins to sit up, or if the pupil pushes up off the floor from an elbow. The maximum limit in terms of number of sit-ups shall be: 50 sit-ups for girls, 100 sit-ups for boys.

3 shuttle run

BOYS AND GIRLS, GRADES 5-12

Equipment. Two blocks of wood, 2 in. x 2 in. x 4 in., and stopwatch. Pupils should wear sneakers or run barefooted.

Description. Two parallel lines are marked on the floor 30 feet apart. The width of a regulation volleyball court serves as a suitable area. Place the blocks of wood behind one of the lines as indicated in *Figure 7*. The pupil starts from behind the other line. On the signal "Ready? Go!," the pupil runs to the blocks, picks one up, runs back to the starting line and *places* the block behind the line; he then runs back and picks up the second block which he carries back across the starting line. If the scorer has two stopwatches or one with a split-second timer, it is preferable

FIGURE 7
Starting the shuttle run.

to have two people running at the same time. To eliminate the necessity of returning the blocks after each race, start the races alternately, first from behind one line and then from behind the other.

Rules. Allow two trials with some rest between.

Scoring. Record the better of the two trials to the nearest tenth of a second.

4 standing broad jump

BOYS AND GIRLS, GRADES 5-12

Equipment. Mat, floor, or outdoor jumping pit, and tape measure.

Description. Pupil stands as indicated in *Figure 8*, with the feet several inches apart and the toes just behind the take-off line. Preparatory to jumping, the pupil swings the arms backward and bends the knees. The jump is accomplished by simultaneously extending the knees and swinging forward the arms.

    1. Allow three trials.

    2. Measure from the take-off line to the heel or other part of the body that touches the floor nearest the take-off line *(Figure 8)*.

    3. When the test is given indoors, it is convenient to tape the tape measure to the floor at right angles to the take-off line and have the pupils jump along the tape. The scorer stands to the side and observes the mark to the nearest inch.

Scoring. Record the best of the three trials in feet and inches to the nearest inch.

FIGURE 8
Measuring the standing broad jump.

5 50-yard dash

Equipment. Two stopwatches or one with a split-second timer.

Description. It is preferable to administer this test to two pupils at a time. Have both take positions behind the starting line. The starter will use the commands "Are you ready?" and "Go!" The latter will be accompanied by a downward sweep of the starter's arm to give the timer a visual signal.

Rules. The score is the amount of time between the starter's signal and the instant the pupil crosses the finish line.

Scoring. Record in seconds to the nearest tenth of a second.

6 softball throw for distance

Equipment. Softball (12-inch), small metal or wooden stakes, and tape measure.

Description. A football field marked in conventional fashion (five-yard intervals), makes an ideal area for this test. If this is not available, it is suggested that lines be drawn parallel to the restraining line, five yards apart. The pupil throws the ball while remaining within two parallel lines, six feet apart *(Figure 9)*. Mark the point of landing with one of the small stakes. If his second or third throw is farther, move the stake accordingly so that, after three throws, the stake is at the point of the pupil's best throw. It was found expedient to have the pupil jog out to his stake and stand there; and then, after five pupils have completed their throws, the measurements were taken. By having the pupil at his particular stake, there is little danger of recording the wrong score.

Rules. 1. Only an overhand throw may be used.
2. Three throws are allowed.
3. The distance recorded is the distance from the point of landing to the nearest point on the restraining line *(Figure 9)*.

Scoring. Record the best of the three trials to the nearest foot.

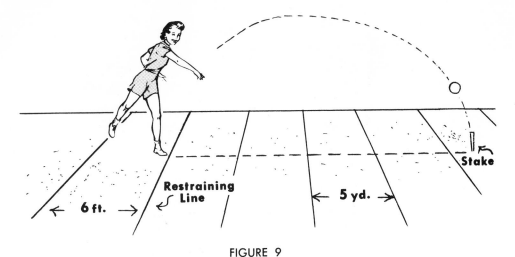

FIGURE 9

Measuring the softball throw for distance. Wherever ball lands, measure
distance perpendicular to starting line.

7 **600-yard run-walk**

BOYS AND GIRLS, GRADES 5-12

Equipment. Track or area marked according to Figures 10-12, and stopwatch.

Description. Pupil uses a standing start. At the signal "Ready? Go!," the subject starts running the 600-yard distance. The running may be interspersed with walking. It is possible to have a dozen subjects run at one time by having the pupils pair off before the start of the event. Then each pupil listens for and remembers his partner's time as the latter crosses the finish. The timer merely calls out the times as the pupils cross the finish.

Rules. Walking is permitted, but the object is to cover the distance in the shortest possible time.

Scoring. Record in minutes and seconds.

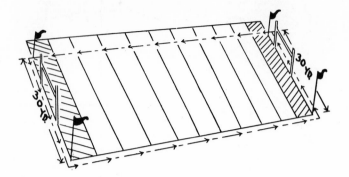

FIGURE 10
Using football field for 600-yard run-walk.

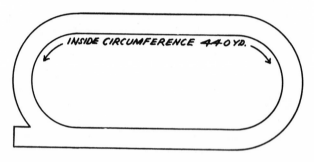

FIGURE 11
Using inside track for 600-yard run-walk.

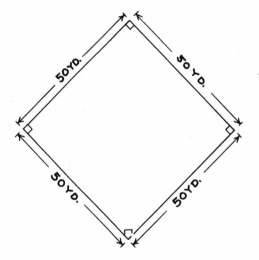

FIGURE 12
Using any open area for 600-yard run-walk.

tables

TABLE 1. MODIFIED PULL-UPS FOR GIRLS
Percentile Scores Based on Age

Percentile	10	11	12	13	14	15	16	17	Percentile
100th	40	40	40	40	40	40	40	40	100th
95th	40	40	40	40	40	40	40	40	95th
90th	40	40	40	40	40	40	40	40	90th
85th	40	40	40	40	40	40	40	40	85th
80th	40	40	40	40	40	40	40	40	80th
75th	40	40	40	40	40	36	40	35	75th
70th	40	40	40	40	36	30	31	30	70th
65th	35	34	33	34	32	25	28	29	65th
60th	30	30	29	30	29	22	25	25	60th
55th	26	27	26	28	25	19	21	23	55th
50th	23	24	24	25	23	16	19	21	50th
45th	20	22	21	22	20	14	17	18	45th
40th	17	20	20	20	19	12	14	15	40th
35th	15	18	18	19	16	11	12	13	35th
30th	12	15	16	17	14	10	11	11	30th
25th	10	12	14	15	13	9	10	10	25th
20th	9	10	12	13	11	8	8	8	20th
15th	7	7	10	10	10	6	6	7	15th
10th	5	5	8	8	7	4	4	5	10th
5th	2	2	5	6	3	1	2	2	5th
0	0	0	0	0	0	0	0	0	0

TABLE 2. SIT-UPS FOR GIRLS
Percentile Scores Based on Age

Percentile	10	11	12	13	14	15	16	17	Percentile
100th	50	50	50	50	50	50	50	50	100th
95th	50	50	50	50	49	37	40	42	95th
90th	50	50	39	36	34	31	32	37	90th
85th	40	40	34	30	30	28	30	30	85th
80th	33	34	30	30	28	26	27	25	80th
75th	30	30	29	27	25	24	25	24	75th
70th	27	29	25	25	24	22	24	23	70th
65th	24	26	24	23	22	20	22	21	65th
60th	22	25	22	21	20	20	21	20	60th
55th	20	23	21	20	20	19	20	18	55th
50th	19	20	20	20	18	18	19	16	50th
45th	17	20	18	19	17	16	18	15	45th
40th	15	18	17	17	15	15	16	15	40th
35th	14	16	15	16	14	14	15	14	35th
30th	12	15	13	15	12	13	13	12	30th
25th	11	13	12	13	11	11	12	11	25th
20th	10	11	10	12	10	10	11	9	20th
15th	8	10	10	10	8	8	10	8	15th
10th	6	8	7	8	6	6	8	6	10th
5th	4	5	5	5	4	4	4	3	5th
0	0	0	0	0	0	0	0	0	0

TABLE 3. SHUTTLE RUN FOR GIRLS
Percentile Scores Based on Age

Percentile	10	11	12	13	14	15	16	17	Percentile
100th	10.0	9.8	9.0	9.0	9.2	9.1	9.0	8.9	100th
95th	11.2	10.9	10.4	10.7	10.5	10.5	10.3	10.4	95th
90th	11.5	11.2	10.8	11.0	10.8	10.8	10.5	10.4	90th
85th	11.7	11.5	11.0	11.2	11.0	11.0	10.8	10.6	85th
80th	11.8	11.6	11.3	11.3	11.2	11.1	11.0	10.8	80th
75th	12.0	11.9	11.5	11.5	11.4	11.2	11.0	11.0	75th
70th	12.1	12.0	11.7	11.6	11.5	11.4	11.2	11.2	70th
65th	12.2	12.0	11.9	11.8	11.6	11.5	11.4	11.3	65th
60th	12.4	12.2	12.0	12.0	11.8	11.8	11.5	11.5	60th
55th	12.6	12.4	12.2	12.0	12.0	12.0	11.5	11.6	55th
50th	12.8	12.5	12.3	12.1	12.0	12.0	11.7	11.8	50th
45th	13.0	12.7	12.5	12.2	12.2	12.1	12.0	12.0	45th
40th	13.1	12.9	12.6	12.4	12.5	12.3	12.0	12.1	40th
35th	13.3	13.0	12.9	12.6	12.5	12.5	12.1	12.3	35th
30th	13.5	13.2	13.0	12.8	12.8	12.8	12.3	12.4	30th
25th	13.6	13.5	13.4	13.0	13.0	13.0	12.5	12.6	25th
20th	14.0	13.7	13.6	13.3	13.1	13.1	12.7	13.0	20th
15th	14.1	14.0	14.1	13.5	13.5	13.4	13.1	13.4	15th
10th	14.7	14.4	14.5	14.0	13.7	14.0	13.5	13.8	10th
5th	15.0	15.0	15.0	14.8	14.0	14.4	14.0	14.2	5th
0	18.9	23.0	23.0	18.0	16.8	23.4	15.0	16.0	0

TABLE 4. STANDING BROAD JUMP FOR GIRLS
Percentile Scores Based on Age

Percentile	10	11	12	13	14	15	16	17	Percentile
100th	6'2"	7'1"	6'11"	6'8"	6'11"	7'0"	7'2"	7'0"	100th
95th	5'4"	5'7"	5'8"	5'9"	6'1"	6'2"	6'5"	6'6"	95th
90th	5'1"	5'4"	5'6"	5'7"	5'9"	6'0"	6'0"	6'2"	90th
85th	4'11"	5'2"	5'3"	5'5"	5'7"	5'9"	5'11"	6'0"	85th
80th	4'10"	5'0"	5'2"	5'4"	5'6"	5'6"	5'8"	5'10"	80th
75th	4'8"	4'11"	5'0"	5'2"	5'4"	5'4"	5'6"	5'8"	75th
70th	4'7"	4'10"	4'11"	5'1"	5'2"	5'3"	5'5"	5'7"	70th
65th	4'6"	4'8"	4'10"	5'0"	5'1"	5'2"	5'3"	5'5"	65th
60th	4'5"	4'8"	4'9"	4'11"	5'0"	5'0"	5'2"	5'3"	60th
55th	4'4"	4'6"	4'7"	4'9"	4'10"	5'0"	5'1"	5'2"	55th
50th	4'3"	4'6"	4'5"	4'8"	4'9"	4'10"	5'0"	5'0"	50th
45th	4'2"	4'4"	4'4"	4'7"	4'8"	4'9"	4'11"	5'0"	45th
40th	4'1"	4'3"	4'1"	4'6"	4'7"	4'8"	4'10"	4'10"	40th
35th	4'0"	4'2"	4'0"	4'5"	4'6"	4'7"	4'9"	4'8"	35th
30th	3'10"	4'0"	3'10"	4'4"	4'5"	4'5"	4'8"	4'7"	30th
25th	3'9"	3'11"	3'9"	4'3"	4'4"	4'4"	4'6"	4'6"	25th
20th	3'8"	3'10"	3'5"	4'2"	4'2"	4'3"	4'4"	4'4"	20th
15th	3'6"	3'8"	3'2"	3'11"	4'0"	4'1"	4'3"	4'2"	15th
10th	3'4"	3'6"	3'6"	3'9"	3'10"	4'0"	4'0"	4'0"	10th
5th	3'2"	3'3"	3'3"	3'6"	3'6"	3'8"	3'10"	3'7"	5th
0	2'5"	2'5"	2'9"	2'7"	2'3"	3'0"	2'6"	3'1"	0

TABLE 5. 50-YARD DASH FOR GIRLS
Percentile Scores Based on Age

Percentile	10	11	12	13	14	15	16	17	Percentile
100th	6.9	6.8	6.2	6.0	6.2	6.7	6.0	6.0	100th
95th	8.0	7.5	7.2	7.4	7.3	7.4	7.1	7.3	95th
90th	8.2	8.0	7.5	7.6	7.5	7.7	7.4	7.6	90th
85th	8.4	8.0	7.9	7.8	7.8	7.8	7.5	7.8	85th
80th	8.5	8.2	8.0	7.9	8.0	8.0	7.7	8.0	80th
75th	8.6	8.3	8.1	8.0	8.0	8.0	7.9	8.1	75th
70th	8.7	8.4	8.2	8.1	8.1	8.1	8.0	8.2	70th
65th	8.8	8.5	8.3	8.2	8.2	8.2	8.1	8.3	65th
60th	8.9	8.6	8.4	8.2	8.3	8.3	8.2	8.4	60th
55th	9.0	8.7	8.6	8.4	8.4	8.5	8.3	8.5	55th
50th	9.1	9.0	8.7	8.5	8.5	8.6	8.4	8.6	50th
45th	9.3	9.0	8.9	8.6	8.6	8.8	8.5	8.8	45th
40th	9.5	9.1	9.0	8.8	8.8	8.9	8.6	8.9	40th
35th	9.5	9.2	9.1	8.9	8.8	9.0	8.7	9.0	35th
30th	9.6	9.2	9.2	9.0	9.0	9.1	8.9	9.2	30th
25th	9.8	9.4	9.3	9.0	9.1	9.2	9.0	9.5	25th
20th	10.0	9.5	9.5	9.2	9.3	9.5	9.3	10.0	20th
15th	10.1	9.7	9.7	9.5	9.5	9.8	9.7	10.5	15th
10th	10.4	10.0	10.0	9.8	10.0	10.1	10.0	10.8	10th
5th	10.8	10.5	10.4	10.5	10.5	10.8	10.9	11.1	5th
0	15.1	14.4	12.5	13.0	12.5	15.1	12.3	13.0	0

TABLE 6. SOFTBALL THROW FOR GIRLS
Percentile Scores Based on Age

Percentile	10	11	12	13	14	15	16	17	Percentile
100th	108	149	152	187	193	170	169	169	100th
95th	69	88	94	106	112	117	120	120	95th
90th	63	78	86	100	102	107	110	112	90th
85th	58	72	82	92	94	99	102	108	85th
80th	56	68	78	88	89	94	99	102	80th
75th	53	65	74	84	85	89	94	97	75th
70th	50	62	70	80	82	86	90	93	70th
65th	47	59	68	77	78	84	87	90	65th
60th	45	56	65	75	75	80	84	86	60th
55th	43	54	62	72	72	78	80	84	55th
50th	41	51	60	69	70	74	76	79	50th
45th	40	50	57	66	67	70	75	75	45th
40th	38	48	55	63	64	67	71	72	40th
35th	37	45	52	60	62	65	69	69	35th
30th	35	43	50	58	59	61	65	66	30th
25th	33	41	48	54	56	58	61	63	25th
20th	31	38	45	50	54	56	59	60	20th
15th	30	36	42	48	50	52	54	54	15th
10th	28	33	40	44	45	48	49	49	10th
5th	26	30	35	39	33	42	44	43	5th
0	13	16	21	19	18	10	28	30	0

TABLE 7. 600-YARD RUN-WALK FOR GIRLS
Percentile Scores Based on Age

Percentile	10	11	12	13	14	15	16	17	Percentile
100th	2:05	2:01	2:01	2:00	1:59	1:52	2:02	2:08	100th
95th	2:30	2:25	2:22	2:24	2:25	2:27	2:23	2:30	95th
90th	2:38	2:33	2:30	2:32	2:33	2:37	2:35	2:35	90th
85th	2:43	2:39	2:36	2:40	2:40	2:46	2:40	2:42	85th
80th	2:49	2:44	2:41	2:43	2:45	2:50	2:48	2:47	80th
75th	2:55	2:49	2:48	2:47	2:52	2:54	2:52	2:54	75th
70th	2:59	2:52	2:54	2:53	2:57	3:00	3:00	3:00	70th
65th	3:02	2:56	2:59	2:58	3:00	3:03	3:02	3:01	65th
60th	3:06	3:01	3:03	3:00	3:05	3:06	3:05	3:04	60th
55th	3:10	3:05	3:07	3:05	3:10	3:10	3:10	3:05	55th
50th	3:14	3:09	3:12	3:08	3:14	3:14	3:15	3:11	50th
45th	3:17	3:12	3:16	3:14	3:17	3:19	3:19	3:13	45th
40th	3:21	3:16	3:21	3:20	3:21	3:24	3:23	3:19	40th
35th	3:25	3:19	3:27	3:24	3:26	3:30	3:27	3:24	35th
30th	3:30	3:24	3:31	3:30	3:30	3:37	3:33	3:34	30th
25th	3:36	3:30	3:40	3:35	3:37	3:45	3:40	3:39	25th
20th	3:40	3:39	3:50	3:45	3:43	3:50	3:47	3:46	20th
15th	3:46	3:50	3:57	3:52	3:52	3:55	3:58	3:58	15th
10th	3:52	3:59	4:05	4:05	4:04	4:00	4:10	4:03	10th
5th	4:16	4:19	4:25	4:31	4:30	4:11	4:32	4:45	5th
0	6:09	6:20	6:23	5:50	7:50	7:00	5:50	6:00	0

TABLE 8. PULL-UPS FOR BOYS
Percentile Scores Based on Age

Percentile	Age								Percentile
	10	11	12	13	14	15	16	17	
100th	12	11	20	14	15	20	18	16	100th
95th	6	6	7	8	10	10	13	12	95th
90th	5	5	6	7	8	9	11	11	90th
85th	4	4	5	6	7	8	10	10	85th
80th	3	4	4	5	6	7	9	10	80th
75th	2	3	4	4	5	6	8	9	75th
70th	2	2	3	4	5	5	7	8	70th
65th	2	2	3	4	4	5	7	7	65th
60th	1	2	2	3	4	5	6	7	60th
55th	1	1	2	3	3	4	6	6	55th
50th	1	1	2	2	3	4	5	6	50th
45th	1	1	1	2	2	4	5	5	45th
40th	0	1	1	2	2	3	4	5	40th
35th	0	0	1	1	2	3	4	4	35th
30th	0	0	1	1	1	2	3	4	30th
25th	0	0	0	1	1	2	3	3	25th
20th	0	0	0	0	1	1	3	3	20th
15th	0	0	0	0	0	1	2	3	15th
10th	0	0	0	0	0	1	2	2	10th
5th	0	0	0	0	0	0	1	1	5th
0	0	0	0	0	0	0	0	0	0

TABLE 9. SIT-UPS FOR BOYS
Percentile Scores Based on Age

Percentile	10	11	12	13	14	15	16	17	Percentile
100th	99	99	99	99	99	99	99	99	100th
95th	99	99	99	99	99	99	99	99	95th
90th	60	67	78	73	99	99	99	99	90th
85th	50	52	60	60	70	73	83	73	85th
80th	47	50	51	54	60	60	73	63	80th
75th	41	42	50	50	53	54	62	60	75th
70th	39	38	44	48	50	50	55	55	70th
65th	35	35	40	44	50	50	51	51	65th
60th	30	31	37	40	44	45	50	50	60th
55th	28	30	33	37	41	41	48	48	55th
50th	26	26	31	35	39	40	44	44	50th
45th	24	25	30	33	36	37	41	40	45th
40th	22	23	28	30	33	35	40	38	40th
35th	20	21	25	30	31	32	36	35	35th
30th	18	20	23	26	30	30	34	32	30th
25th	16	17	20	25	26	29	32	30	25th
20th	14	15	19	22	24	25	30	28	20th
15th	12	12	16	20	21	23	26	25	15th
10th	10	10	12	17	19	20	22	24	10th
5th	6	6	10	12	15	15	18	20	5th
0	0	0	0	1	1	1	3	0	0

TABLE 10. SHUTTLE RUN FOR BOYS
Percentile Scores Based on Age

Percen-tile	Age								Percen-tile
	10	11	12	13	14	15	16	17	
100th	8.7	9.2	9.0	8.1	8.1	8.0	8.2	8.5	100th
95th	10.3	10.4	10.0	9.7	9.4	9.3	9.1	9.0	95th
90th	10.8	10.6	10.2	10.0	9.8	9.5	9.3	9.2	90th
85th	11.0	10.9	10.4	10.2	9.9	9.8	9.4	9.3	85th
80th	11.2	11.0	10.5	10.3	10.0	10.0	9.5	9.5	80th
75th	11.4	11.2	10.8	10.5	10.2	10.0	9.6	9.6	75th
70th	11.6	11.3	10.9	10.6	10.2	10.1	9.8	9.8	70th
65th	11.7	11.5	11.0	10.7	10.4	10.2	10.0	10.0	65th
60th	11.9	11.6	11.1	10.8	10.5	10.4	10.0	10.0	60th
55th	12.0	11.7	11.2	11.0	10.6	10.5	10.2	10.1	55th
50th	12.1	11.8	11.4	11.0	10.8	10.6	10.3	10.3	50th
45th	12.2	12.0	11.5	11.3	10.9	10.7	10.4	10.5	45th
40th	12.3	12.0	11.7	11.5	11.0	10.9	10.5	10.6	40th
35th	12.5	12.2	11.9	11.6	11.1	11.0	10.7	10.8	35th
30th	12.6	12.4	12.0	11.8	11.2	11.2	10.9	10.9	30th
25th	12.9	12.5	12.3	12.0	11.4	11.3	11.0	11.1	25th
20th	13.0	12.8	12.5	12.3	11.5	11.5	11.2	11.3	20th
15th	13.4	13.0	12.7	12.5	11.8	11.7	11.5	11.5	15th
10th	13.7	13.5	13.2	13.0	12.0	12.0	12.0	12.0	10th
5th	14.3	14.0	14.0	13.2	12.5	12.9	12.6	12.5	5th
0	16.0	16.1	16.5	18.0	15.2	15.0	17.5	17.6	0

TABLE 11. STANDING BROAD JUMP FOR BOYS
Percentile Scores Based on Age

Percentile	10	11	12	13	14	15	16	17	Percentile
100th	7'-0"	7'-3"	7'-5"	7'-9"	8'-5"	8'-6"	9'-0"	9'-1"	100th
95th	5'-6"	5'-10"	6'-2"	6'-8"	7'-2"	7'-8"	8'-0"	8'-4"	95th
90th	5'-3"	5'-8"	6'-0"	6'-5"	7'-0"	7'-4"	7'-9"	8'-0"	90th
85th	5'-1"	5'-6"	5'-10"	6'-3"	6'-8"	7'-1"	7'-6"	7'-9"	85th
80th	5'-0"	5'-4"	5'-8"	6'-0"	6'-6"	7'-0"	7'-3"	7'-8"	80th
75th	4'-11"	5'-3"	5'-7"	5'-11"	6'-6"	6'-9"	7'-2"	7'-7"	75th
70th	4'-9"	5'-2"	5'-6"	5'-10"	6'-3"	6'-8"	7'-1"	7'-5"	70th
65th	4'-8"	5'-1"	5'-5"	5'-9"	6'-2"	6'-7"	7'-0"	7'-4"	65th
60th	4'-8"	5'-0"	5'-4"	5'-8"	6'-1"	6'-5"	6'-11"	7'-2"	60th
55th	4'-7"	4'-11"	5'-3"	5'-6"	5'-11"	6'-4"	6'-9"	7'-0"	55th
50th	4'-6"	4'-10"	5'-1"	5'-5"	5'-10"	6'-2"	6'-8"	6'-11"	50th
45th	4'-5"	4'-9"	5'-0"	5'-4"	5'-9"	6'-0"	6'-6"	6'-9"	45th
40th	4'-4"	4'-7"	4'-11"	5'-2"	5'-7"	5'-11"	6'-4"	6'-8"	40th
35th	4'-3"	4'-6"	4'-10"	5'-1"	5'-6"	5'-9"	6'-3"	6'-6"	35th
30th	4'-2"	4'-5"	4'-9"	4'-11"	5'-4"	5'-8"	6'-2"	6'-4"	30th
25th	4'-1"	4'-3"	4'-8"	4'-10"	5'-3"	5'-7"	6'-0"	6'-2"	25th
20th	4'-0"	4'-2"	4'-6"	4'-8"	5'-2"	5'-5"	5'-10"	6'-0"	20th
15th	3'-10"	4'-0"	4'-5"	4'-6"	5'-0"	5'-3"	5'-8"	5'-11"	15th
10th	3'-8"	3'-10"	4'-1"	4'-4"	4'-9"	5'-0"	5'-4"	5'-9"	10th
5th	3'-4"	3'-7"	3'-10"	4'-0"	4'-6"	4'-9"	5'-0"	5'-5"	5th
0	2'-2"	2'-4"	2'-2"	2'-10"	3'-4"	2'-10"	3'-9"	3'-8"	0

Age

TABLE 12. 50-YARD DASH FOR BOYS
Percentile Scores Based on Age

Percentile	10	11	12	13	14	15	16	17	Percentile
100th	6.5	6.1	6.0	5.8	5.6	5.5	5.4	5.4	100th
95th	7.6	7.3	7.0	6.5	6.5	6.2	6.1	6.0	95th
90th	7.9	7.5	7.2	6.9	6.8	6.4	6.2	6.1	90th
85th	8.0	7.7	7.4	7.0	6.9	6.5	6.3	6.2	85th
80th	8.1	7.9	7.5	7.2	7.0	6.7	6.4	6.3	80th
75th	8.3	8.0	7.6	7.3	7.1	6.8	6.5	6.4	75th
70th	8.4	8.1	7.8	7.4	7.2	6.9	6.6	6.5	70th
65th	8.5	8.2	7.9	7.5	7.3	7.0	6.7	6.6	65th
60th	8.6	8.3	8.0	7.6	7.3	7.0	6.8	6.6	60th
55th	8.7	8.4	8.0	7.7	7.4	7.1	6.9	6.7	55th
50th	8.8	8.5	8.0	7.8	7.5	7.1	7.0	6.8	50th
45th	9.0	8.6	8.2	7.9	7.6	7.2	7.0	6.9	45th
40th	9.0	8.7	8.3	8.0	7.7	7.3	7.0	7.0	40th
35th	9.2	8.8	8.4	8.0	7.8	7.4	7.1	7.0	35th
30th	9.3	8.9	8.5	8.2	7.9	7.5	7.2	7.1	30th
25th	9.4	9.0	8.6	8.3	8.0	7.6	7.3	7.2	25th
20th	9.6	9.1	8.8	8.5	8.1	7.8	7.4	7.3	20th
15th	9.7	9.4	9.0	8.6	8.2	8.0	7.6	7.5	15th
10th	10.0	9.7	9.2	9.0	8.5	8.0	7.8	7.6	10th
5th	10.8	10.2	9.6	9.3	8.8	8.5	8.0	7.9	5th
0	13.5	14.3	13.6	12.5	10.1	10.5	9.7	9.3	0

TABLE 13. SOFTBALL THROW FOR BOYS

Percentile Scores Based on Age

Percentile	10	11	12	13	14	15	16	17	Percentile
100th	165	192	183	242	231	247	263	265	100th
95th	122	130	151	171	190	207	214	231	95th
90th	112	122	144	160	178	197	205	221	90th
85th	107	118	136	153	169	189	195	210	85th
80th	103	115	132	148	163	182	190	212	80th
75th	100	113	128	143	158	177	185	198	75th
70th	98	110	124	136	153	171	180	193	70th
65th	95	106	121	133	150	168	178	189	65th
60th	92	103	118	129	147	164	172	185	60th
55th	89	101	114	125	144	159	168	181	55th
50th	87	99	110	121	139	156	165	176	50th
45th	84	96	106	119	135	153	160	172	45th
40th	82	94	102	115	131	150	156	167	40th
35th	80	91	100	112	127	145	154	163	35th
30th	77	88	97	108	123	140	150	161	30th
25th	75	86	94	103	118	135	147	156	25th
20th	71	82	90	98	113	130	140	151	20th
15th	67	77	87	92	106	123	133	143	15th
10th	63	71	83	85	100	115	120	130	10th
5th	54	63	75	73	90	102	102	115	5th
0	31	20	36	36	47	50	48	64	0

TABLE 14. 600-YARD RUN-WALK FOR BOYS
Percentile Scores Based on Age

Percen-tile	10	11	12	13	14	15	16	17	Percen-tile
100th	1:45	1:39	1:45	1:40	1:30	1:23	1:30	1:25	100th
95th	2:15	2:02	2:05	2:00	1:50	1:43	1:40	1:36	95th
90th	2:23	2:15	2:12	2:05	1:56	1:50	1:45	1:44	90th
85th	2:27	2:21	2:16	2:10	2:02	1:55	1:48	1:48	85th
80th	2:30	2:24	2:19	2:13	2:05	1:59	1:51	1:51	80th
75th	2:34	2:27	2:22	2:15	2:08	2:01	1:54	1:54	75th
70th	2:38	2:31	2:26	2:18	2:11	2:05	1:56	1:55	70th
65th	2:41	2:34	2:29	2:21	2:13	2:07	1:59	1:58	65th
60th	2:45	2:37	2:32	2:25	2:18	2:09	2:00	2:00	60th
55th	2:48	2:40	2:35	2:27	2:20	2:10	2:03	2:02	55th
50th	2:51	2:43	2:39	2:29	2:22	2:14	2:05	2:04	50th
45th	2:55	2:47	2:42	2:32	2:25	2:17	2:07	2:06	45th
40th	2:58	2:50	2:46	2:36	2:30	2:20	2:10	2:09	40th
35th	3:03	2:56	2:50	2:40	2:34	2:24	2:12	2:14	35th
30th	3:06	3:01	2:56	2:44	2:37	2:28	2:16	2:17	30th
25th	3:10	3:07	3:02	2:50	2:44	2:31	2:23	2:22	25th
20th	3:15	3:12	3:06	2:57	2:52	2:25	2:30	2:26	20th
15th	3:23	3:20	3:17	3:02	3:00	2:42	2:36	2:35	15th
10th	3:36	3:29	3:33	3:15	3:14	2:55	2:41	2:44	10th
5th	3:48	3:48	3:50	3:39	3:33	3:16	3:02	3:05	5th
0	5:02	5:06	7:00	5:45	5:45	5:37	5:35	5:00	0

Index